MATHEMATICS FOR
DATA PROCESSING

MATHEMATICS FOR DATA PROCESSING

Salvatore DeAngelo
Mastech Computer Systems, Inc.
and
Triton College

Paul Jorgensen
Automatic Electric Labs, Inc.
and
Triton College

McGRAW-HILL BOOK COMPANY
New York   St. Louis   San Francisco   Düsseldorf
London   Mexico   Panama   Sydney   Toronto

mathematics for data processing

Library of Congress Catalog Card Number 73-102458

16203

1234567890 MAMM 79876543210

This book was set in Modern by The Maple Press
Company, and printed on permanent paper and
bound by The Maple Press Company. The
designer was Richard Paul Kluga; the drawings
were done by John Cordes, J. & R. Technical Ser-
vices, Inc. The editors were Donald K. Prentiss
and Andrea Stryker-Rodda. Sally R. Ellyson
supervised the production.

PREFACE

With the growing importance of computers, it is becoming necessary for an informed person to know something of computer power and capabilities. A student enrolled in a data-processing program should acquire a solid background in the mathematics involved. He should also cultivate a feeling for the scope of computers and the types of problems that can be solved on high-speed computing machines. To this end, the treatment, notation, and topics of a data-processing mathematics text should closely connect with computing machines.

A good data-processing curriculum should include early in course sequence a foundation in mathematics designed to carry the student through subsequent courses and familiarize him with practical problems he is likely to encounter in the business data-processing field. We have kept the above notions in mind throughout, and they serve as the overall objectives of this book.

In the introduction (Chapter 1) we characterize high-speed digital computers. It is important for the student to acquaint himself with this because it affords him the means for understanding and appreciating the power of computers as applied to material presented in the text.

Parts 1 and 2 can correspond to the first and second courses of a data-processing mathematics sequence. The inclusion of programming languages in Part 3 is intended to show how the communication between man and machine can be accomplished.

The material in this book should be sufficiently challenging to a student with a good high school algebra background. However, by the study of Chapter 2, an extensive review of basic algebra, and our introductory chapter, students with one or two semesters of high school algebra can readily prepare themselves for the remaining chapters. For those who have been away from the subject matter for a number of years, Chapters 1 and 2 can serve as a refresher. We have assumed no knowledge of calculus throughout this book.

We have attempted to keep the chapters within Parts 1 and 2 as independent as possible, so that the instructor may feel free to choose topics as he sees fit, though with a certain degree of caution. This caution is advised because certain exercises included at the ends of the chapters may involve new ideas from other chapters possibly omitted by some instructors.

Part 1 treats some classical subjects (function, matrix, sequence, number system) in a way that is consistent with the present-day discussion of these topics. The subject matter in Part 1 is used as a base for some of the topics in Part 2 (especially Chapter 9).

With the mathematical background established in Part 1, Part 2 confronts the student with several mathematical topics common to data-processing applications. Chapter 7, Set Theory and Logic, is included not only for its own value but also as a source of examples for the study of Boolean algebra in Chapter 8. In Chapter 9, the notion of an algorithm as an effective computing procedure is considered. The remainder of the chapter consists of examples of algorithms, most of which are extremely useful in data-processing applications. Our experience has shown that it is hardly possible to cover all of Part 2 in a semester course if all the sections in Chapter 9 are treated. Finally, Chapter 10 points out some of the limitations of problem solving with digital computers, and a way to be aware of these limitations.

Part 3 introduces the student to the concept of a programming language and how this vehicle makes communication possible between men and computing machines. The FORTRAN programming language is then presented in considerable detail. This language was chosen because of its wide usage and similarity to standard mathematical notation.

Finally, in Chapter 13, the programming language COBOL is described by means of a simple application, with its associated COBOL program. The language itself is then covered in considerable detail. This chapter is designed to reveal to the student the power of a business-oriented programming language.

The following acknowledgment appears at the request of the CODASYL COBOL committee.

Any organization interested in reproducing the COBOL report and specifications in whole or in part, using ideas taken from this report as the basis for an instruction manual or for any other purpose is free to do so. However, all such organizations are requested to reproduce this section as part of the introduction to the document. Those using a short passage, as in a book review, are requested to mention "COBOL" in acknowledgement of the source, but need not quote this entire section.

COBOL is an industry language and is not the property of any company or group of companies, or of any organization or group of organizations.

No warranty, expressed or implied, is made by any contributor or by the COBOL Committee as to the accuracy and functioning of the programming system and language. Moreover, no responsibility is assumed by any contributor, or by the committee, in connection therewith.

Procedures have been established for the maintenance of COBOL. Inquiries concerning the procedures for proposing changes should be directed to the Executive Committee of the Conference on Data Systems Languages.

The authors and copyright holders of the copyrighted material used herein

FLOW-MATIC (Trademark of Sperry Rand Corporation), Programming for the Univac (R) I and II, Data Automation Systems copyrighted 1958, 1959, by Sperry Rand Corporation; IBM Commercial Translator Form No. F 28-8013, copyrighted 1959 by IBM; FACT, DSI 27A5260-2760, copyrighted 1960 by Minneapolis-Honeywell

have specifically authorized the use of this material in whole or in part, in the COBOL specifications. Such authorization extends to the reproduction and use of COBOL specifications in programming manuals or similar publications.

This text was written with the full support of Automatic Electric Laboratories, Inc., Northlake, Illinois. In this connection, we wish to thank Messrs. John E. Fulenwider, Robert A. Lausch, Heberto Pachon, T. F. Lysaught, and Mrs. Jane Y. Lee, librarian. We also must thank the administration of Triton College, River Grove, Illinois, particularly Dean Gordon Simonsen, for cooperation and advice.

Salvatore De Angelo
Paul Jorgensen

CONTENTS

PART 3

PART ONE

chapter one

INTRODUCTION

1-1 CALCULATING MACHINES

A book on data-processing mathematics implies the use of data-processing equipment to aid in the solution of mathematically oriented problems.

The first machine designed to aid in mathematical computations was conceived by a French mathematician, Blaise Pascal, in the 1600s. Consider the following letter written by Pascal in 1649 on his calculating machine.

Dear Reader, this notice will serve to inform you that I submit to the public a small machine of my invention, by means of which you alone may, without any effort, perform all the operations of arithmetic, and may be relieved of the work which has often times fatigued your spirit, when you have worked with the counters or with the pen. As for simplicity of movement of the operations, I have so devised it that, although the operations of arithmetic are in a way opposed the one to the other—as addition to subtraction, and multiplication to division—nevertheless they are all performed on this machine by a single unique movement. The facility of this movement of operation is very evident since it is just as easy to move one thousand or ten thousand dials, all at one time, if one desires to make a single dial move, although all accomplish the movement perfectly. The most ignorant find as many advantages as the most experienced.   The instrument makes up for ignorance and for lack of practice, and even without any effort of the operator, it makes possible shortcuts by itself, whenever the numbers are set down.[1]

Thus, in the 1600s, a machine was introduced which promised to relieve the user of repetitious, tiring arithmetic operations.   The electronic computer of today reached its present level of popularity because it nicely fulfills the promise made by Pascal in the 1600s and because of the many other options possible.   Options such as automated record keeping and high-speed calculations are among the most important.

Later, in the mid-1800s, Charles Babbage drew up plans for an automatic machine that would carry out long sequences of calculations without human intervention.   Due somewhat to financial difficulties, the machine never actually worked, although the plan served as forerunner of the first computer.

Next in the evolution of machines to aid computation came the adding machines.   These machines are manually operated, and some can add, subtract, multiply, and divide.   They provide the user with a permanent record of input and output on the paper-tape roll.

Finally, the desk calculator evolved.   This is a machine which can function as an adding machine, but in addition it can find square roots, exponentials, and sometimes logarithms.   It allows the user to perform more sophisticated mathematical operations (see Fig. 1-1).

Pascal's calculating machine	Babbage's analytical engine idea	Adding machine	Desk calculator	Electronic computer

Fig. 1-1   Evolution of machines to aid in computations.

1-2 INFORMATION HANDLING

In the early stages of our country's growth, the business establishments that did exist were, for the most part, small one-owner concerns.   Usually, the proprietor kept account of business activities in the best way he saw fit. This might be exemplified by the picture we conjure up when someone mentions "general store."

As our country prospered, the need for record keeping arose.   This meant that the small merchant or businessman had to keep track of his business, not only on a day-to-day basis, but also on a month-to-month and year-to-year basis.   With some businessmen, this meant that volumes of information had to be handled and stored somewhere.   Orderly accounting

[1] Association for Computing Machinery, *Computing Reviews*, front cover, vol. 9, no. 6, June 1968.

procedures came into being almost by necessity. These procedures helped for a time, but when businesses became larger, the information-handling problems again became acute. This was due to the fact that record keeping and information handling were pencil-paper operations. Included in these operations were sortings, recording, summarizing, and calculating. All these functions were performed manually, usually with the help of a bookkeeper.

During this period, certain devices became available which, in a sense, aided in the automation of record keeping. Two of the more important devices were the adding machine and the cash register. In the crudest sense, the devices worked mechanically; that is, their functions were performed through the operation of levers, geared wheels, etc., and not by electrical power. Gradually, the small machines designed to aid in record keeping evolved into the electronic types, and automated record keeping was on its way to becoming a reality.

Perhaps the great need for automated record keeping can be seen in the U.S. Bureau of the Census. Here is an agency that deals with large masses of information that must be gathered and processed in many different ways. As early as the 1800s, the manual (by hand) method of information handling was proving itself to be inefficient and impractical.

The first large-scale operation devoted to automated record keeping took place in 1890 and was part of the 1890 census. Several people involved in the Census Bureau efforts emerged as pioneers in the computer field. One of the most prominent was Dr. Herman Hollerith, Census Bureau statistician and later founder of International Business Machines Corporation.

1-3 COMPUTATIONAL PROBLEMS

Associated with the problems of information handling are those associated with computation. Computational problems are those that involve the operations of addition, subtraction, multiplication, and division. These operations arise in the everyday workings of the business community (such as banks, lending agencies, and credit-card companies) and the scientific community (research laboratories and aerospace companies). When they do occur, they are repetitious. For example, a bank will add each deposit you made to your current balance in order to arrive at a new monthly balance. Here we have repeated additions. If you had a checking account, for each check written, a corresponding amount would be deducted from your current balance. Here we have repeated subtractions. When you consider the number of accounts a typical bank may have, you realize the magnitude of this computational problem. As late as 1960 some large banks were performing these functions manually. A human being can perform a simple four- or five-digit addition in 5 to 10 seconds. When we consider the many other functions a clerk must perform, we can see how the need for machines to aid in computational problems arose. With this aid would come increased efficiency, since human error is reduced; low business operating cost, since efficiency is increased; and more rapid processing of data. An electronic computer nicely fills this need.

1-4 PROBLEM ORIGINATION

Computational problems can arise in several different ways, depending on the environment in which we find ourselves. For example, most of the readers of this text are students. The computational problems met by students come from the exercise problems appearing in their textbooks. These problems can be described as having a written beginning.

Another environment that breeds computational problems is found in a person's normal work day. Here problems usually arise verbally. A supervisor may ask his employee for the day's receipts. A bank manager may ask for total disbursements in a certain period. A scientist may ask a computer programmer for a program (we will meet the terms program and programmer in a later chapter) to interpret certain statistical data. All these problems and many more originate on the job and have a verbal beginning.

Finally, we as individuals can originate computational problems ourselves. This origination may come at our desk or any other place where we are deep in thought. If we are students, we may wish to compute our grade point average. If we are workers, we may wish to compute our year's salary, including the overtime we have worked. We also might wish to project into next year to discover what our income-tax payment will be. These computational problems can be described as personal, and usually begin with a thought process (see Fig. 1-2).

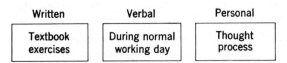

Fig. 1-2 Computational-problem origination.

1-5 SOLVING PROCESS

Some time after the problem has been originated, we begin our solving process. First we decide what must be done. For example, let us say that the boss asked us, "What were the total sales for today?" (Here is a problem that originated verbally, on the job.) You immediately decide what must be done: add together all the individual sales for that day in order to arrive at the total sales figure. Since you know what must be done, you now must decide *how* to do it. Sometimes this decision comes rapidly, but on other occasions much time and thought are devoted to "how to do it," depending on the nature of the problem. Here we must define, in more detail, the steps

involved in achieving our goal.   Often these steps occur to us almost unconsciously.   When this happens, we can quickly follow the problem to its
conclusion.   Other times we must sit and think the problem through in logical
steps in order to achieve a solution.   A valuable aid at this point is a flowchart.
This is a series of boxes connected by arrows indicating our logical flow of
thought.   Flowcharts are sometimes called block diagrams (see Chaps. 4
and 5).

Let us get back to our problem.   We know what must be done: add
individual sales figures.   Now you ask: How to do it?   You may answer:
I'll use the process for adding columns of numbers that I learned in high school.
At this point you might suggest that the *how* step is hardly worth bringing up
since there is this standard way of adding columns of numbers.   The standard
way is not necessarily the easiest.   Consider the following column of numbers
representing individual sales:

```
$  627.35
   978.42
   369.04
 1,672.98
    76.75
```

Standard addition tells us to begin at the rightmost column, add the
digits in that column, bring the "carries," if any, over to the next left column,
and add the carries to that column.   We continue the process through to the
leftmost column.

We arrive at a sum of $3,724.54.   However, many people find it difficult
to keep track of carries and might prefer the following method.

Add the right column of digits.   Place the resulting sum below the
column.   Continue to the next left column.   Place this sum below the
column and below the previous sum one position to the left.   Continue the
process until there are no columns left.   Now add the individual sums in their
position to obtain the total.   The example is illustrated, as follows:

```
$  627.35
   978.42
   369.04
 1,672.98
    76.75
   ───────
       24  ← sum of first column
      2 3  ← sum of second column
      32   ← sum of third column
      29   ← sum of fourth column
     2 4   ← sum of fifth column
     1     ← sum of sixth column
$3,724.54  ← sum of the above
```

Note that only one carry occurred here, instead of five. This simple example was introduced to indicate that at the *how* phase there may be several avenues of approach in the problem-solving process.

The next phase in the problem-solving process was considered unimportant until the advent of computers. This is the data-definition phase. You will learn about data definition in your programming courses. Briefly, by data definition we mean the form (or format) that our data, both input and output, will take. In our example, the input data take the form of dollars-and-cents figures. It so happens that our output data take the same form as the input data. This is not always the case. A simple example is calculation of your telephone bill. Input data consist of message units. Output data are a dollars-and-cents figure.

Next in the problem-solving process is selection of tools to aid us. In our simple example, of course, paper-pencil would be enough. However, if the individual sales were many, you can see how useful an adding machine would be as an aid in the problem-solving process. Problems that are more complex would suggest the use of a desk calculator.

Finally, imagine a problem that calls for a thousand or more additions to be done in a very short time. Problems like this arise daily in the payroll departments of large firms or in the billing departments of various utility companies. In these cases and many others, it makes good sense to enlist the aid of the most sophisticated computational tool, the electronic computer.

Next, we must prepare our input data for the computational tool selected. If our tool selected is pencil-paper or adding machine or desk calculator, then data preparation is straightforward. With adding machine or desk calculator we present input data by depressing certain buttons on a keyboard. With a computer, data preparation is not so straightforward. The input data must be prepared in a form acceptable by the computer. These data are not the only information that must be prepared properly. *The steps leading to solution* (from the *how-to-do-it phase*) must also be prepared in a form acceptable by

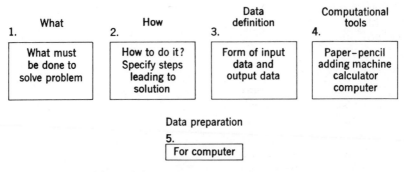

Fig. 1-3   The problem-solving process.

the computer. This fact makes the computer radically different from our other computational tools (see Fig. 1-3).

1-6 THE COMPUTER PROGRAM

A program, more specifically, a computer program, is a set of instructions designed to solve a given problem. The steps leading to solution of a computational problem such as those mentioned at the conclusion of Sec. 1-5 can be called instructions. Thus, when we call upon a computer as a computational tool, the steps leading to solution of our given problem make up the computer program.

In the steps leading to a solution, certain decisions appear. Furthermore, these decisions are based on prior conditions, usually the result of some intermediate arithmetic operation.

As an illustration consider our former example:

$$
\begin{array}{r}
\$ \quad 627.35 \\
978.42 \\
369.04 \\
1,672.98 \\
76.75 \\
\hline
24 \\
2\ 3 \\
32 \\
29 \\
2\ 4 \\
1 \\
\hline
\$3,724.54
\end{array}
$$

A decision-making step during the solution of the problem follows the question: Have I added the digits in the leftmost column? It is easy enough to arrive at a proper answer by merely looking at the problem data. Perhaps we arrive at the answer unconsciously. The main point here is that there indeed are decisions to be made in most computational solutions.

Another example that is more illustrative concerns a checking account. In keeping track of your current balance the bank subtracts the amounts on the written checks from your balance. If any subtraction yields a negative balance, this means there are insufficient funds in your account to cover the check. At this point the check is returned or you are charged a fee. Thus, after every subtraction, a decision must be made concerning your current balance: Are there sufficient funds in this account or insufficient funds? The proper response to this decision is based on the previous subtraction. If the result is positive or zero, there are sufficient funds. If the result is negative, there are insufficient funds.

1-7 THE ELECTRONIC COMPUTER

Let us get back for a moment to the adding machine and see how it is controlled. In order to operate the machine, it is necessary to depress keys on the keyboard and then turn a crank.   If the machine is operated electrically, an "entry" key is depressed.   This is continued until the desired numbers are entered. Other keys are depressed to accomplish the arithmetic operations.   The important thing to remember here is that control of the adding machine occurs *externally* via our physical manipulation.   Moreover, the desk calculator is also controlled by us *externally*.   Each physical activity performed by us can be thought of as a step (or instruction) from the how-to-do-it phase of the problem-solving process.

It is on the point of control that the computer differs so radically from other computational aids.   While the devices mentioned above are controlled externally, the computer is controlled *internally*.   The control comes from the computer program which has been prepared in a form acceptable by the computer.   This is why the data-preparation phase is so important when a computer is used as a computational aid.

The prepared data (usually consisting of a computer program with input data) are put into the computer with the help of certain devices, depending on the medium on which the prepared data exist.   Probably the most familiar medium is the tab card, an 80-column by 12-row pasteboard-paper rectangle. The device to handle this medium is called a card reader.   Devices also exist to handle other media.   The computer can also deliver output data to various devices.   The collection of all the devices mentioned above is referred to as input-output devices, or peripheral units.   We can suggest the analogy with the adding machine by referring to its keyboard input medium and the paper-tape roll as the output medium.

As prepared data are presented to the computer, they are held in the computer's *storage unit*.   This part of the computer holds the instructions from our program and also holds input data.   Output data, when produced, are also held here before delivery to some output device.

When a step in our program calls for some computation to be made, this step is carried out in the computer's *arithmetic unit*.

Finally, when a decision must be made, this step is carried out in the computer's *control unit*.

The three units mentioned above make up the computer's *central processing unit* (CPU).

1-8 THE STORED PROGRAM

Because the problem-solving instructions are held in the storage unit, a program is more properly called a *stored program*.   The instructions are held in a sequential manner, that is, one after the other, in a logical way, corresponding to steps set up in the how-to-do-it phase of our problem-solving process.

When an internal signal is produced, each instruction is performed (or executed) one after the other, beginning with the first instruction in the stored program. Another way of saying this is: The instructions are executed sequentially.

The important thing to remember here is that each instruction is executed at electronic speed. Electronic speeds are measured in thousandths, millionths, or billionths of a second. One thousandth of a second is called a millisecond. One millionth of a second is called a microsecond. One billionth of a second is called a nanosecond. For example, if an addition is performed in a computer in one microsecond, this means that one million additions can be performed in one second. Compare this with a typical human being's ability to perform a five-digit addition of two numbers in 5 to 10 seconds.

It was mentioned earlier that instructions are executed sequentially. This is true unless an instruction within the program itself directs otherwise. Thus an instruction can direct the computer (remember, the instructions control the computer) to bypass the next sequential instruction and execute some other. This is sometimes referred to as *branching*. The *decision* to branch is usually made on the basis of some previous arithmetic result. This brings to the computer user great flexibility in the variety of problems that a computer may aid in solving.

1-9 CONCLUSIONS

We have seen that instructions leading to solution of computational problems can be executed at fantastic speeds. One can get an idea of the speeds involved by keeping in mind the following comparison: 1 nanosecond compared with 1 second is the same as 1 second compared with 30 years, or

$$\frac{1 \text{ nanosecond}}{1 \text{ second}} = \frac{1 \text{ second}}{30 \text{ years}}$$

Thus, with the capability of performing millions of instructions per second, problems never before attempted become simple applications when the computer is used as a computational aid.

chapter two

REVIEW OF BASIC ALGEBRA

INTRODUCTION

The number system with which we are most familiar today began in prehistoric times and reached its present form a few hundred years ago.

The first notion of numbers probably arose as a result of the counting of objects such as leaves, animals, fingers, etc. More specifically, the counting of objects in succession probably led to what we call the *natural numbers*, 1, 2, 3, 4, and so on. These were the only numbers known for a long time. Addition and subtraction as arithmetic operations developed in this context, also.

In time, problems involving the division of quantities, such as a herd of cattle or a piece of property, probably led to the construction of fractions like $\frac{1}{2}$, $\frac{3}{4}$, $\frac{25}{37}$, and so on.

The operation of subtraction (the process of taking something away) evolved, as mentioned above. However, the quantity to be taken away (we have come to call this the subtrahend) was always smaller than the quantity from which something is taken (we have come to call this the minuend). It probably became convenient, for some reason, to take a larger quantity from a smaller one. It became convenient also to express the result of this operation in some way; so the notion of negative numbers came into being. The notion of zero, representing subtraction of equal natural numbers, was introduced.

In the study of geometric figures, the early Greeks found that the lengths of sides of certain figures could not be expressed as natural numbers or even fractions.   At this point the idea of *irrational numbers* evolved ($\sqrt{2}$, $\sqrt{5}$).

All the above types of numbers are part of what we call the *system of real numbers.*

Another type of number evolved when an attempt was made to find the square root of a negative number.   This type we have come to call an imaginary number, or *complex number.*

In this text, when the word number is written, we will mean real number unless specifically stated otherwise.

Real-number Symbolism

The real numbers specifically mentioned above ($\sqrt{2}$, 1, 2, 3, 7, $\frac{1}{2}$, 0, -1, -2, . . .) are called *explicit* real numbers.   However, throughout this text we will have need to refer to real numbers by using letters of the alphabet. When numbers are represented this way, we call these letters number symbols, or merely *literals*.   When the symbol $=$ is used between combinations of literals and/or real numbers, we mean that what is on the left and right of the $=$ sign represent the same number; that is, they are equal.   Thus the symbol $=$ has come to be known (in a mathematical sense) as the equal sign.

2-1   AXIOMS AND OPERATIONS

Long ago, mathematicians decided to *define* the real-number system rigorously. That is, from a basic set of *axioms* and a set of *operations* all the properties of real numbers were stated and proved as theorems.   We will not pursue this development in this text, but some mention of the axioms and operations are in order here.

The operations we will meet are addition, subtraction, multiplication, division, and exponentiation.   We sometimes see these referred to as algebraic operations, arithmetic operations, or fundamental operations.

In a mathematical sense (as opposed to a programming-language sense), the symbols used are addition, $+$; multiplication, $\cdot$; division, $/$ or $\div$; and subtraction, $-$.

axioms of commutativity

Two numbers give the same sum when added in either order.   Also, two numbers give the same product when multiplied in either order.   Thus

$$8 + 5 = 13 \qquad 5 + 8 = 13$$

so

$$8 + 5 = 5 + 8 \tag{2-1}$$

Also

$$7 \times 4 = 28 \qquad 4 \times 7 = 28$$

so

$$7 \times 4 = 4 \times 7 \tag{2-2}$$

In general, if x and y are any two real numbers, then

$$x + y = y + x \tag{2-3}$$

and

$$x \cdot y = y \cdot x \tag{2-4}$$

axioms of associativity

Three numbers give the same sum no matter how the numbers are grouped. Also, three numbers give the same product no matter how the numbers are grouped. Thus

$$(5 + 2) + 6 = 7 + 6 = 13$$

and

$$5 + (2 + 6) = 5 + 8 = 13$$

so

$$(5 + 2) + 6 = 5 + (2 + 6) \tag{2-5}$$

Also

$$(7 \times 3) \times 2 = 21 \times 2 = 42$$

and

$$7 \times (3 \times 2) = 7 \times 6 = 42$$

so

$$(7 \times 3) \times 2 = 7 \times (3 \times 2) \tag{2-6}$$

In general, if x, y, and z are any real numbers, then

$$(x + y) + z = x + (y + z) \tag{2-7}$$

and

$$(xy) \cdot z = x \cdot (yz) \tag{2-8}$$

These four axioms are used to extend the above notions to more than two or three numbers. The extensions allow us to add many numbers in any order and guarantee that we will obtain the same sum every time. A similar statement holds for multiplications and products. For example,

$$7 + 5 + 8 + 2 = 8 + 2 + 5 + 7$$

and

$$9 \times 6 \times 4 \times 3 = 4 \times 6 \times 9 \times 3$$

the distributive axiom

The product of a number x and the sum of two numbers y and z is the same as the sum of the products xy and xz. Thus

$$7 \times (3 + 2) = 7 \times 5 = 35$$

and

$$7 \times 3 + 7 \times 2 = 21 + 14 = 35$$

so

$$7 \times (3 + 2) = 7 \times 3 + 7 \times 2 \qquad (2\text{-}9)$$

In general,

$$x(y + z) = xy + xz \qquad (2\text{-}10)$$

This axiom can be extended to include many numbers inside the parentheses to form a sum. The result will be the sum of the products of every number inside by the number outside. For example,

$$6(4 + 7 + 9 + 10 + 22) = 6 \times 4 + 6 \times 7 + 6 \times 9$$
$$+ \, 6 \times 10 + 6 \times 22$$
$$= 24 + 42 + 54 + 60 + 132$$
$$6(4 + 7 + 9 + 10 + 22) = 312$$

As an exercise, you should form the sum of the numbers in parentheses first, then multiply by 6 to obtain 312.

Inverse

Two types of inverse exist in a real-number discussion.

additive inverse

If X is any real number, then its additive inverse $-X$ exists, so that

$$X + (-X) = 0 \qquad (2\text{-}11)$$

multiplicative inverse

If X is any nonzero real number, then its multiplicative inverse $1/X$ exists, so that

$$X \cdot \frac{1}{X} = 1 \qquad (2\text{-}12)$$

The numbers 0 and 1 on the right, above, are called additive identity and multiplicative identity, respectively. Two important properties of the identities are

$$X + 0 = X \qquad (2\text{-}13)$$
$$1 \cdot X = X \qquad (2\text{-}14)$$

The algebraic sign for subtraction and the negative sign are sometimes confused.

When the symbol $-$ appears between two numbers a and b, the operation of subtraction is suggested. When the sign appears preceding a number, the notion of negative is meant. The notions of negative and positive are easily visualized by introducing what is called the real line (see Fig. 2-1). We select a point on this line and agree to label it the zero point. We further agree that all points to the right will correspond to positive numbers and all points on the left of zero will correspond to negative numbers. We select points at equal distances from each other, starting at zero. These points on the right of zero will correspond to the natural numbers (we can now call them positive integers); these points on the left of zero will correspond to negative natural numbers (or negative integers). Now every point on this line corresponds to a single real number, and conversely, every real number has associated with it one point on this line.

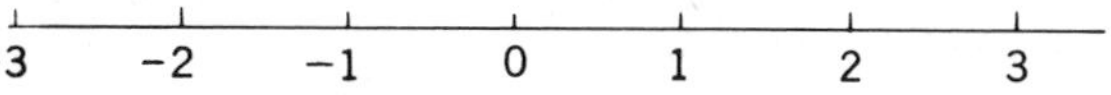

$$
\begin{array}{ccccccc}
-3 & -2 & -1 & 0 & 1 & 2 & 3
\end{array}
$$

Fig. 2-1

At this time it is convenient to introduce the law of signs governing multiplication of signed numbers.

When X and Y are any two numbers

$$(-X)Y = X(-Y) = -XY \qquad (2\text{-}15)$$

and

$$(-X)(-Y) = XY \qquad (2\text{-}16)$$

We have said that X and Y can be any real numbers. In particular, they can be integers, fractions, or irrationals. The above laws allow us to write statements such as

$$-Y = -1 \cdot Y \qquad (2\text{-}17)$$

This follows when we let $X = 1$ in Eq. (2-15).

Also

$$Y = -(-Y) \qquad (2\text{-}18)$$

This follows when we let $X = 1$ in Eq. (2-16).

The Absolute Value

The notion of absolute value of a number is an important one, and we introduce it now.

If X is any real number, then the absolute value of X, written $|X|$, is defined as follows:

$$|X| = X \text{ if } X \text{ is positive or zero}$$

and

$$|X| = -X \text{ if } X \text{ is negative}$$

For example,

$$|7| = 7 \qquad |0| = 0 \qquad |-6| = -(-6) = +6$$

Subtraction

In the operation of subtraction, we seek a number x which will satisfy

$$a + x = b \tag{2-19}$$

The symbol $b - a$ is called the *difference* b minus a.

The subtraction operation and the addition of numbers with unlike sign are tied together by the statement

$$b - a = b + (-a) \tag{2-20}$$

Thus we get the same number when a is subtracted from b or when negative a is added to b.

A simple rule can be stated to accomplish addition of numbers with unlike signs:

To add numbers with unlike signs, first find their absolute values, then take the smaller absolute value from the larger. Prefix to the result the sign of the original number with the larger absolute value.

Example

Add 72 and -86.

First

$$|72| = 72$$
$$|-86| = -(-86) = 86$$

Now take 72 from 86.
The result is 14.
Now 86 is the larger absolute value; so we prefix its original sign. Thus

$$72 + (-86) = -14$$

From Eq. (2-20) we can conclude that

$$72 - 86 = -14$$

When we are asked to add more than two numbers with unlike signs, it is convenient to add the numbers with the same signs together first.

Example

Add 63, -32, 47, -66, -98, 14.

We must find the sum

$$63 + (-32) + 47 + (-66) + (-98) + 14$$

Adding positive numbers, we have

$$124 + (-32) + (-66) + (-98)$$

Now adding the negative numbers together, we get

$$124 + (-196)$$

Now we proceed, as in the previous example, to obtain

$$124 + (-196) = -72$$

From Eq. (2-20), we note that the original sum could have been written

$$63 - 32 + 47 - 66 - 98 + 14$$

Some people prefer to start the problem in the above form and then proceed to add positive numbers together and negative numbers together. It is permissible to do this, but do not lose track of the signs.

Rational Numbers

A rational number is any real number of the form a/b, where a, b are integers and b is not zero. For example,

$$\frac{2}{3} \qquad \frac{-6}{7} \qquad \frac{72}{-45} \qquad \frac{10}{12} \qquad \frac{17}{1}$$

are all rational numbers. You have probably, in the past, referred to numbers like these as fractions.

Many theorems on rational numbers exist. We will state the ones which will be most useful to us.

$$\frac{a}{1} = a \tag{2-21}$$

$$-\frac{a}{b} = \frac{-a}{b} = \frac{a}{-b} \tag{2-22}$$

$$\frac{a}{b} = \frac{1}{b} \cdot \frac{a}{1} = a \cdot \frac{1}{b} \tag{2-23}$$

$$\frac{a}{b} \cdot \frac{c}{d} = \frac{ac}{bd} \tag{2-24}$$

$$\frac{a}{b} = \frac{ax}{bx} \qquad \text{where } x \text{ is a nonzero number} \qquad (2\text{-}25)$$

$$\frac{a}{b} + \frac{c}{d} = \frac{ad + bc}{bd} \qquad (2\text{-}26)$$

$$\frac{a}{c} + \frac{b}{c} = \frac{a + b}{c} \qquad (2\text{-}27)$$

$$\frac{a}{b} - \frac{c}{d} = \frac{ad - cb}{bd} \qquad (2\text{-}28)$$

$$\frac{a/b}{c/d} = \frac{a}{b} \cdot \frac{d}{c} \qquad (2\text{-}29)$$

Most of the manipulations with fractions that you are accustomed to are based on the above theorems.

For example, from Eq. (2-25),

$$\frac{2}{3} = \frac{2 \times 2}{3 \times 2} = \frac{4}{6} \qquad \text{also} \qquad \frac{2}{3} = \frac{2 \times 9}{3 \times 9} = \frac{18}{27}$$

Fractions like $\frac{2}{3}$ and $\frac{4}{6}$ and $\frac{18}{27}$ are called equivalent fractions.

Equation (2-27) can be extended to any number of fractions with the same denominator. Thus

$$\frac{a}{c} + \frac{b}{c} + \frac{d}{c} + \frac{e}{c} = \frac{a + b + d + e}{c} \qquad (2\text{-}30)$$

A fraction in lowest terms can be defined after we introduce the notion of factor. We assume a, b, and x are integers.

If there is a number x such that

$$ax = b \qquad (2\text{-}31)$$

then a is called a factor of b. Also, b is called a multiple of a.

Example

12 is a multiple of 4 since

$$3 \times 4 = 12$$

Also, we see that 4 is a factor of 12, and 3 is a factor of 12.

If two numbers have the same factor, then this number is said to be a common factor between them. For example,

$$15 = 3 \times 5 \qquad \text{and} \qquad 21 = 3 \times 7$$

Thus 3 is a common factor between 15 and 21.

A fraction is said to be in lowest terms if there are no common factors other than 1 between numerator and denominator.

Addition of fractions with unlike denominators involves the notion of least common denominator (LCD). First we make sure all denominators are positive. We can do this by using Eq. (2-22).

The LCD of several fractions is a number which is the product of all the *different* prime factors of the denominators. (There is an extension of this definition, which will be stated after we discuss exponents.) Then we use Eq. (2-25) to write the fractions with the same denominator (the LCD we have just found). Now we can use Eq. (2-30) to form the sum.

For example, add

$$\tfrac{1}{10} \qquad \tfrac{2}{15} \qquad \tfrac{5}{6}$$

We write the denominators and their prime factors.

$$10 = 2 \times 5 \qquad 15 = 3 \times 5 \qquad 6 = 2 \times 3$$

Now the *different* prime factors are 2, 3, and 5. The product of these is the LCD. Thus

$$LCD = 2 \times 3 \times 5 = 30$$

Now we use Eq. (2-25).

$$\frac{1}{10} = \frac{1 \times 3}{10 \times 3} = \frac{3}{30}$$

$$\frac{2}{15} = \frac{2 \times 2}{15 \times 2} = \frac{4}{30}$$

$$\frac{5}{6} = \frac{5 \times 5}{6 \times 5} = \frac{25}{30}$$

Thus

$$\frac{1}{10} + \frac{2}{15} + \frac{5}{6} = \frac{3}{30} + \frac{4}{30} + \frac{25}{30}$$

We use Eq. (2-30) on the right side of this to obtain

$$\frac{3 + 4 + 25}{30} = \frac{32}{30}$$

We should always check our resulting fraction to see if it is in lowest terms. We do this by eliminating common factors in numerator and denominator. In our case

$$\frac{32}{30} = \frac{2 \times 16}{2 \times 15} = \frac{16}{15}$$

Our final result then is

$$\frac{1}{10} + \frac{2}{15} + \frac{5}{6} = \frac{16}{15}$$

Another way of describing a rational number is as follows.

Division

The symbol a/b can be called the *quotient* of a divided by b. When the division is actually carried out, we will obtain a repeating or a terminating decimal number.

A repeating decimal number is one where one or more digits (digits are the numbers 0, 1, 2, 3, 4, 5, 6, 7, 8, 9) repeat to the right of the decimal point.

A terminating decimal number is one which ends in zero to the right of the decimal point.

Example

$$13\tfrac{3}{5} = 2.60000$$

So the rational number $13\tfrac{3}{5}$ can be written as a terminating decimal number.
Also

$$2\tfrac{2}{7} = 0.285714285714285714 \ldots$$

Here the rational number $2\tfrac{2}{7}$ can be written as a repeating decimal number. Note that the six digits 2, 8, 5, 7, 1, 4 repeat.

Once we are sure which digits repeat in a repeating decimal number, there is a shorter way of writing it. We place a heavy line over the first complete set of digits that repeat. Thus we can write $2\tfrac{2}{7}$ as $2\tfrac{2}{7} = 0.\overline{285714}$.

We can use this notation for terminating decimal numbers also. Thus

$$13\tfrac{3}{5} = 2.6\overline{0}$$

means that the final zero repeats.

Division has its basis in the finding of numbers x which satisfy the statement

$$ax = b \qquad\qquad (2\text{-}32)$$

When a, b are integers, we call this x the quotient and write

$$x = \frac{b}{a}$$

2-2 INEQUALITIES

A statement that one real number is greater than or less than another real number is called an *inequality*.   The statement *"a is less than b"* is an inequality.   We express this symbolically as

$$a < b$$

The symbol $<$ means "is less than."

On the other hand, if *"a is greater than b,"* we write

$$a > b$$

The symbol $>$ means "is greater than."

For any real number a, we say that

$$a > 0 \text{ if and only if } a \text{ is positive}$$

Also

$$a < 0 \text{ if and only if } a \text{ is negative}$$

The phrase "if and only if" appears frequently in mathematics textbooks. It usually appears between two conditions.   Its meaning follows.

If we have a statement about two conditions A and B which reads

Condition A if and only if condition B

this means

If *condition A is true, then condition B is true*

and simultaneously,

If *condition B is true, then condition A is true*

Now for two numbers a and b we have

$$a < b \text{ if and only if } b - a > 0$$

Also

$$a > b \text{ if and only if } b - a < 0$$

Frequently, the condition of equality is included when we speak of a relationship between two numbers.   In that case the symbol $\leq$ is used.   This symbol is read "is less than or equal to."   Similarly, the symbol $\geq$ means "is greater than or equal to."

We can give a geometric interpretation to this idea of inequality.

Let a and b be real numbers.   Let P_a be the point associated with a, and

P_b be the point associated with b.   (Refer to Fig. 2-1.)   Then

> $a < b$ *if and only if* P_a *is to the left of* P_b
> $a > b$ *if and only if* P_a *is to the right of* P_b

Examples

> $3 < 5$ *since* $5 - 3 = 2$, *which is positive*
> $-4 < -3$ *since* $-3 - (-4) = 1$, *which is positive*
> $4/15 < 3/5$ *since* $3/5 - 4/15 = 5/15 = 1/3$

However,

> $7 > 2$ *since* $2 - 7 = -5$, *which is negative*

Also

> $1/2 - 5/8 = -1/8$, *which is negative; so* $5/8 > 1/2$

It should be clear that

> *If* $a < b$, *this means* $b > a$

It can easily be shown that the following statements are true.

1. The sense of an inequality (that is, the direction in which the inequality sign points) is not changed when any real number is added to both sides of the inequality.

    > Symbolically,
    > *If* $a < b$
    > *then* $a + c < b + c$

2. The sense of an inequality is not changed when both sides are multiplied by some nonzero positive number; that is,

    > *If* $a < b$
    > *and if* $c > 0$
    > *then* $ac < bc$

3. The sense of an inequality is reversed when both sides are multiplied by some negative number.

    > *If* $a < b$
    > *and if* $c < 0$
    > *then* $ac > bc$

4. *If* $a < b$
    then $\dfrac{1}{a} > \dfrac{1}{b}$ *when* $a \neq 0$ *and* $b \neq 0$

Statements similar to the above can be made with the inequality sign reversed. You should satisfy yourself about the above statements by substituting numbers for a, b, and c.

For example, let

$$a > b$$

Now multiply both sides by -1. This falls under statement 3. We obtain

$$-a < -b$$

2-3 EXPONENTS

When equal factors are multiplied together, we express the resulting product with a certain shortened notation. For example, $a \cdot a$ can be written as a^2; $a \cdot a \cdot a$ is written as a^3; in general, a^m, where m is a positive integer, means that a occurs m times in the product. The number m is called an *exponent*, and a is called the *base*. a^m is called the *mth power of a*. For example,

$$a^7 = a \cdot a \cdot a \cdot a \cdot a \cdot a \cdot a$$

and

$$a^5 = a \cdot a \cdot a \cdot a \cdot a$$

So

$$\frac{a^7}{a^5} = \frac{a \cdot a \cdot a \cdot a \cdot a \cdot a \cdot a}{a \cdot a \cdot a \cdot a \cdot a}$$

But the same number a appears in numerator and denominator on the right; seven times in the numerator and five in the denominator. We cancel five in the denominator with five in the numerator, leaving a product of two a's in the numerator. Thus

$$\frac{a^7}{a^5} = a^2$$

In general, the following *laws of exponents* are valid. We assume m and n are integers.

$$1^m = 1$$

that is, 1 raised to any power is 1.

$$a^m \cdot a^n = a^{m+n} \tag{2-33}$$

Example

$$3^2 \times 3^3 = (3 \times 3)(3 \times 3 \times 3) = 3 \times 3 \times 3 \times 3 \times 3 = 3^5 = 3^{2+3}$$

$$\frac{a^m}{a^n} = a^{m-n} \tag{2-34}$$

$$\frac{5^4}{5^2} = \frac{5 \times 5 \times 5 \times 5}{5 \times 5} = 5 \times 5 = 5^2 = 5^{4-2}$$

$$(a^m)^n = a^{mn} \tag{2-35}$$

Thus

$$(2^2)^4 = 2^2 \times 2^2 \times 2^2 \times 2^2 = 2 \times 2 \times 2 \times 2 \times 2 \times 2 \times 2 \times 2$$
$$= 2^8 = 2^{2 \cdot 4}$$

$$\left(\frac{a}{b}\right)^m = \frac{a^m}{b^m} \tag{2-36}$$

Example

$$\left(\frac{4}{5}\right)^3 = \frac{4}{5} \times \frac{4}{5} \times \frac{4}{5} = \frac{4 \times 4 \times 4}{5 \times 5 \times 5} = \frac{4^3}{5^3}$$

$$(ab)^m = a^m b^m \tag{2-37}$$

Thus

$$(3 \times 7)^4 = (3 \times 7)(3 \times 7)(3 \times 7)(3 \times 7)$$
$$= 3 \times 7 \times 3 \times 7 \times 3 \times 7 \times 3 \times 7$$
$$= 3 \times 3 \times 3 \times 3 \times 7 \times 7 \times 7 \times 7 = 3^4 \times 7^4$$

We usually do not write the exponent m when $m = 1$. Thus

$$a^1 = a$$

As definitions, the following are true also.

$$a^0 = 1 \qquad \text{when } a \neq 0 \tag{2-38}$$

Example

$$2^0 = 1, \ (-5)^0 = 1, \ (6x)^0 = 1$$

$$a^{-m} = \frac{1}{a^m} \qquad \text{when } a \neq 0 \tag{2-39}$$

Example

$$4^{-5} = \frac{1}{4^5} = \frac{1}{4 \times 4 \times 4 \times 4 \times 4} = \frac{1}{1,024}$$

$$3x^{-2} = \frac{3}{x^2}$$

$$(2x)^{-3} = \frac{1}{(2x)^3} = \frac{1}{8x^3}$$

Example

Write as a single real number without an exponent:

$$\frac{(\frac{1}{3})^5}{(\frac{1}{3})^4}$$

We obtain [from Eq. (2-34)]

$$\frac{(\frac{1}{3})^5}{(\frac{1}{3})^4} = (\frac{1}{3})^{5-4} = \frac{1}{3}$$

As an application consider the following statements:

All positive odd integers (some of which are 1, 3, 5, 7, 9, 11, 13, 15, 17, . . .) can be given by the formula

$2k + 1$ where k takes on values 0, 1, 2, 3, 4, . . .

For instance, when $k = 0$, we obtain 1; when $k = 1$, we obtain 3; when $k = 2$, we obtain 5; and so on.

Now let us evaluate -1 raised to some odd powers.

$$(-1)^1 = -1$$
$$(-1)^3 = (-1)(-1)(-1) = (+1)(-1) = -1$$

We can show that -1 raised to any odd power is -1; that is,

$$(-1)^n = -1 \qquad \text{when } n \text{ as odd} \tag{2-40}$$

To show that Eq. (2-40) is true, write n as an odd integer.

$$(-1)^n = (-1)^{2k+1}$$

Now use Eq. (2-33).

$$(-1)^{2k+1} = (-1)^{2k} \cdot (-1)^1$$

But from Eq. (2-35), $(-1)^{2k}$ can be written

$$(-1)^{2k} = [(-1)^2]^k$$

Since $(-1)^2 = (-1)(-1) = +1$, we obtain

$$(-1)^{2k} = +1^k = 1$$

and thus

$$(-1)^n = (-1)^{2k+1} = +1 \times (-1)^1 = +1 \times (-1) = -1$$

So we have shown

$$(-1)^n = -1 \qquad \text{when } n \text{ is odd}$$

(See Exercise 2-13 for n even.)

Now, since any negative number, $-b$, can be written $(-1) \cdot b$, you should be able to see that

$$(-b)^n = -b^n \qquad \text{when } n \text{ is odd} \tag{2-41}$$

For example,

$$(-6)^3 = -6^3 = -216$$
$$(-2)^5 = -2^5 = -32$$

In words, a negative number raised to any odd power is negative.

A perfect mth power is a number b that can be written as some base a raised to the power m. Thus, if

$$b = a^m$$

b is called a perfect mth power. When m is 2, we call b a *perfect square;* when m is 3, we call b a perfect cube.

Example

Since

$$16 = 4^2$$

we say that 16 is a perfect square. Also, since

$$16 = 2^4$$

we say that 16 is a perfect 4th power.

Problem

Write as a power of 3

$$\frac{27 \times 81}{243}$$

solution: Here we are asked to write the above as 3 raised to some power (a power of 3). So we should try to find as many factors of 3 as possible in the above members. First we find that

$$\frac{27 \times 81}{243} = \frac{3^3 \times 9^2}{3 \times 81} = \frac{3^3 \times (3^2)^2}{3 \times 9^2} = \frac{3^3 \times 3^4}{3 \times (3^2)^2} = \frac{3^7}{3 \times 3^4} = \frac{3^7}{3^5} = 3^2$$

Thus

$$\frac{27 \times 81}{243} = 3^2$$

We now give a more complete definition of LCD, first mentioned in Sec. 2-2.

Least Common Denominator (LCD)

The LCD of several fractions is a number which is the product of all the different prime factors of the denominators. Each prime factor should appear in the LCD to the highest power that it appears in any one denominator.

Now we proceed as in Sec. 2-2.

Example

Add

$$\frac{1}{9}, \quad \frac{5}{12}, \quad \frac{3}{8}$$

The denominators and their prime factors are

$$9 = 3^2 \qquad 12 = 3 \times 2^2 \qquad 8 = 2^3$$

The different prime factors are 2 and 3. The highest power to which 3 appears is 2. The highest power to which 2 appears is 3. Hence the LCD is

$$\text{LCD} = 3^2 \times 2^3 = 9 \times 8 = 72$$

Then

$$\frac{1}{9} = \frac{1 \times 8}{9 \times 8} = \frac{8}{72}$$

$$\frac{5}{12} = \frac{5 \times 6}{12 \times 6} = \frac{30}{72}$$

$$\frac{3}{8} = \frac{3 \times 9}{8 \times 9} = \frac{27}{72}$$

So

$$\frac{1}{9} + \frac{5}{12} + \frac{3}{8} = \frac{8}{72} + \frac{30}{72} + \frac{27}{72} = \frac{65}{72}$$

2-4 POSITIONAL NUMBERING SYSTEMS

As we mentioned earlier in this chapter, the notion of number arose as a result of counting. We have seen that these numbers are combinations of certain symbols used over and over again. The symbols used to represent actual (or explicit) real numbers are 0, 1, 2, 3, 4, 5, 6, 7, 8, 9. The *position* in which one of these symbols falls has meaning. Thus 91 has a different meaning from 19. The symbols 0, 1, 2, 3, 4, 5, 6, 7, 8, and 9 are called *digits*.

In general, the position of a digit in a number determines to what extent this digit is to be counted in the ultimate value of the number.

The method of representing numbers in the manner we are most familiar with is really a shorthand notation for the sum of each digit present times a nonnegative power of 10.   For example, 612 is shorthand notation for

$$6 \times 10^2 + 1 \times 10 + 2$$

Note that each digit is multiplied by a different power of 10, depending on its position in the number.   For integers, this idea is generalized by saying that, from right to left, each succeeding digit is to be multiplied by successive powers of 10, beginning with 10^0 (note that $10^0 = 1$). 10^0 is included in the generalization because it will facilitate symbolic description of this notion.

Nonintegers, when written with a decimal point, are also shorthand notation for the sum of each digit present times a negative power of 10.   For example, .237 is shorthand notation for

$$2 \times 10^{-1} + 3 \times 10^{-2} + 7 \times 10^{-3}$$

Note that each digit to the right of the decimal point is multiplied by a different negative power of 10.   For numbers less than 1, we generalize this by saying that, from left to right, each succeeding digit is to be multiplied by successive negative powers of 10.

Composite numbers (numbers that have an integer part and a fractional part) are also sums of powers of 10.   For example, 421.546 is shorthand notation for

$$4 \times 10^2 + 2 \times 10 + 1 + 5 \times 10^{-1} + 4 \times 10^{-2} + 6 \times 10^{-3}$$

In general, every digit is multiplied by some power of 10.   The number 10 is called the *base (or radix) of this positional numbering system*.   This system is called the base 10, or decimal, numbering system.   Numbers expressed in this system (whether in shorthand notation or as sums of powers of 10) are called base 10 numbers, or decimal numbers.

Note that this base 10 system has 10 digits (0, 1, 2, 3, 4, 5, 6, 7, 8, 9) with which to express numbers.   Also note that the use of the word decimal is different from what you have been accustomed to.   Previously, the word decimal number meant any number written with a decimal point.   Now the word decimal number means any base 10 number.

Perhaps now you have an idea as to why we name the digital positions in a base 10 number.

For example, in the number

679.542

we say that the digit 6 is in the *hundreds* position because, in the expanded form of this number, 6 is multiplied by 10^2 ($10^2 = 100$).   Similarly, 7 is in the *tens* position.   By convention (since 9 is multiplied by 10^0, or 1), we say that 9 is in the units position.

For digits to the right of the decimal point we recall that

$$10^{-1} = \frac{1}{10} = .1 = \text{one tenth}$$

$$10^{-2} = \frac{1}{10^2} = \frac{1}{100} = .01 = \text{one hundredth}$$

$$10^{-3} = \frac{1}{10^3} = \frac{1}{1,000} = .001 = \text{one thousandth}$$

This is why we say that 5 is in the *tenths* position, 4 is in the *hundredths* position, 2 is in the *thousandths* position.

We list the names of other positions in the following diagram.

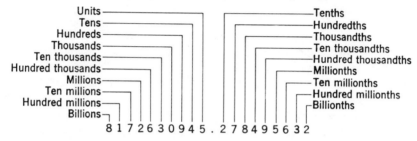

This description of our decimal numbering system should suggest to you the possibility of other positional numbering systems with bases other than 10. For example, a positional system with base 5 would have all its numbers expressible as combinations of the digits 0, 1, 2, 3, 4. A positional system with base 7 would have all its numbers expressible as a combination of the digits 0, 1, 2, 3, 4, 5, 6.

In general, if the number system has base b, then the permissible digits in that system will be 0, 1, 2, 3, 4, . . . , $b - 2$, $b - 1$. Thus, in any number system with base b, the highest-value digit in that system is $b - 1$.

When discussing numbers with different bases, we use a convention that has been adopted to identify to which system a number belongs. The convention suggests placing the base b at the lower right side of the number. Thus

413_5 would be a base 5 number
728_{10} would be a base 10 number

A number system which has gained importance since the advent of the computer is the base 2 (or binary) system. Here only two digits, 0 and 1, are used to express any binary number. Thus

1011_2 would be a base 2 number

Since base 10 is the number system with which we are most familiar, we may sometimes wish to convert to base 10 a number which is not in base 10.

We can accomplish this by merely writing out the number as a sum of powers of the base.

Example

Convert 413_5 to a base 10 number.

First we write 413_5 as a sum of powers of 5.   Thus

$$4 \times 5^2 + 1 \times 5 + 3 = 100 + 5 + 3 = 108_{10}$$

This number, 108_{10}, is called the *base* 10 *equivalent* of 413_5.

The point that separates integer part and fractional part in a composite number is called a radix point.   For example, in

$$241.303_5$$

241 is the integer part, 303 is the fractional part, and the point separating these is called the radix point.   In the past, you have probably referred to this as a decimal point.   This is because you were dealing with decimal (that is, base 10) numbers.   However, it is more properly called a radix point.

All the systems we have mentioned so far had bases smaller than 10. It is conceivable to have bases greater than 10.   But since we have only 10 digits at our disposal (0 to 9), new symbols must be introduced to represent values up to one less than the base.   For example, in the positional number system with base 12, we need 12 digits.   Then any base 12 number will be a combination of some of these 12 digits.   We have 10 digits (0 to 9) to represent values 0 to 9, but what shall we use for values 10 and 11?   We cannot use 10 for digit 10 because this takes up two positions (recall that a digit should take up only one position).   Moreover, 10 in base 12 is really $1 \times 12 + 0$, or 12. By the same reasoning, 11 cannot be used for digit 11 in this base 12 system. So we arbitrarily introduce symbols to represent digits 10 and 11.   The symbols t and e are commonly used to represent digits 10 and 11, respectively.

Thus the 12 digits permitted in the base 12 (also called duodecimal) system are

$$0, 1, 2, 3, 4, 5, 6, 7, 8, 9, t, e$$

and any duodecimal number is a combination of these digits.

Example

$t2e$

is a base 12 number.   We can find its base 10 equivalent in the usual way if we remember to change t and e to 10 and 11, respectively, when the number is written in expanded form.   Thus $t2e$ becomes

$$10 \times 12^2 + 2 \times 12 + 11 = 1,440 + 24 + 11 = 1,475$$

and we have

$$t2e_{12} = 1475_{10}$$

Fractional numbers and composite numbers exist in this system and are constructed in a manner similar to that previously discussed in other positional systems.

Another system has gained in importance due to the ever-expanding field of computer technology. This is the system with *base* 16, *the hexadecimal system*. We will meet this system in Chap. 6.

2-5 SCIENTIFIC AND FLOATING-POINT NOTATION

Before the advent of computers, man found himself dealing with very large and very small numbers. Distances between planets and galaxies and atoms are expressed with very large and very small numbers. Scientific notation allows us to express very large or very small numbers in a convenient form as a number between 1 and 10 times some integral power of 10.

For example,

$$275,000 = 2.75 \times 10,000 = 2.75 \times 10^5$$
$$.326 = 3.26 \times \tfrac{1}{10} = 3.26 \times 10^{-1}$$

When an integer is written by itself, it is implied that a decimal point appears to the right of it. Thus

25 *implies* 25.

Symbolically, scientific notation is defined as follows:
If M is any number written with a decimal point, then we can write

$$M = a \cdot 10^n$$

where $1 \leq a < 10$. a is formed by rewriting the digits in M with a decimal point placed just after the first nonzero digit on the left; n, the power of 10, can be found as follows: Count the number of places that the decimal point has moved in forming a from M; the number obtained is n; it will be positive if the point has moved left, negative if moved right, and zero if not moved at all.

Examples

$$5 = 5. \times 10^0 \qquad .5 = 5. \times 10^{-1}$$
$$50 = 5. \times 10^1 \qquad 1 = 1. \times 10^0$$
$$100 = 1 \times 10^2 = 10^2$$

Note that n will be negative if $0 < M < 1$, positive if $M > 10$, and zero if $1 < M < 10$. It is important to remember that every move of the point one place to the left means that we are dividing by 10; a move one place to the right means that we are multiplying by 10.

Scientific notation allows us to compute with large and small numbers in a very convenient fashion. For example, if we were asked to divide 100,800,000 by 840,000, you can see that the process of long division would become unwieldy. However, if we used scientific notation, we would have

$$\frac{100,800,000}{840,000} = \frac{1.008 \times 10^8}{8.4 \times 10^5}$$

Now we can use Eq. (2-24) to write

$$\frac{1.008 \times 10^8}{8.4 \times 10^5} = \frac{1.008}{8.4} \frac{10^8}{10^5}$$

We carry out the divisions and obtain

$$\frac{100,800,000}{840,000} = .12 \times 10^3 = 120.0$$

If we were asked to write the result in scientific notation, we would have

$$1.2 \times 10^2$$

Floating-point notation is another way of writing real numbers. Here we express the real number M as

$$M = b \cdot 10^m$$

where $0 < b < 1$, and m is an appropriate power of 10. Numbers written this way are called floating-point numbers. b is called the *mantissa*, and m is the *exponent*. Thus

$$16.25 = .1625 \times 10^2$$

Note that b is formed in a manner similar to forming a in scientific notation. In forming b we place the decimal point preceding the first nonzero digit on the left. m is found by counting the number of decimal places moved as we did in scientific notation.

When the leftmost digit of the mantissa is not a zero, we say the floating-point number is *normalized*. For example,

$$.0326 \times 10^2$$

is a *nonnormalized* floating-point number; but

$$.875 \times 10^{-3}$$

is a *normalized* floating-point number.

Floating-point notation is a common way of representing numbers within a computer. There usually is a fixed number of positions devoted to mantissa and a fixed number of positions devoted to exponent.

There is no need for a position to represent the decimal point and no need for positions to represent 10. This is so because 10 is present in every floating-point number.

The following is a hypothetical but realistic way that floating-point numbers might be represented internally within a computer.

Mantissa   Exponent

Then internally, the number $.875 \times 10^{-3}$ would appear as

| + | 8 | 7 | 5 | 0 | | − | 0 | 3 |

There is always a fixed number of positions with which to represent mantissa and exponent. How then, you may ask, can we represent a number whose floating-point form yields a mantissa with more digits than there are positions available? This question is best answered after we discuss the notions of *rounding* and *truncation*.

Let us assume we have a number M written with seven digits. For instance,

276.4932

would be such a number.

It is sometimes desirable (sometimes necessary) to express such a number with fewer digits. The two methods used to accomplish this are rounding and truncation. The digits to be dropped are on the right. Several examples will illustrate.

Examples

Let us say we wish to express the above number with four digits. The method of *chopping off* the undesired digits on the right is called *truncation*. Thus

276.4 *is the truncated form of* 276.4932

We say that 276.4932 has been *truncated* to four digits.

We could have used the process of *rounding* to express 276.4932 in four digits. In this procedure we look at the leftmost digit of *the digits to be dropped*. *If it is five or greater, we add one to the rightmost of the digits remaining.* If it is less than five, we do nothing to the remaining digits.

In our example we have

276.4932

The digits to be dropped are 932. The leftmost of these is 9. It is greater than 5; so we add 1 to the rightmost of the digits remaining. The digits remaining are 276.4. The rightmost is 4; so we add 1 to 4. The result is

276.5

This is the rounded form of 276.4932.

It should be clear to you that 276.4932 rounded to three digits is 276. Also

276.4932 *truncated to three digits is* 276

We can round and truncate integers, but we must remember to replace the digits dropped by zeros. For example,

5,472 *rounded to the hundreds position*

(another way of saying this is "the nearest hundred") is 5,500. But the same number truncated to the nearest hundred is 5,400.

Now we can see how a number can be expressed in a fewer number of digits.

Truncation and roundoff are two modes of representation when there are too many digits in the original number. For example, 642.76 represented internally would be

Rounded							
+	6	4	2	8	+	0	3

Truncated							
+	6	4	2	7	+	0	3

So keep in mind that rounding and truncation yield approximations to the original number. Thus, in the above example,

$.6428 \times 10^3$ and $.6427 \times 10^3$

are approximations to the original number $.64276 \times 10^3$.

Thus we see that a number represented internally may be only an approximation to the original number. Because of this, certain arithmetic operations may lead to erroneous results!

For example, let us add 473.46 and 42.568. We obtain

```
    473.46
+    42.568
   _____
   516.028
```

Now let us perform the addition when the two numbers are represented in floating-point form with four-digit mantissas. First we write the numbers and their floating-point forms.

$$473.46 \qquad .4735 \times 10^3$$
$$42.568 \qquad .4257 \times 10^2$$

Now we can add numbers written in floating-point form when the powers of 10 of the numbers are the same (this is true for scientific notation also). When the powers are the same, we merely add the mantissas and write the result times the common power of 10. So in our case, before we add, we must adjust the powers of 10. Let us adjust $.4257 \times 10^2$ so that the exponent is 3. Then we have

$$.4257 \times 10^2 = .04257 \times 10^3$$

But we can have only a four-digit mantissa. So we round off .04257 to obtain

$$.0426 \times 10^3$$

Now we add according to the rule above.

$$.4735 \times 10^3$$
$$+.0426 \times 10^3$$
$$\overline{.5161 \times 10^3}$$

Thus the sum is $.5161 \times 10^3$. In ordinary decimal notation this is

$$516.1$$

Note that this is quite different from the true sum of 516.028!

Sometimes the addition of mantissas will yield a number with mantissa greater than 1. For example, add

$$.9423 \times 10^3$$

and

$$.7582 \times 10^2$$

Adjusting the number with smaller exponent and adding, we have

$$.9423 \times 10^3$$
$$.0758 \times 10^3$$
$$\overline{1.0181 \times 10^3}$$

Now we adjust the resulting sum to obtain a *normalized floating-point number*. This will be accomplished if we move the decimal point in 1.0181 one place to the left (this is the same as dividing 1.0181 by 10), while at the same time increasing the exponent by 1 (this is the same as multiplying 10^3 by 10).

Both steps must be taken. This is so because performing only one step will yield a completely different number. We write the number obtained after each step to demonstrate this.

	Ordinary notation
1.0181×10^3	$1,018.1$
$\dfrac{1.0181}{10} \times 10^3 = .10181 \times 10^3$	101.81
$1.0181 \times (10^3 \times 10) = 1.0181 \times 10^4$	$10,181.$
$\dfrac{1.0181}{10} \times (10^3 \times 10) = .10181 \times 10^4$	$1,018.1$

The Associative Law

It is easy to see that the associative law for real-number addition *may not hold* inside a limited digit machine (like a computer). This means $a + (b + c)$ is not necessarily the same as $(a + b) + c$. We will use standard decimal representation to show this. The equivalent floating-point representation appears to the right of a, b, and c.

$$a = 141.6 \qquad .1416 \times 10^3$$
$$b = 604.9 \qquad .6049 \times 10^3$$
$$c = 543.8 \qquad .5438 \times 10^3$$

Now $b + c = 1,148.7$.

Using four digits after rounding, we have

$$b + c = 1,149$$

Adding a to this, we have

$$a + (b + c) = 141.6 + 1,149 = 1,290.6$$

Using four digits after rounding, we find

$$a + (b + c) = 1,291$$

But now

$$a + b = 746.5$$

and

$$(a + b) + c = 746.5 + 543.8 = 1,290.3$$

Using four digits after rounding, we obtain

$$(a + b) + c = 1,290$$

As an exercise you should follow through the above examples, using floating-point notation throughout.

Sometimes we may be interested in the difference between true value and computed value of a quantity. In our case we have

$$516.028 - 516.1 = -.072$$

This difference is sometimes called the *error*. The *absolute value* of this difference is called the *absolute error*. From above, the absolute error is

$$|516.028 - 516.1| = |-.072| = -(-.072) = .072$$

A better measure of the error is obtained when we divide the absolute error by the computed value. The result is called *relative error*. Multiplying the relative error by 100 gives *percent error*. In our case,

$$\frac{.072}{516.1} = .0001 \text{ relative error}$$

Thus we have a .01 percent error between computed value and true value. This topic will be discussed again in Chap. 10.

2-6 NONINTEGRAL EXPONENTS

We have demonstrated the laws of exponents when the exponents are integral values. The laws are true for nonintegral exponents also. By nonintegral we mean exponents which are not integers. This is the same as saying that we mean exponents which are fractional (rational) and irrational. We discuss fractional exponents first.

The notions of fractional exponent and of an integral root are tied together with the following definition.

Let a be a number whose nth power is equal to b. That is, let

$$a^n = b \tag{2-42}$$

Then we say that a is an nth root of b. When n is 2, a is called a square root of b. When n is 3, a is called a cube root of b. For example,

$$2^2 = 4$$

so 2 is a square root of 4. Also,

$$(-2)^2 = 4$$

so -2 is a square root of 4.

As another example,

$$2^3 = 8$$

so 2 is a cube root of 8.   Also,

$$(-2)^3 = -8$$

so -2 is a cube root of -8.

There is a symbolic way of representing nth roots.   This is accomplished by introducing the symbol $\sqrt{}$, called the *radical*.   It is used to denote nth roots in the following way.

If $a^n = b$ then $a = \sqrt[n]{b}$

is read "a equals the principal nth root of b." n is sometimes called the *index* of the radical, and b is called the *radicand*.   By *principal nth root* we mean the positive real nth root when b is positive and n is even.   For example, we know

$$2^2 = 4$$

and

$$(-2)^2 = 4$$

so 2 and -2 are 2d roots (square roots) of 4.   But 2 (since it is positive) is the principal square root.   So

$$2 = \sqrt{4} \qquad \text{and} \qquad -2 = -\sqrt{4}$$

When the index of the radical is 2, we do not write it.

Principal nth root also means negative nth root when b is negative and n is odd.   For example,

$$(-2)^3 = -8$$

so

$$-2 = \sqrt[3]{-8}$$

Finally, principal nth root means positive nth root when b is positive and n is odd.   For example,

$$2^3 = 8$$

so

$$2 = \sqrt[3]{8}$$

We have not covered the case when b *is negative and n is even*.   This is because no real number raised to an even power will yield a negative number (see Exercise 2-13).   Another way of saying this is: The nth root of a negative number when n is even does not exist as a real number.   For example,

$$\sqrt{-4}$$

does not exist as a real number, since no real number, when squared, will equal -4.

The notion of nth root and the notion of fractional exponents are tied together by the relationship

$$\sqrt[n]{b} = b^{1/n} \tag{2-43}$$

The notions developed previously with integral exponents can be extended to fractional exponents. We state the results:

$$(b^{1/n})^m = b^{m/n} = (b^m)^{1/n} \tag{2-44}$$

For example,

$$(4^{1/2})^3 = (2)^3 = 8$$

and

$$(4^{1/2})^3 = 4^{3/2} = (4^3)^{1/2} = (64)^{1/2} = 8$$

Using radicals instead of fractional exponents, we would have

$$(\sqrt{4})^3 = (2)^3 = 8$$

and

$$(\sqrt{4})^3 = \sqrt{4^3} = \sqrt{64} = 8$$

So we note that

$$4^{3/2} = (\sqrt{4})^3$$

or

$$4^{3/2} = \sqrt{4^3}$$

Another extension is

$$(b^{1/n})^{1/m} = b^{1/nm} = (b^{1/m})^{1/n} \tag{2-45}$$

For example,

$$(16^{1/4})^{1/2} = 16^{1/8} = (16^{1/2})^{1/4}$$

or

$$\sqrt{\sqrt[4]{16}} = \sqrt[8]{16} = \sqrt{\sqrt[4]{16}}$$
$$(b^{1/n})^n = (b^n)^{1/n} = b \tag{2-46}$$

Example

$$(2^{1/2})^2 = (2^2)^{1/2} = 2$$

or

$$(\sqrt{2})^2 = \sqrt{2^2} = 2$$

In general,

$$\sqrt[n]{b^n} = b \tag{2-47}$$
$$(ab)^{1/n} = a^{1/n}b^{1/n} \tag{2-48}$$

or

$$\sqrt[n]{ab} = \sqrt[n]{a}\,\sqrt[n]{b} \tag{2-49}$$

Finally,

$$\left(\frac{a}{b}\right)^{1/n} = \frac{a^{1/n}}{b^{1/n}} \tag{2-50}$$

or

$$\sqrt[n]{\frac{a}{b}} = \frac{\sqrt[n]{a}}{\sqrt[n]{b}} \tag{2-51}$$

As illustrations we have

$$\sqrt{125} = \sqrt{25 \times 5} = \sqrt{25}\,\sqrt{5} = 5\,\sqrt{5}$$
$$\sqrt{\frac{7}{16}} \frac{\sqrt{7}}{\sqrt{16}} = \frac{\sqrt{7}}{4} = \frac{1}{4} \times \sqrt{7}$$

An illustration using several of the results above is

$$\left(\frac{a^3 b^9}{c^6}\right)^{1/3} \cdot \left(\frac{c^{12}}{a^4 b^8}\right)^{1/4} = \frac{ab^3}{c^2} \cdot \frac{c^3}{ab^2} = bc$$

Usually, when radicals or fractional exponents appear in a problem, it is desirable to remove them as best we can. One process that can help is to seek perfect nth powers under radicals of index n. Then we apply Eq. (2-47) to remove the radical.

Problem 1

Simplify (this means remove radical or fractional exponent to the extent possible)

$$\sqrt[3]{192}$$

solution: We observe that 192 can be factored in many ways. For instance, $192 = 2 \times 96 = 3 \times 64 = 4 \times 48$. But in our efforts to *factor the radicand* 192, we keep in mind that perfect 3d powers are sought, since this is a radical of order 3. We note that 64 is a perfect 3d power since $4^3 = 64$.

So the proper factorization is

$$\sqrt[3]{192} = \sqrt[3]{64 \times 3}$$

or

$$\sqrt[3]{192} = \sqrt[3]{4^3 \times 3}$$

Now we can use Eqs. (2-49) and (2-47) to obtain

$$\sqrt[3]{192} = 4\sqrt[3]{3}$$

Problem 2

Simplify

$$\sqrt[3]{27 \cdot x^3}$$

solution:

$$\sqrt[3]{27 \cdot x^3} = \sqrt[3]{3^3 \cdot x^3} = \sqrt[3]{(3 \cdot x)^3} = 3x$$

We must keep in mind that a number expressed in radical form is merely another way of expressing that number in exponential form. From this we can see that radicals can be combined according to the distributive law only if they have the same index and same radicand. For example, $\sqrt{2}$ is different from $\sqrt{3}$ even though it has the same index. Likewise, $\sqrt[3]{8}$ is different from $\sqrt{8}$ even though it has the same radicand.

Now, in applying the distributive law to radicals, a multiplication between radicals is necessary. When radicals of different order are to be multiplied, it is convenient to convert the different orders to some common one.

For example, multiply

$$\sqrt{2} \text{ and } \sqrt[3]{3}$$

Writing with fractional exponents gives a better idea of what is happening.

$$\sqrt{2} = 2^{1/2} \qquad \sqrt[3]{3} = 3^{1/3}$$

We construct a common index by multiplying $1/2$ by $3/3$ and by multiplying $1/3$ by $2/2$. Then

$$2^{1/2} = 2^{3/6} \qquad 3^{1/3} = 3^{2/6}$$

and

$$\sqrt{2} \times \sqrt[3]{3} = \sqrt[6]{2^3} = \sqrt[6]{3^2} = \sqrt[6]{2^3 \times 3^2} = \sqrt[6]{72}$$

Now you see how we can perform operations like

$$\sqrt{2} \times (1 + \sqrt[3]{3}) = \sqrt{2} + \sqrt[6]{72}$$

As another example, we have

$$\frac{7}{2}\sqrt[4]{3} + 8\sqrt[4]{3} = \left(\frac{7}{2} + 8\right)\sqrt[4]{3} = \frac{23}{2}\sqrt[4]{3}$$

You may have noticed that in some examples the answers were sometimes expressed with radicals, sometimes without radicals. If you look back, you will see the latter only when the radicand was a perfect nth power. When the radicand was not a perfect nth power, we could express the result as a radical only with index n. That is,

$$\sqrt[n]{a}$$

is a rational number (note that integers are included here) only if a is a perfect nth power. If a is not a perfect nth power, then $\sqrt[n]{a}$ is an *irrational number*. One characteristic of an irrational number is that it can be represented as a never-ending nonrepeating decimal number. For example, $\sqrt{2}$ is an irrational number. You may have memorized its decimal representation as 1.414. This decimal number is only an *approximation* to $\sqrt{2}$, because the actual decimal number is a never-ending one.

2-7 LOGARITHMS

A special way of thinking about exponents is a good thing to remember when the word *logarithm* is mentioned. In fact, as we shall see, a logarithm is merely another way of writing an exponent.

Logarithms first gained prominence in the seventeenth century as an aid in *computation*. At present, we have the computer to aid us in computation; so the importance of logarithms as a computational aid has decreased. However, in more advanced mathematics courses, the notion of logarithm is needed; so we will introduce, but not dwell on it, here.

Let b be a positive number different from 1. Then, if

$$b^y = x \tag{2-52}$$

the exponent y is called the *logarithm* (the word is sometimes shortened to log) of x to the base b. It is written symbolically as

$$y = \log_b x \tag{2-53}$$

Equation (2-52) is the exponential form; Eq. (2-53) is the logarithmic form of the same relationship. Some examples follow.

$$2 = \log_5 25$$

because

$$5^2 = 25$$

Also,

$$5 = \log_2 32$$

since

$$2^5 = 32$$

A word of warning. Always pay special attention to the roles played by b, y, and x in Eq. (2-52). y is the exponent; b is the base that must be raised to the power y in order to obtain x.

Since b is positive, then x must be positive. This is so because any positive number raised to any real power is positive. (This statement requires proof, but we will not pursue it.) Note that we said *to any real power*. This includes negative numbers. Thus logarithms can be negative numbers.

For example,

$$-3 = \log_2 \tfrac{1}{8}$$

because

$$2^{-3} = \frac{1}{2^3} = \frac{1}{8}$$

We are restricted to integers as exponents, as demonstrated by this example.

$$\tfrac{3}{4} = \log_{16} 8$$

since

$$16^{3/4} = (\sqrt[4]{16})^3 = 2^3 = 8$$

Note that this can also be written

$$.75 = \log_{16} 8$$

Since logarithms are exponents, you may have guessed that a set of laws exist governing operations with logarithms, similar to the laws of exponents. This is true; in fact, the *properties of logarithms* have their basis in the laws of *exponents*. We repeat some of the laws of exponents that are used in deriving the properties of logarithms.

$$b^y b^z = b^{y+z} \tag{2-54}$$

$$\frac{b^y}{b^z} = b^{y-z} \tag{2-55}$$

$$(b^y)^z = b^{yz} \tag{2-56}$$

It is easy to show (see Exercises) the following properties of logarithms; b again is the base, and x and w are positive.

The log of a product is equal to the sum of the logs. Symbolically,

$$\log_b xw = \log_b x + \log_b w \qquad\qquad (2\text{-}57)$$

The log of a quotient is equal to the difference of the logs. That is,

$$\log_b \frac{x}{w} = \log_b x - \log_b w \qquad\qquad (2\text{-}58)$$

Finally, if r is a real number,

$$\log_b x^r = r \log_b x \qquad\qquad (2\text{-}59)$$

Logarithms became important as a computational aid because problems which involved the tedious operations of multiplication and division could be solved using the simple operations of addition and subtraction.

An illustration will be helpful at this point.

Problem

Calculate

$$\frac{(4.53) \cdot (6.98)}{7.45}$$

solution: In solving this, we could use floating-point notation, but the operations of multiplication and division would still have to be done. Using the notions of logarithm, we can solve this more simply by addition and subtraction.

Let x be the result. Then

$$x = \frac{(4.53) \cdot (6.98)}{7.45}$$

Now take the log of x to some base b. Then

$$\log_b x = \log_b \frac{(4.53) \cdot (6.98)}{7.45}$$

Now we use two of the properties of logs, Eqs. (2-51) and (2-58), to obtain

$$\log_b x = \log_b 4.53 + \log_b 6.98 - \log_b 7.45$$

If we can find each of the three numbers on the right, we can combine them and obtain a single real number; call it y. Then we would have

$$\log_b x = y$$

Note that b is known and y is known.   If there were some way to find b raised to the power y (this is the definition of log), we would have our desired result x.   That is,

$$x = b^y$$

As you can see from above, the selection of the base b is an all-important step.

Long ago, near the time of the discovery of logarithms, a base of 10 was selected, because our familiar number system is founded on powers of 10. Extensive *log tables* have been constructed which give the logs to the base 10 of many numbers.

The logarithms of all positive numbers to the base 10 are called *common logarithms*.

The task of constructing base 10 logarithm tables is not as forbidding as one might think if it is recalled that any positive number P can be written in scientific notation as

$$P = x \cdot 10^n \tag{2-60}$$

where n is an integer, and x is between 1 and 10.   Now we find the log of P and use Eqs. (2-57) and (2-59) to obtain

$$\log P = \log x + \log 10^n \tag{2-61}$$

or

$$\log P = \log x + n \tag{2-62}$$

(*Note:* When it is understood that we are speaking of common logs, we do not explicitly write the 10 in $\log_{10}$.   In common logarithms log means log to the base 10.)

The integer n is called the *characteristic* of $\log P$, and the number $\log x$ is called the *mantissa* of $\log P$.

For example,

$$758 = 7.58 \times 10^2$$

Then

$$\log 758 = \log 7.58 + 2$$

Note that $\log 7.58 + 2$ *does not mean* $\log (7.58 + 2)$.   To avoid possible confusion, we write

$$\log 758 = 2 + \log 7.58$$

Also,

$$75.8 = 7.58 \times 10^1$$

Then

$$\log 75.8 = 1 + \log 7.58$$

As a final example,

$$7.58 = 7.58 \times 10^0$$
$$\log 7.58 = 0 + \log 7.58 = \log 7.58$$

The following proposition is proved in more advanced courses.

If x is between 1 and 10, then $\log x$ is between 0 and 1. (Exercise 2-37 gives some insight into this idea.)

This is why $\log x$ in Eq. (2-61) or (2-62) is always between 0 and 1. In constructing log tables, only the mantissas are given, since the characteristics can be obtained by inspection.

For example,

$$.000357 = 3.57 \times 10^{-4}$$

Then

$$\log .000357 = -4 + \log 3.57$$

In this and other examples you will see that the characteristic is the power of 10 obtained when the number is written in scientific notation.

When negative characteristics arise, they are written as some positive number minus 10. In the previous example,

$$\log .000357 = -4 + \log 3.57 = 6 + \log 3.57 - 10$$

This convention has been adopted for ease in handling the additions and subtractions of logarithms.

Since there are many texts which give a good treatment of logarithmic manipulations, we end our discussion here.

2-8 SYMBOLS OF GROUPING

In this text and in your contact with computer languages you will need a background knowledge of symbols of grouping.

Sometimes we group together several explicit real numbers and/or literals when they are to be considered as a single real number. In mathematics textbooks you will see such grouping symbols as the parentheses ( ), brackets [ ], and braces { } used most often.

You have seen the parentheses used before in this chapter. They were introduced in the section on real-number axioms. In that section, the arithmetic operation which appeared inside was to be performed first. Thus

$$a + (b + c)$$

meant: Obtain the sum $b + c$ first, then add the result to a.   However,

$$(a + b) + c$$

meant: Obtain the sum $a + b$ first, then add the result to c.

There are three important reasons why symbols of grouping are used:

1. To signify that what is inside is to be taken as a single real number
2. To specify that the arithmetic operation appearing inside is to be performed first
3. To facilitate reading the symbolic statement

Most of the time reasons 1 and 3 are implied when symbols of grouping are used.

Let us assume we have literals or explicit numbers connected by combinations of addition, subtraction, multiplication, division, or exponentiation. The resulting configuration is called an *expression*.   An example is

$$(a + 5x^2 - b)$$

The parentheses are included to emphasize reason 1 above.   The distinct members of the expression are a, $5x$, and b.   These parts, with their signs preceding, are called *terms* of the expression.   When a term consists of a product of a known value and an unknown value, the known value is called the coefficient of the term.   Thus, in the term $+5x^2$, the coefficient is $+5$.

When two or more terms differ in coefficient only, we can apply the *distributive law* to obtain a single term.   Thus

$$-6y + 12y$$

can be *simplified* by the distributive law to yield

$$(-6 + 12)y$$

or

$$6y$$

The process is called *combining like terms*.

Often we will be asked to add or subtract expressions.   For example, subtract $-2a + 5x^2 - b$ from $a + 5x^2 - b$.   Symbolically, this means

$$(a + 5x^2 - b) - (-2a + 5x^2 - b)$$

The parentheses are included here to emphasize reasons 1 and 3.   If we are asked to *simplify* the above, we must remove as much as possible all symbols of grouping and combine like terms.

The following rules will help us in the removal of grouping symbols.

A pair of grouping symbols preceded by a plus sign can be removed unconditionally.

A pair of grouping symbols preceded by a minus sign can be removed if the sign of each enclosed term is changed.

Two similar rules can be stated, with the word "removed" replaced by "inserted."

These rules are consequences of Eq. (2-20) and the distributive law.

So, in our problem above, we have

$$(2 + 5x^2 - b) - (-2a + 5x^2 - b)$$

or

$$a + 5x^2 - b + 2a - 5x^2 + b$$

Now $+5x^2$ and $-5x^2$ can be combined to yield a zero term.   Similarly, $-b$ and $+b$ yield zero, and we are left with

$$a + 2a$$

or

$$(1 + 2)a$$

or

$$3a$$

Thus

$$(a + 5x^2 - b) - (-2a + 5x^2 - b) = 3a$$

(*Note:* When no sign precedes a pair of grouping symbols, the plus sign is assumed.)

Recall, from the distributive law, that we have

$$-4(6x - 4y + 3a) = -24x + 16y - 12a$$

We use this concept to handle problems like the following:

Simplify

$$(5a + 25x - 12y) - 4(6x - 4y + 3a)$$

The result is

$$5a + 25x - 12y - 24x + 16y - 12a$$

or

$$-7a - x + 4y$$

When we are asked to simplify expressions in which pairs of grouping symbols enclose other pairs of grouping symbols, we usually proceed by removing the innermost pair first, combining as we go along, thus:

Simplify

$$-\{5x - 3[x - 4(x - y) + 7y]\}$$

First,

$$-[5x - 3(x - 4x + 4y + 7y)]$$

Then, combining like terms,

$-[5x - 3(-3x + 11y)]$

Once again,

$-(5x + 9x - 33y)$

Combining, we have

$-(14x - 33y)$

Finally,

$-14x + 33y$

In an answer such as this, the plus term is written first, without its sign.

$33y - 14x$

The meaning is the same.

Near the beginning of this section, reasons were given for the use of grouping symbols.   The second of those reasons is one of the rules for expression construction in the FORTRAN computer language.

For example, in

$3 - 4(7 - 2)$

$(7 - 2)$ would be computed first, yielding

$3 - 4 \times 5$

Now, another FORTRAN rule is this: *When no parentheses appear in an expression, the operations of multiplication and division are performed before addition or subtraction.*   Thus we obtain

$3 - 20$

Finally, we have

-17

As a final illustration of this point, consider

$-[17 - 6(5 + 2) - 12(6 + 4) - 13]$

The computer would evaluate this (via the FORTRAN language) in the following way:

A. $-(17 - 6 \cdot 7 - 12 \cdot 10 - 13)$
B. $-(17 - 42 - 120 - 13)$
C. $-(-25 - 120 - 13)$
D. $-(-145 - 13)$
E. $-(-158)$
F. 158

[*Note:* When only additions or subtractions appear within parentheses (as in B), they are performed from left to right.]

The symbols for arithmetic operations in the FORTRAN language are slightly different than those normally used in mathematics. The following table will clarify this.

Operation	Mathematical symbol	FORTRAN symbol
Addition	$+$	$+$
Subtraction	$-$	$-$
Multiplication	$\cdot$ $\times$ ("ex") Adjacent letters or numbers	*
Division	$\div$ $-$ $/$	/
Exponentiation	Small exponent to the upper right of the base	**

Examples

In the following list, capital letters denote the FORTRAN equivalent.

	$a + b$	A + B
	$a - b$	A − B
	$a \cdot b$	A*B
or	$a \times b$	A*B
or	ab	A*B
	$a \div b$	A/B
or	$\dfrac{a}{b}$	A/B
or	a/b	A/B
	a^b	A**B

Exercises

2-1.   In the following equations, name the literals and the explicit real numbers.

a. $A = 2h$ b. $x = a + b$ c. $y = a - b$

d. $6 = 5 - b$ e. $10 = 20 - 10$ f. $100 = 2k$

2-2. A consequence of the distributive axiom is $x(y - z) = xy - xz$. Use this to find

   a. $3(5 - 2)$ b. $4(8 - 5)$

2-3. Perform these operations:

   a. $4 + (-3)$ b. $\frac{3}{2} \div \frac{1}{5}$ c. $-4 - 5$
   d. $-6(x - y)$ e. $\frac{3}{4} \times \frac{4}{3} \times \frac{2}{5}$ f. $\frac{17}{25} + \frac{2}{3}$
   g. $\frac{17}{25} - \frac{2}{3}$ h. $-\frac{4}{3} + \frac{15}{3}$ i. $\frac{1}{2}(\frac{2}{3} + \frac{4}{9} - \frac{2}{7})$
   j. $62[37 + (-26)]$

2-4. Reduce to lowest terms

   a. $\frac{16}{8}$ b. $2a/8a$ c. $\frac{11}{22}$
   d. $\frac{36}{21}$ e. $-\frac{42}{49}$

2-5. Equation (2-25) tells us $a/b = ax/bx$. From this, which of the following pairs are equal?

   a. $\dfrac{4}{5}, \dfrac{20}{25}$ b. $\dfrac{ax + ay}{ax - ay}, \dfrac{x + y}{x - y}$ c. $\dfrac{1}{2}, \dfrac{2}{3}$

   d. $\dfrac{-1}{x + y}, \dfrac{1}{-x - y}$

2-6. A positive integer n is said to be a prime number if its only factors are 1 and the number n itself. Thus 3 is a prime since its only factors are 1 and 3. Thus $3 = 1 \times 3$. The integer 6 is not a prime, since it can be factored as $6 = 2 \times 3$. State which of the following numbers are primes.

   a. 60   b. 7   c. 13
   d. 14   e. 15   f. 16
   g. 17   h. 27   i. 101
   j. 105

2-7. *Refer to Fig.* 2-1. The distance between two points on the real line is defined as the absolute value of their difference (this makes distance a positive quantity). Find the distance between

   a. 6 and -3 b. -3 and 6   c. $\frac{1}{2}$ and $\frac{1}{4}$
   d. 0 and -1 e. -50 and $+50$ f. -100 and 0

2-8. Find the sum of

   a. $\frac{1}{3} + \frac{1}{5} + \frac{1}{7}$ b. $\frac{3}{10} + \frac{4}{15} + \frac{2}{3}$
   c. $\frac{3}{10} - \frac{4}{15} + \frac{2}{3}$ d. $\frac{4}{21} + \frac{16}{15} + \frac{31}{35}$

2-9.   Show that

a. $\dfrac{xy + xz}{x} = y + z$ b. $\dfrac{xy/wz}{y/z} = \dfrac{x}{w}$

c. $\dfrac{ab + ac}{df} \cdot \dfrac{d}{a} = \dfrac{b + c}{f}$

2-10.   When b and a are integers, with $a \neq 0$, we have

$$\frac{b}{a} = q + \frac{r}{a}$$

where q, an integer, is called the quotient, and r, an integer, is called the remainder.   When $b = 6$ and $a = 4$, we have

$$\frac{b}{a} = \frac{6}{4}$$

Now

$$\begin{array}{r} 1 \\ 4\overline{)6} \\ \underline{4} \\ 2 \end{array}$$

Thus

$$\tfrac{6}{4} = 1 + \tfrac{2}{4}$$

In every case r has the property $0 \leq r \leq (a - 1)$.   We can also write

$$b = aq + r$$

2-11.   Find q and r when b/a is

a. $\tfrac{10}{5}$ b. $\tfrac{16}{3}$ c. $-\tfrac{12}{4}$

d. $\tfrac{15}{2}$ e. $\tfrac{30}{16}$

2-12.   State symbolically (with inequality signs) the relationship between

a. $\tfrac{3}{7}, \tfrac{5}{8}$ $0, 1$ $-\tfrac{2}{3}, \tfrac{3}{2}$ $2, -2$
b.   If $a > 1$, what can you say about a^2 and a?
c.   If $0 < a < 1$, what can you say about a and a^2?

2-13.   All positive even integers can be given by the formula $2k$, where k takes on values $1, 2, 3, 4, 5, \ldots$.   Show that -1 to any even power is positive.   In particular, show that

a. $(-1)^n = 1$ when n is even
b. $(-9)^n = 9^n$ when n is even
c. $(-a)^n = a^n$ when a is positive and n is even

2-14.   Write without exponents

   a. $\dfrac{a^3}{a^2}$ b. $\dfrac{6^7 \times 6^3}{6^4/6}$ c. $[(2^3)^2]^3$

   d. $\dfrac{9^4 \times 3^7}{81^2 \times 27}$ e. $\dfrac{(-5)^2}{5^3}$ f. $\dfrac{8 \times 2^2}{2^4}$

   g. $\dfrac{13^8}{13^7}$ h. $\dfrac{(\frac{1}{4})^3}{(\frac{1}{4})^4}$

2-15.   Write with as few bases as possible

   a. $x^3 y^2 y^{-3}$ b. $\dfrac{x^3 y^6 z^9}{x^2 y^4 z^6}$ c. $b^4 \cdot b^4 \cdot b$

   d. $10x^2 y^5 / 2y^3$

2-16.   Write the base 10 equivalent of

   a. 1011_2 b. 244_5 c. 1000_2

   d. 1620_7 e. 11111_2 f. 1241_5

   g. 10_2 h. 10_5 i. 10_7

   j. $2et_{12}$ k. $ttee_{12}$ l. $t00t_{12}$

   m. 10_{12}

2-17.   Can 10,634 be a base 5 number?   If not, why not?

2-18.   Write in scientific notation

   a. .000015   b. 93,000,000   c. 10,324,569

2-19.   Compute, using scientific notation,

   a. $\dfrac{(1,500) \cdot (45,000)}{300}$ b. $\dfrac{(.0145) \cdot (301)}{.062}$

2-20.   Round off, then truncate, the following numbers to three digits.

   a. .46375   b. 3.4586   c. .00057

   d. 562.9

2-21.   The notion of *significant digits* in a number is sometimes important.

   i.   All nonzero digits in a number are significant digits.
   ii. Zeros appearing between nonzero digits are significant digits.
   iii. Trailing zeros in an integer and leading zeros in a number
        less than 1 are nonsignificant.   For example,
        345.02   has five significant digits
        340   has two significant digits
          .0054 has two significant digits

As illustrations we will round the following numbers to three significant digits.

a. 5,286	b. 457.903	c. 0.0007863
5,290	458	0.000786

2-22.   Round these numbers to two significant digits:

a. 41.3   b. .0652   c. 93,872,435

2-23.   Add, assuming four-digit mantissas, by adjusting the number with the smaller exponent.

a. $.35627 \times 10^3$ b. $.26785 \times 10^7$ c. $.35406 \times 10^5$
    $.24812 \times 10^2$ $.98723 \times 10^4$ $.43782 \times 10^1$

d. Find the percent error between true value and computed value for parts a to c when rounding is used; to the same when truncation is used.

2-24.   Adjust the following numbers as required.

a. Rewrite with an exponent of 3:

$.263 \times 10^2$ $.263 \times 10^4$ $.982 \times 10^{-1}$ 1.26×10^5

b. Rewrite as normalized floating-point numbers:

$.00635 \times 10^5$ 76.55×10^{-2} $.00037 \times 10^{-6}$

2-25.   Verify whether or not the associative law for addition is obeyed for the following numbers.   Use truncated three-digit representation.

a. 14.29	b. 72.00	c. 1.325
36.98	66.00	2.017
47.56	19.00	6.128

2-26.   Consider a radical sign with a radicand of 343.   The index is 3.   To what real integer does this correspond?

2-27.   We find $5^4 = 625$ and $(-5)^4 = 625$.   From this, what is the principal 4th root of 625?   Write it symbolically.

2-28.   Find the square roots of:

a. ¼   b. ⁴⁄₈₁   c. 625
d. 121

2-29.   Express without radicals or fractional exponents:

        a. $\sqrt[5]{.00032}$ (*Hint:* Write the radicand as some number times an appropriate power of 10.)

        b. $8^{2/3}$ c. $(-.064)^{2/3}$ d. $(\tfrac{1}{32})^{1/5}$

        e. $(.0016)^{1/4}$ f. $\sqrt{\sqrt{16}}$

2-30.   Simplify these sums:

        a. $\sqrt{20} + 2\sqrt{45} - 3\sqrt{5}$

        b. $\sqrt[3]{x^6 y} + \sqrt[3]{y^4 z^3} + \sqrt[3]{y^{10}}$

        c. $\sqrt{\dfrac{a}{b^3}} + \sqrt{\dfrac{a^3}{b^3}}$

2-31.   Show that 1.414 is a better approximation to $\sqrt{2}$ than 1.41.   You can accomplish this by appealing to the definition of square root. a is an nth root of b if

$$a^n = b$$

Let $n = 2$, $b = 2$, $a = 1.414$.

    Find a^2 for both 1.414 and 1.41.   Then calculate the relative error between each a^2 and 2.   The smaller the error, the closer the approximation!

2-32.   Show that the properties of logarithms are true.
        Hint: Let $x = b^y$, $w = b^z$; this means

$$y = \log_b x \qquad z = \log_b w$$

Now write

$$xw = b^y \cdot b^z = b^{y+z}$$

But by Eqs. (2-52) and (2-53), this means

$$\log_b xw = y + z$$

Now substitute for y and z, and thus Eq. (2-57) follows.
    Show that Eqs. (2-58) and (2-59) are true by using similar arguments.

2-33.   Write in logarithmic form:

        a. $5^{-3} = \tfrac{1}{125}$ b. $3^4 = 81$ c. $9^3 = 729$

        d. $10^0 = 1$ e. $8^0 = 1$ f. $2^0 = 1$

        g. $27^{2/3} = 9$

2-34. Write in exponential form:

a. $\log_{10} 10 = 1$ b. $\log_{10} \frac{1}{10} = -1$ c. $\log_8 64 = 2$
d. $\log_2 64 = 6$ e. $\log_8 1 = 0$ f. $\log_{10} .001 = -3$
g. $\log_b b = 1$ h. $\log_b 1 = 0$

2-35. Find as a single real number:

a. $\log_{10} 10^2$ b. $\log_2 1^3$ c. $\log_8 64$
d. $\log_{10} .01$ e. $\log_b b^{50}$

2-36. Write as a sum or difference of logs:

a. $\log_{10} 15$ b. $\log_2 (1.5)$ c. $\log_2 \frac{3}{2}$
d. $\log_8 \frac{15}{7}$ e. $\log_5 \frac{25}{2}$

2-37. Find the log to the base 10 of:

a. .00001   b. .0001   c. .001   d. .01
e. .1   f. 1   g. 10   h. 100
i. 1,000   j. 10,000   k. 100,000

2-38. Simplify:

a. $(b^2 + a) - b(a + b)$ b. $a - (3b + a)$
c. $a(b + c) - b(a - c)$ d. $2\{x + 3[x + 2(x + 1)]\}$
e. $\frac{1}{2}(\frac{1}{3} - \frac{1}{4}) + \frac{1}{3}(\frac{1}{2} - \frac{1}{4})$
f. $[(3a + 4b) - \frac{1}{6}(36a - 90b) + 5]$

2-39. As practice in the insertion of grouping symbols:

a. Write as a sum of two expressions, one with x and y terms, the other with a and b terms,

$$4a + x - y - b$$

$$\frac{a}{2} + 3y - 5b - 5x + \frac{3}{2}a$$

b. Write in grouping symbols preceded by a minus sign

$$x - y + 2a$$

c. Factor out -3 from

$$60x - 21y + 9a - 12b$$

2-40. Write the steps in the computer evaluation of:

$$-\{5 - 3[2 + 4(7 + 6) + 12 - 1] - 9\}$$

2-41. If A = 6, B = 7, C = 8, find:

a. A + B − C   b. (A + B)/C   c. A + B/C
d. A∗B + C   e. A∗(B + C)   f. C∗∗A

chapter three

FUNCTIONS, EQUATIONS, AND GRAPHS

INTRODUCTION

The computer usually functions as a tool that is used between the time a problem is defined and the problem is solved. In order to use this tool properly, we must communicate with it in a language that it "understands." Sometimes problems can be solved by combining certain quantities according to the rules of addition, multiplication, subtraction, division, and exponentiation. We then ask the computer to *evaluate* the resulting *expression*. Equating an expression to some symbol suggests the notions of *function* and *equation*. Interpretation of intermediate evaluations suggests the notion of a *graph*. These notions form the basis of this chapter.

3-1 EXPRESSIONS

When we wish to specify a relationship between real numbers, symbols and letters will be used in place of these real numbers. This is done to emphasize the fact that more than one set of values may satisfy the relationship being discussed. These symbols and letters, jointly referred to as *literals*, are called constants and variables, according to the meaning attached to them in the relationship. Symbols that represent a fixed number in a given discussion are called *constants*. Symbols that are to be determined in a given discussion are called *variables*. Lowercase letters near the beginning of the alphabet, a, b, c, usually characterize constants, while those near the end of the alphabet, w, x, y, z, characterize variables. Explicit real numbers, 2, 5, -6, $1\frac{1}{2}$, $\sqrt{3}$, . . . , appearing in a relationship are also referred to as *constants*.

Any relationship formed by combining literals and/or explicit real numbers according to the rules of addition, subtraction, multiplication, division, and exponentiation is called an *algebraic expression*.

For example, the expression for the area of a triangle is

$$\frac{bh}{2} \tag{3-1}$$

where b = base, and h = height. Here b and h are literals, and 2 is an explicit real constant.

Variables in an expression are also called unknowns. More will be said about these in a later section.

In the expression

$$ax^2 - by^2 + c \tag{3-2}$$

x and y are understood to be variables (or unknowns), and a, b, c are understood to be constants.

If the expression consists of sums and/or differences, the distinct parts, together with their preceding sign, are called *terms* of the expression. Thus, in Eq. (3-2), $-by^2$ is a term, ax^2 is a term, and c is a term. The distinct parts of a term are called factors of that term. Thus, in Eq. (3-2), $-b$ is a factor of $-by^2$.

Consider the following algebraic expression:

$$\frac{ax^2 - by^2}{x + y} \tag{3-3}$$

where a and b are constants, x and y are variables.

Note that there is a division by an expression involving the unknowns. An expression of this type is called *fractional*. If there is no division by an expression involving unknowns, we call it *integral*. Thus

$$ax^2 - by^2 \tag{3-4}$$

is an *integral expression*.

In the expression

$$a\sqrt{x} + b\sqrt[3]{y} \tag{3-5}$$

note that the square root and cube root of the variables x and y are desired. Expressions of this type, where roots of variables are indicated, are called *irrational expressions.*   If no roots of variables appear, the expression is called *rational.*   Thus

$$ax + by \tag{3-6}$$

is a *rational expression.*

Note that the words integral, fractional, rational, and irrational have nothing to do with the value of the expression.   They merely serve to describe certain algebraic expressions.

Some mention of a very important class of algebraic expression is worthwhile here.

Expressions involving a single variable which are integral and rational are called *polynomials* in that variable.

For example,

$$5x^3 - 3x^2 + x - 1 \tag{3-7}$$

is called a polynomial in x.

The highest integral power to which the variable appears is called the *degree* of the polynomial.   In Eq. (3-7) we have a third-degree polynomial. The general form of a polynomial is

$$a_n x^n + a_{n-1} x^{n-1} + \cdots + a_1 x + a_0 \tag{3-8}$$

where n is a positive integer, and a_n, a_{n-1}, . . . , a_1, a_0 are constants.   The n, $n - 1$, . . . , 1, 0 appearing below the a's are called subscripts.   The use of subscripts greatly expands our notational capacity and allows us to express certain relationships in a clear and concise form.   The a's, together with their subscripts, are called *coefficients* of the *terms* in which they appear.   Thus, in Eq. (3-8), a_n is the coefficient of the term $a_n x^n$.

An example of a polynomial of degree 4 is

$$6x^4 + \tfrac{3}{2}x^3 - \tfrac{5}{8}x^2 - x + 1 \tag{3-9}$$

When compared with Eq. (3-8), we see that $n = 4$, $a_n = a_4 = 6$, $a_{n-1} = a_3 = \tfrac{3}{2}$, $a_{n-2} = a_2 = -\tfrac{5}{8}$, $a_{n-3} = a_1 = -1$, $a_{n-4} = a_0 = +1$.

Polynomials have acquired special names, depending on the value of n. For example, when $n = 4$, in Eq. (3-8), the resulting expression is called a quartic.   When $n = 3$, it is called a cubic expression; when $n = 2$, a quadratic; and when $n = 1$, a linear expression.

The product of two expressions is found by applying the distributive law several times.   A convenient way of accomplishing it is to multiply every term of one expression by every term of the other, and then combine like terms.

For example, multiply

$$(4a + 5b)(3a - 7b)$$

First, $(4a)(3a - 7b)$ yields

$12a^2 - 28ab$

Then $(+5b)(3a - 7b)$ yields

$15ab - 3b^2$

So the product is the expression

$12a^2 - 28ab + 15ab - 35b^2$

Combining like terms, we obtain the final result

$(4a + 5b)(3a - 7b) = 12a^2 - 13ab - 35b^2$

The concepts hold for expressions involving more than two terms.   For example,

$$(6a^2 - 3x)(a + 7x - 2ax) = 6a^3 + 42a^2x - 12a^3x - 3ax - 21x^2 + 6ax^2$$

There are no like terms in the product, except for an ax, which is common to four terms.   We may factor this out if we wish.   Thus

$$(6a^2 - 3x)(a + 7x - 2ax) = 6a^3 - 21x^2 + ax(42a - 12a^2 + 6x - 3)$$

Factoring

With a little practice we should be able to express certain simple expressions in terms of their *prime factors*.   For example, the prime factors of $a^2 - b^2$ are $a + b$ and $a - b$.   Thus, for all real a and b

$$a^2 - b^2 = (a + b)(a - b) \tag{3-10}$$

More examples follow.   The expression will appear on the left, and the steps leading to the factored form on the right.

Example 1

$$ab - a - b + 1 = a(b - 1) - (b - 1)$$

Note that $(b - 1)$ is a common factor of both terms.   Thus

$$ab - a - b + 1 = (a - 1)(b - 1)$$

Example 2

$$\begin{aligned} a^2b - b^2 - a^2c + bc &= a^2b - a^2c - b^2 + bc \\ &= a^2(b - c) - b(b - c) \\ &= (a^2 - b)(b - c) \end{aligned}$$

Example 3

The identity

$$(x - y)^2 = x^2 - 2xy + y^2$$

is helpful in factoring expressions like

$$a^2 - b^2 + 2bc - c^2 = a^2 - (b^2 - 2bc + c^2)$$
$$= a^2 - (b - c)^2$$
$$= [a + (b - c)][a - (b - c)]$$
$$= (a + b - c)(a - b + c)$$

Example 4

$$(a + 2c)^2 - 4b^2 = [(a + 2c) - 2b][(a + 2c) + 2b]$$
$$= (a + 2c - 2b)(a + 2c + 2b)$$
$$= [a + 2(c - b)][a + 2(c + b)]$$

Here we have the difference of two squares on the left. The expression (3-10) is used here.

The foregoing examples demonstrate factoring of an expression. Thus, to factor an expression is to resolve it into its *prime factors*. Note that a prime factor of an expression is another expression. More specifically, a prime factor is an expression which has no factors other than itself or some constant.

We point out that factoring is the reverse of multiplication. That is, when we multiply expressions, several applications of the distributive law occur. Then we combine like terms to form the final result.

The reverse process begins with the separation of combined terms. At this point the greatest difficulty is met, since there are many ways that certain terms can be broken up. The second step is to apply the distributive law in order to replace $xy + xz$ by $x(y + z)$, etc.

The best advice we can offer to overcome the difficulties in factoring is *practice*.

Learning known identities (see Exercise 3-1) will help in the factoring of expressions. Two of the more important ones are

$$x^2 + 2xy + y^2 = (x + y)^2 \qquad\qquad (3\text{-}11)$$
$$x^2 - 2xy + y^2 = (x - y)^2 \qquad\qquad (3\text{-}12)$$

In applying identities to our factoring we try to associate the given expression with some identity. For example, factor

$$9a^4 - 12a^2b + 4b^2$$

We can associate this expression with the second of the above identities. In particular, $9a^4$ plays the role of x^2, $12a^2b$ plays the role of $2xy$, and $4b^2$ plays the role of y^2.

From Eq. (3-12) note that we seek x from x^2; that is, we seek the square root of x^2. In our case we seek the square root of $9a^4$. It is easier to see this if we write $9a^4$ as $(3a^2)^2$. Thus, if x^2 is $9a^4$, then x is $3a^2$. Similarly, if y^2 is $4b^2$, then y is $2b$. Thus we can write

$$9a^4 - 12a^2b + 4b^2 = (3a^2 - 2b)(3a^2 - 2b) = (3a^2 - 2b)^2$$

Example 5

Factor

$$9a^2b^2 + 30ab + 25$$

We note that

$$9a^2b^2 + 30ab + 25 = (3ab)^2 - 2 \cdot 15ab + (5)^2$$

So, from Eq. (3-11), we have

$$9a^2b^2 + 30ab + 25 = (3ab + 5)^2$$

We can sometimes factor expressions of the form $x^2 + px + q$ because

$$(x + a)(x + b) = x^2 + (a + b)x + ab$$

If we can find numbers a and b, so that $a + b = p$ and $ab = q$, then we will have found the factors of $x^2 + px + q$.

There is a theorem, proved in higher mathematics courses, which states the conditions for a and b existing as integers. We use the theorem without proof.

Example 6

Factor

$$x^2 + 11x + 18$$

We seek two numbers, a and b, so that

$$a + b = 11 \quad \text{and} \quad ab = 18$$

Since the sum and product are positive, a and b must be positive. Now

$$18 \times 1 = 18 \quad 6 \times 3 = 18 \quad 9 \times 2 = 18$$

But, of the above factors, only $9 + 2 = 11$. Hence

$$a = 9 \quad b = 2$$

and thus

$$x^2 + 11x + 18 = (x + 9)(x + 2)$$

Example 7

Factor

$$x^2 - 9x - 22$$

Here $\quad ab = -22 \quad$ and $\quad a + b = -9$

Since ab is negative, then a and b have opposite signs. Also, since $a + b$ is negative, then the one whose absolute value is greatest must be negative.

Therefore

$$-22 \cdot 1 = -22 \qquad -11 \cdot 2 = -22$$

At this point, we note that $-11 + 2 = -9$. So $a = -11$, $b = 2$, and hence

$$x^2 - 9x - 22 = (x - 11)(x + 2)$$

As further practice, factor

$$x^2 - 13x + 22$$

Here $ab = 22$ and $a + b = -13$.

(*Hint*: Since the product is positive and sum is negative, both a and b must be negative.)

Addition and Subtraction of Fractions

You are likely to come across fractions where the denominators are expressions, as in

$$\frac{x}{x^2 - y^2}$$

When you are asked to add or subtract fractions in which an expression appears as denominator, you should recall the statement on least common denominator from Chap. 2. Then you should remember the following statement on LCD for expressions in denominators.

To find the LCD of two or more expressions, factor each expression into its prime factors. The LCD is the product of these prime factors, each prime appearing to the highest power which it appears in any of the given expressions.

Example

Given

$$\frac{1}{x^2 - y^2} + \frac{1}{(x + y)^2} + \frac{1}{x - y}$$

Factor the first denominator.

$$x^2 - y^2 = (x + y)(x - y)$$

The second denominator is already prime.

$$(x + y)^2$$

The third denominator is already prime.

$$(x - y)$$

Hence the LCD is

$$(x + y)^2 (x - y)$$

To add or subtract fractional expressions we write each term as a fraction, with the LCD as denominator. To accomplish this we use a theorem which states: *Multiplying numerator and denominator of a fraction by the same non-zero expression does not change the value of the fraction.* Thus

$$\frac{1}{x^2 - y^2} + \frac{1}{(x+y)^2} + \frac{1}{x-y}$$

$$= \frac{x+y}{(x+y)^2(x-y)} + \frac{x-y}{(x+y)^2(x-y)} + \frac{(x+y)^2}{(x+y)^2(x-y)}$$

$$= \frac{x+y+x-y+(x+y)^2}{(x+y)^2(x-y)}$$

$$= \frac{2x+(x+y)^2}{(x+y)^2(x-y)}$$

Example

From the laws of signs for fractions, we note that

$$\frac{x}{y-3} = \frac{x}{-(3-y)} = -\frac{x}{3-y} = \frac{-x}{3-y}$$

The use of this law allows us to make certain adjustments to numerator and denominator. Thus, add

$$\frac{3x}{y-2x} + \frac{3xy}{4x^2-y^2}$$

Now we note that $4x^2 - y^2 = (2x - y)(2x + y)$. Also, the first fraction can be rewritten

$$\frac{-3x}{2x-y}$$

So we see that our LCD is $4x^2 - y^2$. Then

$$\frac{-3x(2x+y)}{(2x-y)(2x+y)} + \frac{3xy}{4x^2-y^2} = \frac{-6x^2-3xy+3xy}{4x^2-y^2}$$

or

$$\frac{3x}{y-2x} + \frac{3xy}{4x^2-y^2} = \frac{-6x^2}{4x^2-y^2}$$

We have constructed expressions according to the rules of addition, subtraction, multiplication, division, and exponentiation. Expressions also exist within a programming language. They are first constructed by a person called a programmer. The construction obeys the rules mentioned above and also the *rules of combination* within the programming language itself.

For example, if a, b, A, and B are real numbers,

$$a + (-b) \tag{3-13}$$

is a valid expression.   It is a simple matter to mentally simplify Eq. (3-13) to

$$a - b \tag{3-14}$$

The computer, however, is not able to abstract mentally, as human beings can.   Thus, in the medium used to communicate with the computer, the programming language, an expression of the form

$$\text{A} + -\text{B} \tag{3-15}$$

is not permitted.   But

$$\text{A} + (-\text{B}) \tag{3-16}$$

is a valid expression.   This demonstrates one rule of combination in a programming language: No two arithmetic operators, $+$, $-$, $*$, $/$, $**$, can appear in succession.

As another example, consider

$$\frac{a + bc}{d} \tag{3-17}$$

In a programming language, an equivalent expression would be

$$(\text{A} + \text{B}*\text{C})/\text{D} \tag{3-18}$$

Note that

$$\text{A} + \text{B}*\text{C}/\text{D} \tag{3-19}$$

is *not* equivalent to Eq. (3-17).   Equation (3-19) tells us to multiply B by C, divide the result by D, and add that result to A.

Thus, in a programming language, parentheses may be used to specify the order in which arithmetic operations are to occur.   In Eq. (3-18) multiplication is done first, then addition, and last, division.   In Eq. (3-19), the order is multiplication, division, addition.

In a programming language, any sequence of constants and variables connected by arithmetic operators according to the rules of combination of that language is called an *expression*.

3-2 FUNCTIONS

The notion of function is the next logical step after a discussion of expressions. Think of an expression in one variable, x.   For example,

$$6x^2 - 4x + 1 \tag{3-20}$$

Now consider the *numerical value* that expression (3-20) takes on when the variable x is a certain numerical value, say, $x = 2$. Then expression (3-20) becomes $6 \times 4 - 4 \times 2 + 1$, or 17.

We express this fact mathematically in the following way:

$$17 = 6x^2 - 4x + 1 \qquad \text{when } x = 2 \tag{3-21}$$

Now Eq. (3-20) will yield a certain result for each different value of x. That is, Eq. (3-20) will yield a *variable*, which we will call y. We express this symbolically as

$$y = 6x^2 - 4x + 1 \tag{3-22}$$

Note that the value y depends on x. Mathematically, this is stated: y is a function of x. The proper definition of function follows.

A variable y is a function of a variable x if to each value of x there is associated one and only one value of y. x is called the independent variable, and y is called the dependent variable.

A symbolic convention for the above two statements is

$$y = f(x) \tag{3-23}$$

Equation (3-23) is read: y equals f of x. (The right side of the equal sign does not mean f times x.) Symbols other than f, y, and x are sometimes used.

The right side of the equal sign in Eq. (3-23) is usually an expression when the specific relationship between independent and dependent variable is known. But sometimes an expression is difficult, if not impossible, to construct. For example, consider the following statement: A person's weight depends on the food he eats. If W is weight and f is food, we may express the statement in functional notation as follows:

$$W = g(f) \tag{3-24}$$

[In Eq. (3-24) it was convenient to use g instead of f to symbolize function. This is because we chose to represent the independent variable as f. The choice of g was arbitrary.] That is, a certain intake of food f will yield a certain weight W. Here it is impossible to construct an expression for the right side of Eq. (3-24).

As another example, consider the expression for volume V of a sphere.

$$V = \tfrac{4}{3}\pi r^3 \tag{3-25}$$

where r is the radius. Note that the volume depends on the radius, that is, V is a function of r. Symbolically,

$$V = f(r) \tag{3-26}$$

Since r represents a physical quantity, the radius, we assume that r is a positive number. So it would be more proper to express Eq. (3-26) in the following way:

$$V = f(r) \qquad \text{where } r \text{ is positive} \tag{3-27}$$

We will not usually bother to write functions this way when it is understood that the independent variable must be positive. Here, the independent variable is said to be *limited to positive values*. Many other functions that we will meet will have some limitation on the independent variable.

The previous concepts can be extended to functions of more than one variable. Let us take two independent variables as an example and state the definition of function: *If a value z corresponds to a pair of values x and y, then z is said to be a function of the two variables x and y.* We write

$$z = f(x,y) \tag{3-28}$$

As an illustration, consider the volume V of a cylinder, with radius r and height h.

$$V = \pi r^2 h \tag{3-29}$$

Here the volume V is a function of the two variables r and h. Symbolically,

$$V = f(r,h) \tag{3-30}$$

where

$$f(r,h) = \pi r^2 h \tag{3-31}$$

We can also express a function symbolically when the variable x is replaced by any of its particular values.

Example

In Eq. (3-22) we have

$$y = f(x) \tag{3-32}$$

where

$$f(x) = 6x^2 - 4x + 1 \tag{3-33}$$

If we wish to express the fact that y is 43 when x is 3, we write

$$43 = f(3) \tag{3-34}$$

In general, if a is a particular value of x and b is the result when x is a, then we write

$$b = f(a) \tag{3-35}$$

The following problems illustrate the concepts developed above.

Problem 1

If a function is given by

$$f(x) = 16x^3 - 17\sqrt{x} \qquad\qquad (3\text{-}36)$$

express the function when x is replaced by half its value.

solution: Half the value of x is merely $x/2$.   Replacing x in (2.17) by $x/2$, we have

$$f\left(\frac{x}{2}\right) = 16\left(\frac{x}{2}\right)^3 - 18\sqrt{\frac{x}{2}} \qquad\qquad (3\text{-}37)$$

If we are asked to *simplify the resulting expression*, Eq. (3-37) becomes

$$f\left(\frac{x}{2}\right) = 2x^3 - \frac{18\sqrt{x}}{\sqrt{2}} \qquad\qquad (3\text{-}38)$$

Now recall that a rational number is not changed if we multiply numerator and denominator by the same quantity.   We make use of this fact and multiply the coefficient of $\sqrt{x}$ by $\sqrt{2}/\sqrt{2}$.   Then

$$\frac{18}{\sqrt{2}} \times \frac{\sqrt{2}}{\sqrt{2}} = \frac{18\sqrt{2}}{2} = 9\sqrt{2} \qquad\qquad (3\text{-}39)$$

Thus Eq. (3-38) simplifies to

$$f\left(\frac{x}{2}\right) = 2x^3 - 9\sqrt{2}\sqrt{x} \qquad\qquad (3\text{-}40)$$

Problem 2

Here we wish to find a function of a function.
Let

$$y = f(x) \qquad\qquad (3\text{-}41)$$

and

$$u = g(v) \qquad\qquad (3\text{-}42)$$

where

$$f(x) = 6ax^2 + x \qquad\qquad (3\text{-}43)$$

and

$$g(v) = v - 1 \qquad\qquad (3\text{-}44)$$

Find $f(u)$.

solution: Essentially, we are asked to find $f(x)$ when x is replaced by u. So we have

$$f(u) = 6au^2 + u \tag{3-45}$$

The solution to this exercise is now complete.

Problem 3

Continue Prob. 3-2 and find $f(v - 1)$ and simplify to a polynomial in v.
solution: From Eq. (3-45) we have f as a function of the variable u. But from Eqs. (3-42) and (3-44)

$$u = v - 1 \tag{3-46}$$

Hence

$$f(v - 1) = 6a(v - 1)^2 + (v - 1) \tag{3-47}$$

Simplifying in this case means gathering all like powers of v and expressing the right side of Eq. (3-47) as a polynomial.
First

$$(v - 1)^2 = (v - 1)(v - 1) = v^2 - 2v + 1 \tag{3-48}$$

and

$$6a(v - 1)^2 = 6av^2 - 12av + 6a \tag{3-49}$$

Finally,

$$6a(v - 1)^2 + v - 1 = 6av^2 - 12av + v + 6a - 1 \tag{3-50}$$

Thus the solution to Problem 3 is

$$f(v - 1) = 6av^2 + (1 - 12a)v + (6a - 1) \tag{3-51}$$

Note that Eq. (3-51) is a second-degree polynomial in v.

Problem 4

Let z be a function of two variables,

$$z = f(x,y) \tag{3-52}$$

where

$$f(x,y) = \frac{1 - 2x}{1 + 3y} \tag{3-53}$$

Find (*a*) $f(y,x)$; (*b*) $f(4,5)$; (*c*) $f(5,4)$.

solution: (*a*) Here we merely replace x by y and y by x.

$$f(y,x) = \frac{1 - 2y}{1 + 3x} \tag{3-54}$$

(b) In this case $x = 4$ and $y = 5$. Then

$$f(4,5) = \frac{1 - 2 \cdot 4}{1 + 3 \cdot 5} = \frac{-7}{16} \qquad (3\text{-}55)$$

or

$$f(4,5) = -\tfrac{7}{16} \qquad (3\text{-}56)$$

(c) Here we have

$$f(5,4) = \frac{1 - 2 \cdot 5}{1 + 3 \cdot 4} = \frac{-9}{13} \qquad (3\text{-}57)$$

or

$$f(5,4) = -\tfrac{9}{13} \qquad (3\text{-}58)$$

Note that

$$f(4,\ 5) \neq f(5,\ 4) \qquad (3\text{-}59)$$

Problem 5

Let

$$f(x) = x^2 - x + 1 \qquad (3\text{-}60)$$

Find $f(x + a) - f(x)$, where a is a constant.

solution:

$$\begin{aligned}
f(x + a) &= (x + a)^2 - (x + a) + 1 \\
&= x^2 + 2ax + a^2 - x - a + 1 \\
&= x^2 + (2a - 1)x + a^2 - a + 1
\end{aligned} \qquad (3\text{-}61)$$

Then

$$\begin{aligned}
f(x + a) - f(x) &= x^2 + (2a - 1)x + a^2 - a + 1 - x^2 + x - 1 \\
&= 2ax + (a^2 - a)
\end{aligned} \qquad (3\text{-}62)$$

Problem 6

If

$$y = f(x) = 5x^2 + 9 \qquad (3\text{-}63)$$

Find $f(y)$ in terms of x.

solution: First, we replace x by y to obtain $f(y)$.

$$f(y) = 5y^2 + 9 \qquad (3\text{-}64)$$

But $y = 5x^2 + 9$. Then

$$f(y) = 5(5x^2 + 9)^2 + 9 \qquad (3\text{-}65)$$

Expanding the right side of (2.46), we have

$$f(y) = 5(25x^4 + 90x^2 + 81) + 9$$
$$= 125x^4 + 450x^2 + 405 + 9$$
$$= 125x^4 + 450x^2 + 414 \qquad (3\text{-}66)$$

Problem 7

Express the area A of a triangle as a function of its base b when the triangle is inscribed in a circle and the base coincides with part of the diameter. The circumference of the circle is 16.

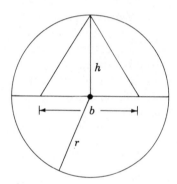

solution:

Area of triangle $= \frac{1}{2}bh$ where $h = r$
Circumference of circle $= 2\pi h = 16$

$$h = \frac{8}{\pi} \qquad (3\text{-}67)$$

Hence

$$A = \frac{1}{2}b\,\frac{8}{\pi} \qquad (3\text{-}68)$$

or

$$A = \frac{4b}{\pi} \qquad (3\text{-}69)$$

Thus the area A of the triangle is expressed as a function of the base b.

Problem 8

Find the function which expresses a man's weekly gross pay w, before taxes, if his monthly gross pay is given by P.

solution: It is *not* correct merely to divide P by 4 to get weekly gross pay. This is because some months have 5 weeks. The proper method is to multiply P by 12 (number of months in a year) and divide that result by 52 (number of weeks in a year).

Thus the solution to Prob. 8 is given by

$$w = \frac{12P}{52} \tag{3-70}$$

This section thus far has dealt with the notion of function from a strictly mathematical point of view. We move now to the notion of function from a programming-language point of view.

Perhaps the most important distinction is this:

Mathematically, a function is used to represent symbolically a certain relationship between variables; in a computer language, a function is used to save computational steps. What we have previously defined as independent variables are called *arguments* in the programming-language context.

In the illustration which follows, lowercase letters refer to a strictly mathematical discussion, while uppercase letters refer to a computer-language discussion.

Let a function be given by

$$f(x) = 6x^3 + 7.5x - 7 \tag{3-71}$$

In a language, functions are usually *named* by more than one letter. So, playing the same role as f in Eq. (3-71), might be the four-letter symbol FUNC. Then, equivalent to Eq. (3-71), we would have

$$\text{FUNC(X)} = 6*X**3 + 7.5*X - 7 \tag{3-72}$$

Here X is called the argument of the function FUNC.

We use a statement like Eq. (3-72) in the following way:

$$D = 2*\text{FUNC(2)} + 3 \tag{3-73}$$

Equation (3-73) states: The value of the function FUNC(X) when X = 2 is to be multiplied by 2, and then 3 is added to that product. The final result is to be called D.

Equation (3-73) merely serves as an introduction to the use of a function. In normal use, within a statement like Eq. (3-73), the argument of the function will appear as a symbol, say, W. Then

$$D = 2*\text{FUNC(W)} + 3 \tag{3-74}$$

will yield a different value for D with each different value of W. Equation (3-74) is equivalent to

$$D = 2*(6*W**3 + 7.5*W - 7) + 3 \tag{3-75}$$

Thus there is a savings in writing when functional notation is used. The savings in computational steps is realized when we think of W taking on different values. Because we have written a general form of our function, Eq. (3-72), the right side of Eq. (3-72) will result in a certain numerical value when W is a numerical value. FUNC(W) symbolically refers to this certain numerical value. Thus we perform Eq. (3-74) after assigning a different value to W. The result D will be different each time.

Example

Refer to Eq. (3-74).

Suppose we wish to find values for D when W is assigned the values 2, 3, and 4.

The following *statements* will accomplish this

$$W = 2 \tag{3-76}$$
$$10 \ D = 2*FUNC(W) + 3 \tag{3-77}$$

$$W = W + 1 \tag{3-78}$$
$$GO \ TO \ 10 \tag{3-79}$$

In Eq. (3-76) we assign the value 2 to W. In Eq. (3-77) we find D when W = 2. The dots following Eq. (3-77) signify that something is done with this value D that was just found. Here we also are told when to end our computations. In this case we end when D has been found for W = 4. Equation (3-78) tells us to increment the current value of W by 1. Equation (3-79) tells us to perform Eq. (3-77) again.

Equation (3-78) may look strange to you. In a language context, a statement like Eq. (3-78) means: Take the current value of W, add 1 to it, and let this sum be the *new* current value of W. Mathematically, the relationship

$$x = x + 1 \tag{3-80}$$

cannot be satisfied for any value of x. So Eq. (3-80) is said to be invalid, mathematically.

But a relationship like Eq. (3-78), in a language context, *is* valid. This is because the equal sign = takes on a different meaning from what we are accustomed to. In a language context the sign = means *replacement* rather than equality.

Equations (3-76) to (3-78) are called *arithmetic statements*. In general, an arithmetic statement consists of an *expression* to the right of the = sign and a symbol to the left of the = sign (see Chap. 12).

3-3 EQUATIONS

In many real-life situations we can think of statements of equality. For example, 1 day equals 24 hours; 12 inches equals 1 foot; a man's age equals the sum of the ages of his wife and son increased by 5. All the above, of course, are word statements. In the first two there are no unknown quantities. In the third, if the ages of the wife and son are given, the only unknown quantity is the man's age.

Symbols and letters, used in place of known and unknown quantities, allow us to express statements of equality in a concise form. In the last statement above, if w, s, and m are symbols for wife's age, son's age, and man's age, then symbolically, the statement becomes

$$m = w + s + 5 \tag{3-81}$$

Here the symbol $=$ means equality.

Thus, once we know what each symbol represents, symbolic statements of equality tell us all there is to know about the relationship between knowns and unknowns.

The notion of *variable* is still present in a discussion on *statements of equality*. In Eq. (3-81), m, w, and s are variables. When w and s are assigned specific values, we say the variables w and s are known. When we speak of ages as variables, it is understood that we are referring to positive quantities. In a statement like Eq. (3-81) it is assumed that m, w, and s will all be positive. Thus there is some *limitation on the variables*. When a statement of equality assumes some limitation (that is, some condition) on the variables, we call it a *conditional equality*. This is the proper definition of *equation*. Thus *an equation is a conditional equality*.

When a statement of equality is true for *all* values of the variables, we call it an *identity*. Identities are usually written with the identity symbol $\equiv$ replacing the symbol of equality $=$.

An example of an identity is

$$(x + y)(x - y) \equiv x^2 - y^2 \tag{3-82}$$

The above example is true for all real values of the variables x and y. Note that the left side of Eq. (3-82) is merely the factored form of the right side. In general, we can say that the statement of equality between an expression and the product of its factors is an *identity*.

Thus another identity is

$$(x + y)(x + y) \equiv x^2 + 2xy + y^2 \tag{3-83}$$

We have stated that an equation is a conditional equality. That is, the equality is true for *some* values of the unknowns. These values are called *roots (or solutions)* of the equation.

For example, the root of

$$11 = x + 5 \tag{3-84}$$

is

$$x = 6 \tag{3-85}$$

This is the only real number which will satisfy Eq. (3-82). The roots of

$$0 = x^2 - 7 \tag{3-86}$$

are

$$x = + \sqrt{7} \tag{3-87}$$

and

$$x = - \sqrt{7} \tag{3-88}$$

Note that in Eq. (3-84) the unknown x appeared to the *first* power and there was *one* root. In Eq. (3-86) the unknown x appeared to the *second* power and there were *two* roots. These examples serve as illustrations of a certain *theorem: Every polynomial equation, in which the degree of the polynomial is n, has exactly n roots.* The phrase "exactly n roots" needs some amplification. So consider the following polynomial equation of degree 3:

$$0 = x^3 - 5x^2 + 7x - 3 \tag{3-89}$$

This equation can be factored in the following form:

$$0 = (x - 3)(x - 1)^2 \tag{3-90}$$

Equation (3-90) is merely a different way of writing Eq. (3-89). [You should verify that the factors $(x - 3)$, $(x - 1)^2$ on the right side of Eq. (3-90) give the right side of Eq. (3-89) when multiplied together.]

Now we can see that the only values of x which satisfy Eq. (3-90) [and hence satisfy Eq. (3-89)] are

$$x = 3 \tag{3-91}$$

and

$$x = 1 \tag{3-92}$$

These two values each satisfy the definition of root as defined previously. However, the theorem in our case ($n = 3$) states that Eq. (3-89) should have *three* roots. What is the third root? This question is answered when we examine Eq. (3-90), the factored form of Eq. (3-89). Now the factor $(x - 1)$ appears to the power 2. The root involved in this factor is $x = 1$. These last two sentences are another way of saying that *the root $x = 1$ is of multiplicity* 2. When this occurs, the root involved is counted twice (its multiplicity). Thus, in Eq. (3-90), the root $x = 1$ is counted twice, and the root $x = 3$ is counted once, making a total of three roots. In general, when a factor appears to the power m, we say that the root involved is of multiplicity

m, and that root is to be counted m times.   (m is an integer, less than or equal to n.)

The results of another important theorem allow us to form a polynomial equation when only the roots are known.   For example, if $r_1, r_2, \ldots , r_n$ are roots of a polynomial equation, we can form the equation by merely equating to zero the product of the factors $(x - r_1), (x - r_2), \ldots , (x - r_n)$.

Problem:

Form the polynomial equation whose roots are 5, -3, 2.

solution: Construct the factors $(x - 5)$, $[x - (-3)]$, and $(x - 2)$.

Now $[x - (-3)] = (x + 3)$; so we have

$$(x - 5)(x + 3)(x - 2) = 0$$

When the multiplications on the left are carried out, the polynomial equation that we seek is obtained.   You should verify that the product of the above factors is $x^3 - 4x^2 - 11x + 30$.   Thus the final result is

$$x^3 - 4x^2 - 11x + 30 = 0$$

Some of the more important types of equations that we will meet are linear, in which the highest power of the unknowns is 1, and quadratic, in which the highest power of the unknowns is 2.

3-4 LINEAR EQUATIONS IN ONE UNKNOWN

The general form of this type of equation is

$$ax + b = 0 \qquad \text{with } a \neq 0 \tag{3-93}$$

where a and b are constants.

The solution, or root, of Eq. (3-93) is easily found to be

$$x = -\frac{b}{a} \tag{3-94}$$

Most equations which require application of Eq. (3-94) begin with a form different from Eq. (3-93).

For example, solve the following equation for x.

$$4.5(2x - 3) = 2.5(2x + 5) \tag{3-95}$$

Carrying out the indicated multiplication, we have

$$9.0x - 13.5 = 5.0x + 12.5 \tag{3-96}$$

Subtract $5.0x$ from both sides.

$$4.0x - 13.5 = 12.5 \tag{3-97}$$

Subtract 12.5 from both sides.

$$4.0x - 26.0 = 0 \tag{3-98}$$

or

$$4.0x + (-26.0) = 0 \tag{3-99}$$

When we compare this result with Eq. (3-93), we see that

$$a = 4.0 \tag{3-100}$$
$$b = -26.0 \tag{3-101}$$

Thus the solution to Eq. (3-95) is

$$x = \frac{26.0}{4.0} \tag{3-102}$$

or

$$x = 6.5 \tag{3-103}$$

Substitute this value back into the original equation. This is done to make sure the result obtained is indeed a solution.

$$4.5(2 \times 6.5 - 3) \stackrel{?}{=} 2.5(2 \times 6.5 + 5)$$
$$4.5(10) \stackrel{?}{=} 2.5(18)$$
$$45.0 = 45.0 \tag{3-104}$$

Thus Eq. (3-103) is a solution of Eq. (3-93).

In general, we perform certain operations on both sides of the original equation. This should result in an equivalent equation (*an equivalent equation is one which has the same roots as the original*). These manipulations are continued until an equation of the form (3-93) is obtained. The root is then found by Eq. (3-94). This root is then substituted back in the original equation. This is done to make sure the root obtained is indeed a root of the original equation. If the original equation is satisfied, the problem is complete.

The following operations lead to an equivalent equation.

A value added to or subtracted from both sides
Multiplying or dividing both sides by the same nonzero value

You should now go back to the example of Eq. (3-95) and follow it through again, observing the points made in the preceding two paragraphs.

As another example, solve the following equation for w.

$$\frac{2w + 5}{2} + \frac{3w}{w - 1} = w \tag{3-105}$$

Multiply both sides by $2(w - 1)$. This is done to free the equations of fractions. Then we have

$$(2w + 5)(w - 1) + 3w \cdot 2 = 2w(w - 1) \tag{3-106}$$

Now carry out the multiplication.

$$2w^2 + 3w - 5 + 6w = 2w^2 - 2w \tag{3-107}$$

Now subtract $2w^2$ from both sides (that is, cancel $2w^2$). Then

$$3w + 6w - 5 = -2w \tag{3-108}$$

Collect the terms involving w and simplify.

$$11w - 5 = 0 \tag{3-109}$$

Thus, from Eqs. (3-93) and (3-94) the solution for w is

$$w = \frac{5}{11} \tag{3-110}$$

Now substitute this value in Eq. (3-105) to see if it is indeed a solution.

$$\frac{2(\frac{5}{11}) + 5}{2} + \frac{3(\frac{5}{11})}{\frac{5}{11} - 1} \stackrel{?}{=} \frac{5}{11}$$

$$\frac{\frac{10}{11} + \frac{55}{11}}{2} + \frac{\frac{15}{11}}{\frac{5}{11} - \frac{11}{11}} \stackrel{?}{=} \frac{5}{11}$$

$$\frac{65}{22} + \frac{\frac{15}{11}}{-\frac{6}{11}} \stackrel{?}{=} \frac{5}{11}$$

$$\frac{65}{22} - \frac{15}{6} \stackrel{?}{=} \frac{5}{11}$$

$$\frac{195 - 165}{66} \stackrel{?}{=} \frac{5}{11}$$

$$\frac{30}{66} \stackrel{?}{=} \frac{5}{11}$$

$$\frac{5}{11} = \frac{5}{11}$$

Thus $\frac{5}{11}$ is a true solution of Eq. (3-105).

It should be pointed out at this stage that the computer does not lend itself readily to aid in the solution of equations like (3-95) and (3-105). However, the ability to solve equations of this type becomes important when word problems are involved. We will meet these in a later section.

3-5   QUADRATIC EQUATIONS IN ONE UNKNOWN

The general form of this type of equation is

$$ax^2 + bx + c = 0 \qquad \text{with } a \neq 0 \tag{3-111}$$

where a, b, and c are constants.

As usual, we seek values of the unknown x which satisfy Eq. (3-111). We proceed now to derive the quadratic formula. This is a general formula which will give the roots of any quadratic equation. We will apply a procedure called *completing the square* to Eq. (3-111) (see prob. 3-17).

First, subtract c from both sides of Eq. (3-111) and then divide both sides by a.

$$x^2 + \frac{b}{a}x = -\frac{c}{a} \tag{3-112}$$

Now take one-half the coefficient of x, square it, and add the result to both sides of Eq. (3-112).

$$x^2 + \frac{b}{a}x + \frac{b^2}{4a^2} = -\frac{c}{a} + \frac{b^2}{4a^2} \tag{3-113}$$

A perfect square now exists on the left side of Eq. (3-113).

$$\left(x + \frac{b}{2a}\right)^2 = -\frac{c}{a} + \frac{b^2}{4a^2} \tag{3-114}$$

Simplifying the right side, we have

$$\left(x + \frac{b}{2a}\right)^2 = \frac{b^2 - 4ac}{4a^2} \tag{3-115}$$

When the square roots of both sides are taken, we have

$$x + \frac{b}{2a} = \pm \frac{\sqrt{b^2 - 4ac}}{2a} \tag{3-116}$$

Finally,

$$x_1, x_2 = \frac{-b \pm \sqrt{b^2 - 4ac}}{2a} \tag{3-117}$$

This result is called the quadratic formula.

Note that two values for x are obtained. This is consistent with the theorem mentioned in Sec. 3-3.

You should satisfy yourself that the values for x given by Eqs. (3-117) do indeed satisfy the original equation (3-111).

As an example, solve by the quadratic formula

$$3x^2 - 5x + 1 \tag{3-118}$$

Here $a = 3$, $b = -5$, $c = 1$. So

$$x_1 = \frac{5 + \sqrt{25 - 12}}{6} = \frac{5 + \sqrt{13}}{6}$$

$$= \frac{5 + \sqrt{13}}{6} \tag{3-119}$$

$$x_2 = \frac{5 - \sqrt{13}}{6} \tag{3-120}$$

The expression under the radical sign in Eqs. (3-117) is called the *discriminant* of the quadratic (3-111).   A closer look at it will tell us something about the roots of Eq. (3-111).

If $b^2 - 4ac$ is positive, the roots x_1 and x_2 are real and unequal.
If $b^2 - 4ac$ is zero, the roots x_1 and x_2 are real and equal.
If $b^2 - 4ac$ is negative, the roots are imaginary and written

$$x_1 = u + iv \qquad x_2 = u - iv$$

where u and v are real numbers and $i^2 = -1$.

Factoring the quadratic equation is another way of arriving at the roots. The following identity is fundamental in a discussion of factoring.   Here d, e, f, and g are real, with d and g not zero.

$$(dx + e)(gx + f) = dgx^2 + (eg + fd)x + ef \tag{3-121}$$

The right side of this equation has the general quadratic form.   The left side is the product of two linear factors.

When Eq. (3-111) is written as the product of two linear factors, the product law tells us how roots may be found.   The product law states: *If the product of two factors is zero, then at least one of the factors is zero.*   (Note that in this statement the possibility that both may be zero is included.)

Thus, when Eq. (3-111) is written

$$(dx + e)(gx + f) = 0 \tag{3-122}$$

then

$$dx + e = 0 \tag{3-123}$$

or

$$gx + f = 0 \tag{3-124}$$

or both are zero.

The solutions for x of Eqs. (3-123) and (3-124) are the two roots of the quadratic equation in question.

Problem 1

Solve by factoring

$$5x^2 + 6x + 1 = 0 \qquad\qquad (3\text{-}125)$$

solution: We wish to write Eq. (3-125) as the product of two linear factors [see Eq. (3-121)]. That is, we want to find d, g, f, e, where

$$(dx + e)(gx + f) = 5x^2 + 6x + 1 \qquad\qquad (3\text{-}126)$$

Now, from Eq. (3-121) we see that $dg = 5$ and $ef = 1$. We seek two numbers d and g whose product is 5. The numbers are 5 and 1 or -5 and -1. We also seek two numbers e and f whose product is $+1$. The numbers are $+1$ and $+1$ or -1 and -1. But the product of e and g added to the product of f and d must equal 6. That is, $eg + fd = 6$.

The proper selection for d, e, f, and g is $d = 5$, $e = 1$, $g = 1$, $f = 1$. This combination yields 6 when $eg + fd$ is calculated. You should satisfy yourself that $d = -5$, $g = -1$, $e = +1$, $f = +1$ and $d = 5$, $g = 1$, $e = -1$, $f = -1$ are both incorrect sets of values for d, e, f, g.

Thus

$$5x^2 + 6x + 1 = (5x + 1)(x + 1) = 0 \qquad\qquad (3\text{-}127)$$

Then

$$5x + 1 = 0 \qquad\qquad (3\text{-}128)$$

and

$$x + 1 = 0 \qquad\qquad (3\text{-}129)$$

or

$$x = -\tfrac{1}{5} \qquad\qquad (3\text{-}130)$$
$$x = -1 \qquad\qquad (3\text{-}131)$$

Now we substitute each of these values back into our original equation (3-125) and find that each value for x satisfies Eq. (3-125). Hence Eqs. (3-130) and (3-131) are the two roots. The problem is now solved.

[It is interesting to note that, since the product of two negative numbers is positive, $d = -5$, $e = -1$, $f = -1$, $g = -1$ also yield correct solutions of Eq. (3-125).]

A simpler application of the product law occurs when we are asked to solve a quadratic equation with no constant term. That is,

$$ax^2 + bx = 0 \qquad\qquad (3\text{-}132)$$

Here we merely apply the distributive law and then the product law to the left side of Eq. (3-132).   Thus

$$x(ax + b) = 0 \qquad\qquad\qquad (3\text{-}133)$$

or

$$x = 0 \qquad\qquad\qquad (3\text{-}134)$$

$$x = -\frac{b}{a} \qquad\qquad\qquad (3\text{-}135)$$

These are the two solutions of Eq. (3-132).

Problem 2

As another exercise, solve for w.

$$\frac{w - 4}{w + 1} - \frac{15}{4} = \frac{w + 1}{w - 4} \qquad\qquad\qquad (3\text{-}136)$$

solution: We multiply both sides of the equation by $4(w + 1)(w - 4)$ to rid the equation of fractions.   Then we have

$$4(w - 4)^2 - 15(w - 4)(w + 1) = 4(w + 1)^2 \qquad\qquad\qquad (3\text{-}137)$$

Expanding and canceling $4w^2$ from both sides,

$$-32w + 64 - 15w^2 + 45w + 60 = 8w + 4 \qquad\qquad\qquad (3\text{-}138)$$

Multiply by -1 and gather like terms.

$$15w^2 - 5w - 120 = 0 \qquad\qquad\qquad (3\text{-}139)$$

Divide by 5.

$$3w^2 - w - 24 = 0 \qquad\qquad\qquad (3\text{-}140)$$

The quadratic formula is now used to find the roots.

$$x_1 = 3 \qquad\qquad\qquad (3\text{-}141)$$
$$x_2 = -\frac{8}{3} \qquad\qquad\qquad (3\text{-}142)$$

When x_1 and x_2 are substituted back into Eq. (3-136), we find that the original equation is satisfied.   Thus x_1 and x_2 are the solutions.

In Probs. 1 and 2, the roots were easily obtained.   This is because the original equations lent themselves to easy solutions.   Unfortunately, this is usually not the case in real-life situations.   This fact, coupled with certain limitations within a computer, may lead to *erroneous results* when the computer is used as an aid to solution.   Problem 3 will illustrate.

Problem 3

Find the roots of the quadratic equation

$$x^2 - 10^5 x + 1 = 0 \tag{3-143}$$

solution: The quadratic formula is used, and we obtain

$$x_1 = \frac{10^5 + \sqrt{10^{10} - 4}}{2} \tag{3-144}$$

$$x_2 = \frac{10^5 - \sqrt{10^{10} - 4}}{2} \tag{3-145}$$

The difference under the radical sign is found to be

9,999,999,996

The square root of this number is

99,999.999979999999998 . . .

Then x_1 and x_2 become

$$x_1 = 99999.9999899999999989 \ldots \tag{3-146}$$
$$x_2 = 0.000010000000001 \ldots \tag{3-147}$$

The foregoing results were obtained by hand. The procedure becomes tedious, and hence it is realistic to look to the computer as an aid in computation.

Let us see how a computer using eight-digit floating-point arithmetic can aid us.

First of all, the difference under the radical sign is computed. 10^{10} in floating-point form is written

.1 × 10^{11}

In eight-digit floating-point form we have

.10000000 × 10^{11}

The integer 4 in floating-point form is written

.4 × 10^1

Now, to subtract two numbers in floating-point form, their powers of 10 must be the same. So, for example, the integer 4 must be written as some number times 10^{11}, or

.00000000004 × 10^{11}

But only eight digits are permitted to the right of the decimal point. Hence the last two 0's and the 4 do not appear at all. The two decimal numbers are then subtracted.

$$\begin{array}{r} .10000000 \\ -.00000000 \\ \hline .10000000 \end{array}$$

In eight-digit floating-point form this is

$$.10000000 \times 10^{11}$$

The computer calculates the square root of this product to be 10^5. Thus x_1 and x_2 are found to be

$$x_1 = 10^5 = 100,000.0 \tag{3-148}$$
$$x_2 = 0.0 \tag{3-149}$$

Note the discrepancy between the roots calculated by hand and the computer-evaluated roots. This example is used to point out that the computer should not be thought of as a cure-all for tedious problems. Some care is needed in the pursuit of computer-aided solution to problems.

The above notion of error is discussed further in Chap. 10.

Sometimes equations in which the unknowns appear under radical signs can be reduced to linear or quadratic form by squaring both sides of the equation at least once or until the radical sign is eliminated. But here it must be emphasized that this process may lead to an equation that is not equivalent to the original. That is, solutions may be obtained which are not solutions of the original equation. Such roots are called *extraneous*. We determine whether or not a root is extraneous by direct substitution into the original equation. If an identity occurs, the root obtained is a true root.

Problem

Solve for x:

$$\sqrt{x} = x - 12 \tag{3-150}$$

solution: Square both sides to eliminate the radical.

$$x = (x - 12)^2 \tag{3-151}$$

or

$$x = x^2 - 24x + 144 \tag{3-152}$$

Add $-x$ to both sides.

$$0 = x^2 - 25x + 144 \tag{3-153}$$

Use the quadratic formula to solve this.

$$x_1, x_2 = \frac{25 \pm \sqrt{(25)^2 - 576}}{2}$$

$$= \frac{25 \pm \sqrt{625 - 576}}{2}$$

$$= \frac{25 \pm 7}{2}$$

Then

$$x_1 = 16 \qquad\qquad\qquad\qquad\qquad\qquad (3\text{-}154)$$
$$x_2 = 9 \qquad\qquad\qquad\qquad\qquad\qquad (3\text{-}155)$$

Substitute these values into Eq. (3-150).

First, x_1.

$$\sqrt{16} \stackrel{?}{=} 16 - 12$$
$$4 \equiv 4$$

Thus x_1 is a true solution.

Now, x_2.

$$\sqrt{9} \stackrel{?}{=} 9 - 12$$
$$3 \neq -3$$

Thus x_2 is not a root of the original equation. It is an *extraneous root*.

Thus far we have been exercising our ability to solve problems which are presented to us symbolically. That is, we are asked to solve an equation where the unknown is some symbol and the known quantities are given as real numbers or symbols different from the symbol assigned to the unknown. However, in real-life situations, problems are usually presented to us in words. From these words we try to determine the known and the unknown quantities. Then, if possible, we set up a relationship between the known and the unknown quantities. This relationship is frequently an equation (a conditional equality). We then try to *solve* the resulting equation. That is, we try to find a value or values of the unknowns which *satisfy* the equation. Problems arising as described in this paragraph are called *word problems*. We begin with a few simple exercises.

Problem 1

The sum of the digits of a two-digit number is 14. If the order of the digits is reversed, the number is increased by 18. Find the number.

solution: Let the two digits be n and m, with n in the tens place and m in the units place. The number that we seek, then, is nm.

Now we know from the problem statement that

$$n + m = 14 \tag{3-156}$$

Thus

$$n = \text{the tens-place digit}$$
$$14 - n = \text{the units-place digit}$$

Now recall that the decimal number system is a positional number system. That is, each digit of a number is understood to be multiplied by a certain power of 10, depending on its position. We use this fact in the next step of the solution.

The required number has the value

$$10n + (14 - n)$$

The value with digits reversed is

$$10(14 - n) + n$$

But from the problem statement we know that

$$10(14 - n) + n = 10n + (14 - n) + 18 \tag{3-157}$$

Now we merely solve this equation for n. Note that it is a linear equation in n.

Expanding and gathering all terms in n on the left side, we have

$$-10n + n - 10n + n = 18 + 14 - 140 \tag{3-158}$$

Simplify and multiply by -1. Then

$$18n = 108 \tag{3-159}$$

or

$$n = 6 \tag{3-160}$$

From Eq. (3-156) we have

$$m = 8 \tag{3-161}$$

The required number, then, is 68.

Problem 2

Twelve home owners on a block will share equally in the cost of one powerful TV antenna. If two more home owners agree to join the group, the cost to each member of the new group will be $1 less than the original equal share.

Find the cost of the antenna.

solution: Let P be the price of the antenna. Then if x is an equal share (in dollars) of the original group, we have

$$12x = P \tag{3-162}$$

But two more home owners will reduce the cost to each by $1. That is,

$$14(x - 1) = P \tag{3-163}$$

Now we can equate (3-162) and (3-163).

$$12x = 14(x - 1) \tag{3-164}$$

Solve for x,

$$14 = 14x - 12x \tag{3-165}$$
$$14 = 2x \tag{3-166}$$

Thus

$$x = 7 \tag{3-167}$$

The cost of the antenna is [from Eq. 3-162)] 12×7, or $84.

3-6 THE CARTESIAN PLANE

Graphical representation of data, although an old idea, has seen renewed interest in recent years, due in some part to the huge volumes of data generated by computers.

The *cartesian plane* forms the basis of this representation. Let two infinite lines intersect at right angles and call the point of intersection 0. Now mark off points equidistant from 0 on all the lines. This distance we call a unit distance. Continue marking unit distances beyond the first mark. The positive portions of these lines are arbitrarily selected to the right of 0 and above 0. Portions to the left and below 0 are then negative. Now assign integer values to the points marked. We then have Fig. 3-1.

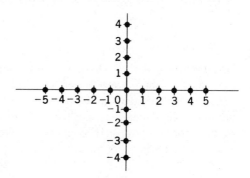

Fig. 3-1

The lines, the open spaces between them, and the origin are collectively referred to as the cartesian plane. We sometimes call the horizontal line the x axis and the vertical line the y axis. The axes divide the cartesian plane into four quadrants, as in Fig. 3-2.

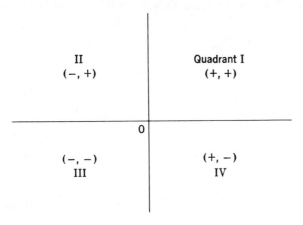

Fig. 3-2

Any point P can be uniquely described by dropping perpendiculars from the point to the axes. Then we obtain a value x_1 on the x axis and y_1 on the y axis. x_1 is called the abscissa of P, and y_1 is called the ordinate of P. x_1 and y_1 together are called the coordinates of P. Conversely, any two real numbers x and y, where x is an abscissa and y is an ordinate, correspond to one and only one point P. The pair (x,y), written within parentheses, is called an *ordered pair*. Here the word order is used to denote the fact that the first member is the abscissa and the second is the ordinate of P.

The other symbols in Fig. 3-2 tell us the sign that the abscissa and the ordinate take on in a quadrant. Thus any point lying in quadrant IV has a positive abscissa and a negative ordinate. If a point lies on an axis, then one of its coordinates is zero. This point does not lie in any quadrant.

Problems

In a previous section, the notion of function was introduced. In that section, two real numbers were called the independent and the dependent variable. When a numerical value is assigned to the independent variable, we obtain a value for the dependent variable. If every pair of values so obtained are used to describe a point in the plane, we obtain a series of points, all of which correspond to our original function.

Example

Consider the function

$$y = 7x + 3 \qquad\qquad (3\text{-}168)$$

Now, for the following x values, corresponding y values are obtained.

x	-2	-1	0	1	2
y	-11	-5	3	10	17

Integer values for x were selected for the sake of simplicity.   We could just as well have selected fractional values for x.

If we consider each x, y pair as the coordinates of a point P with the x as abscissa and y ordinate, we obtain a set of points which describe the function (3-168).   See Fig. 3-3.

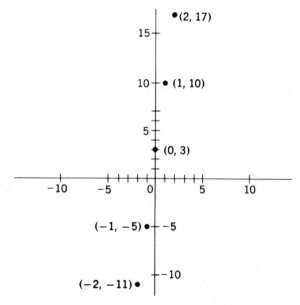

Fig. 3-3

This procedure suggests the notion of a *graph*, that is, a set of points. The process of finding points on a graph is called *plotting*.

We have thus far seen how a graph may be used to describe a certain type of function. x and y are symbolically used as coordinates of a point. Other data can be graphically represented, using similar procedures. For example, consider the list of outside temperatures over the last 24 hours. This list is usually given in the daily newspaper as part of the weather report.

Hour	Temp.	Hour	Temp.
Noon	87°	1 A.M.	75°
1 P.M.	88°	2	74°
2	89°	3	73°
3	92°	4	73°
4	92°	5	73°
5	91°	6	74°
6	90°	7	74°
7	89°	8	76°
8	87°	9	78°
9	82°	10	80°
10	80°	11	81°
11	80°	Noon	83°
Midnight	78°		

Of course, a glance at this list will tell us what the temperature was for a specific hour. But construction of a *graph* containing the above information will yield results which are more vivid than a mere list of numbers.

Before a graph is constructed, we must decide what information is to be displayed. From the above list it is clear that we wish to display time and temperature. These two quantities will be the coordinates of a point in the graph we are about to construct. Next, we must decide which quantity will be displayed on the horizontal axis and which on the vertical. A rule of thumb is this: If we can construct a function using the given information, then place the independent variable on the horizontal axis and the dependent variable on the vertical. If this cannot be done, construct the graph with the horizontal axis as the longer. In our case we have $t = f(h)$, where h signifies hour and t is temperature. Here f is meant to suggest that h is the independent variable and t is dependent. Now we must select the scale and units for each of our quantities. From the list, units are easily selected to be hour and Fahrenheit degrees. The proper increments along the axes and the highest and lowest values of units must be determined next. This is what we mean by scale. We take increments of one hour along the horizontal axis beginning at noon on one day and ending at noon on the next. We take increments of one degree along the vertical axis beginning at 70° and ending at 95°. (We could just as easily have begun at 72° and ended at 94°. The main point is that all temperatures in the list be included.) See Fig. 3-4.

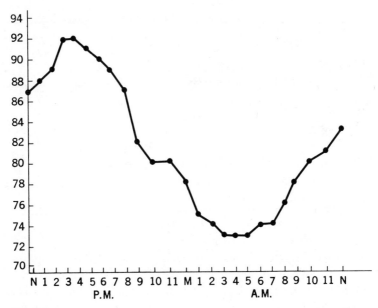

Fig. 3-4

Although the points are connected by line segments, these segments are not to be interpreted as a meaningful part of the graph. They are included only to add vividness to the data being graphed. For example, between 5 and 6 P.M. there could have been a sudden shower, causing a rapid decrease in temperature. When the shower ended, temperature would have increased to its starting point. Thus there would be no indication on the graph of this significant change.

3-7 LINEAR EQUATION IN TWO UNKNOWNS

The general form of this type of equation is

$$ax + by + c = 0 \tag{3-169}$$

All symbols correspond to real numbers, and x, y are the unknowns.

If either $a = 0$ or $b = 0$, Eq. (3-169) becomes a linear equation in one unknown, and the student is referred to Sec. 3-4.

Unless otherwise specified, a and b are not zero.

By a solution of Eq. (3-169) we mean a pair of values x, y which satisfy Eq. (3-169). For a given value of x, we can find the corresponding y, and conversely, for a given y, we can find the corresponding x. Thus an infinite number of pairs (x,y) are solutions to Eq. (3-169).

A graphical interpretation of Eq. (3-169) is seen in the following example.

$$2x + 5y - 10 = 0 \tag{3-170}$$

We seek solutions of this equation.

Let us find y when $x = 0$.

$$+5y - 10 = 0 \tag{3-171}$$

or

$$y = +2 \tag{3-172}$$

Thus the pair (0,2) is a solution of Eq. (3-170).

Now we find x when $y = 0$.

$$2x - 10 = 0 \tag{3-173}$$

or

$$x = 5$$

Thus the pair (5,0) is also a solution of Eq. (3-170).

Now let us interpret the pairs obtained as being points in the coordinate plane.   Then the first pair (0,2) has x coordinate zero, y coordinate 2.   The second (5,0) has x coordinate 5, y coordinate zero.   See Fig. 3-5.

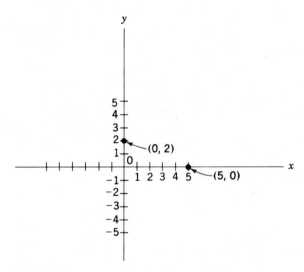

Fig. 3-5

Two theorems from the subject of analytic geometry are applicable here. The first is: The graph of every linear equation is a straight line.   The second is: Two points obtained from a linear equation in two unknowns are enough to determine the graph of that linear equation.

Thus we may join the two points in Fig. 3-5 by a line segment.   Furthermore, extending that line segment in both directions will yield the graph of
Eq. (3-170).   See Fig. 3-6.

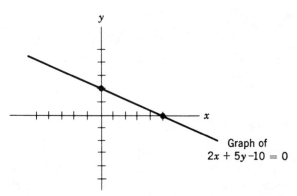

Fig. 3-6

The infinite number of pairs which are solutions to Eq. (3-170) correspond
to points on the line in Fig. 3-6.

Now let us find the graph of the following equation:

$$2x - 5y + 20 = 0 \tag{3-174}$$

Points on the axes are found as in the preceding problem.   These are (0,4) and
(−10,0).   A line through these points yields Fig. 3-7.

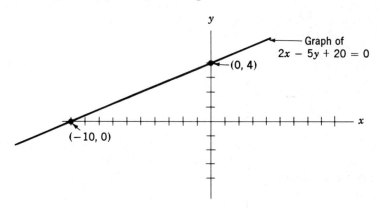

Fig. 3-7

Now let us solve Eq. (3-174) for y in terms of x.

$$y = \tfrac{2}{5}x + 4 \tag{3-175}$$

Note that the coefficient of x on the right of this equation is $\tfrac{2}{5}$.

Now, from the preceding example, let us solve Eq. (3-170) for y in terms of x.

$$y = -\tfrac{2}{5}x + 2 \tag{3-176}$$

Note that the coefficient of x in this case is $-\tfrac{2}{5}$. Equations (3-175) and (3-176) will serve as an introduction to the concept of *slope* of a line, which we define as follows.

When a linear equation in two unknowns is written in the form

$$y = mx + b \tag{3-177}$$

the quantity m is an indication of the angular measure from the horizontal axis to the line represented by Eq. (3-177). This m is called the *slope* of the line. It is positive when the angle is greater than 0° but less than 90°. It is negative when the angle is greater than 90° and less than or equal to 180°. The quantity b in Eq. (3-177) is the y coordinate of the point where the line crosses the y axis. (What is the x coordinate of this point?) This point is called the y intercept of the line, and Eq. (3-177) is called the slope-intercept form of a linear equation. The *slope* of a line has certain interesting properties. These properties serve as an aid in graphical interpretation of linear equations. One interesting property is: The slope increases from zero to an unlimited positive number as the angle of inclination increases from 0 to 90°. Also, as the angle increases from 90 to 180°, the absolute value of the slope (remember, slope is negative for an angle between 90 and 180°) decreases from an unbounded positive number to zero.

Some examples follow.

Problem 1

Find the graph of

$$22x - y + 5 = 0 \tag{3-178}$$

solution: We find y when $x = 0$, then x when $y = 0$. This will give us two points, which are sufficient to determine the graph of a straight line. The points are $(0,5)$, $(-\tfrac{5}{22},0)$. When Eq. (3-178) is written in the form of (3-177), we have

$$y = 22x + 5 \tag{3-179}$$

From this we see that the slope m is 22, a relatively large positive number. The graph is given in Fig. 3-8.

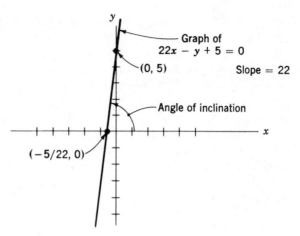

Fig. 3-8

Problem 2

Find the graph of

$$2x + y - b = 0 \tag{3-180}$$

when b takes on integral values 0, 1, 2, 3, 4.

solution: Note that, for each fixed value of b, we obtain one linear equation. Since we require b to take on five values, we will obtain five equations, and thus five graphs. Now, when Eq. (3-180) is written in slope-intercept form, we have

$$y = -2x + b \tag{3-181}$$

From Eq. (3-181) we can see that the five lines will all have the same slope (in this case, -2).

The five equations from Eq. (3-180) are

$$
\begin{array}{lll}
2x + y = 0 & \text{or} & y = -2x \\
2x + y - 1 = 0 & \text{or} & y = -2x + 1 \\
2x + y - 2 = 0 & \text{or} & y = -2x + 2 \\
2x + y - 3 = 0 & \text{or} & y = -2x + 3 \\
2x + y - 4 = 0 & \text{or} & y = -2x + 4
\end{array}
$$

The standard form is on the left, the slope-intercept form on the right. Let us examine the first set (when $b = 0$). We can easily find one point on this line by letting $x = 0$ or $y = 0$. In either case we obtain the origin [the point $(0,0)$]. To obtain a second point let x be some nonzero value. When we substitute this value back into the top equation, the corresponding y value is obtained. Thus we obtain another point on the line. For example, let $x = \frac{1}{2}$, the $y = -1$, and the point $(\frac{1}{2}, -1)$ is a second point on the graph. We can now construct the line.

We can get an idea about the graph of a line by examining its slope. In $y = -2x$, we see that the slope is negative. Thus the line should be inclined at an angle greater than 90° from the horizontal axis. When the line is constructed, we see that this is indeed true.

The remaining four equations can be graphed according to the methods described in Prob. 1 above. You should satisfy yourself that the results obtained in this problem are valid. The lines are graphed on the same set of axes in Fig. 3-9.

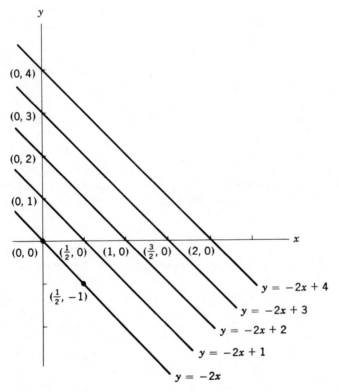

Fig. 3-9

Note that the lines in Fig. 3-9 have the same slope. That is, they are all inclined at the same angle from the horizontal axis. *Lines having the same slope are said to be parallel.*

As further practice find the graph of

$$y = mx \tag{3-182}$$

when m takes on the values 1, 2, 3, 10, -10, -3, -2, -1.

Now let us examine

$$ax + by + c = 0 \tag{3-183}$$

when either $a = 0$ or $b = 0$. First $a = 0$. Then, for any value of x, y is always a fixed quantity, depending on the values c and b. That is,

$$y = -\frac{c}{b} \tag{3-184}$$

This is a line parallel to the horizontal axis.

We can give an interpretation to the slope in the following way.

Write Eq. (3-183) in slope-intercept form.

$$y = -\frac{0}{b}x - \frac{c}{b} \tag{3-185}$$

or

$$y = 0x - \frac{c}{b} \tag{3-186}$$

Note that the slope m in this case is zero. That is, the angle of inclination from the horizontal axis to the line is 0°. Thus, if a line is parallel to the horizontal axis, its slope is zero.

Next, $b = 0$. Then Eq. (3-183) becomes

$$ax + 0y + c = 0 \tag{3-187}$$

That is,

$$x = -\frac{c}{a} \tag{3-188}$$

Thus, for any value of y, x is always a fixed quantity.

This is a line parallel to the y axis. Note that in Eq. (3-187) an attempt to obtain the slope-intercept form will necessitate a division by zero. This is interpreted by saying that the slope is infinite. Thus a line parallel to the y axis has infinite slope. Now, since the y axis is perpendicular to the x axis, any line parallel to the y axis is also perpendicular to the x axis, and the inclination from the x axis to the line is 90°.

Example

Graph the equation

$$x = \frac{5}{2} \tag{3-189}$$

Here we have an equation in the form of (3-188), where

$$-\frac{c}{a} = \frac{5}{2} \tag{3-190}$$

or

$$c = -5 \tag{3-191}$$

and

$$a = 2 \tag{3-192}$$

If Eq. (3-189) is written in standard form, we have

$$2x - 5 = 0 \tag{3-193}$$

or

$$2x + 0y - 5 = 0 \tag{3-194}$$

Thus Eqs. (3-189), (3-193), and (3-194) are all equivalent equations, giving the straight line in Fig. 3-10.

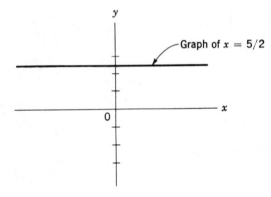

Fig. 3-10

As further practice in graphing do the following exercises: Graph on the same set of axes

$$4x + 3y - 12 = 0$$

and

$$x + y + 1 = 0$$

3-8 QUADRATIC EQUATIONS IN TWO UNKNOWNS

The form of quadratic equation that we will consider is

$$y = ax^2 + bx + c \tag{3-195}$$

Here the two unknowns are x and y. a, b, and c are real numbers, with a not zero.

It is a simple matter to obtain a value for y when a value for x is substituted into Eq. (3-195). Note that in a previous section we discussed Eq. (3-195) when $y = 0$. The values of x we obtained in that section were called solutions. They can also be referred to as the *zeros* of the function $f(x)$, where

$$f(x) = ax^2 + bx + c \qquad\qquad\qquad (3\text{-}196)$$

We can interpret Eq. (3-195) geometrically if x and y values are thought of as being coordinates of points in the plane. The function (3-195) or (3-196) is one of a larger set of functions whose graphs are smooth curves. The roots (or solutions, or zeros) of Eq. (3-195) may correspond to the points where the graph crosses the x axis ($y = 0$). However, the graph of Eq. (3-195) may not cross the x axis at all. So let us examine a few quadratic equations in the form of Eq. (3-195).

Example 1

Graph the equation

$$y = 3x^2 - 4x + 1 \qquad\qquad\qquad (3\text{-}197)$$

We set up the following table of x and corresponding y values.

x	0	1	-1	2	-2	$\frac{1}{3}$	$-\frac{1}{3}$	$\frac{2}{3}$
y	1	0	8	5	21	0	$\frac{8}{3}$	$-\frac{1}{3}$

The graph is given in Fig. 3-11.

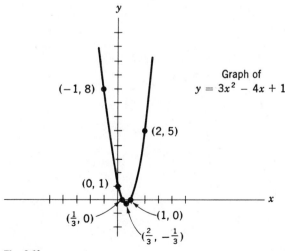

Fig. 3-11

Now let us examine the discriminant of Eq. (3-197).

$$b^2 - 4ac = (-4)^2 - 4 \times 3 \times 1 \qquad (3\text{-}198)$$

or

$$b^2 - 4ac = 4 \qquad (3\text{-}199)$$

Note that this result is positive. Algebraically, this means that the two roots of Eq. (3-197) are real numbers and are distinct from one another. Graphically, a positive discriminant means that the curve corresponding to Eq. (3-197) crosses the x axis at two different points. The x coordinates of these points are the solutions of Eq. (3-197). From the table, the roots are $x_1 = 1$ and $x_2 = \frac{1}{3}$. (You should verify that these are indeed valid by using methods of a previous section.)

Note that y changes sign as it passes through x_1 and x_2.

Example 2

Graph the equation

$$y = -2x^2 + 3x - 2 \qquad (3\text{-}200)$$

This time let us first construct the discriminant.

$$b^2 - 4ac = (3)^2 - 4(-2)(-2) \qquad (3\text{-}201)$$

or

$$b^2 - 4ac = -7 \qquad (3\text{-}202)$$

Note that it is negative. In a previous section we saw that a negative discriminant corresponded to *no real roots*. Graphically, this means that the curve does not cross the x axis.

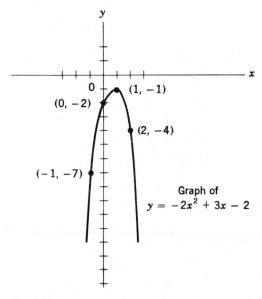

Graph of
$y = -2x^2 + 3x - 2$

Fig. 3-12

From the following table of x and y values the graph of Eq. (3-200) is constructed in Fig. 3-12.

x	0	1	−1	2	−2	$\frac{3}{4}$	$-\frac{3}{4}$
y	−2	−1	−7	−4	−16	$-\frac{7}{8}$	$-4\frac{3}{8}$

Example 3

Graph

$$y = x^2 - 2x + 1 \tag{3-203}$$

Here the discriminant is found to be zero.

$$b^2 - 4ac = (-2)^2 - 4 \times 1 \times 1 = 0 \tag{3-204}$$

Algebraically, this means the two roots of Eq. (3-203) are real and equal. Graphically, this means that the curve touches the x axis at only one point. The x coordinate of that point is the common value of the two roots.

See Fig. 3-13.

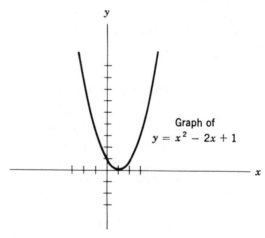

Graph of
$y = x^2 - 2x + 1$

Fig. 3-13

The curves we have constructed in this section are called parabolas. The graph of a quadratic equation

$$y = ax^2 + bx + c \qquad a \neq 0 \tag{3-205}$$

will always be a parabola. The parabola will open upward if a is positive (Figs. 3-11 and 3-13) or downward if a is negative (Fig. 3-12). Note that if a parabola opens upward, it has a lowest point; if it opens downward, it has a highest point. These two points are called the minimum and maximum, respectively. In the upward or downward case, the point is called the *vertex* of the parabola.

It is proved in an analytic geometry course that when a quadratic equation is written

$$y - k = p(x - h)^2 \qquad p \neq 0 \tag{3-206}$$

then h and k are the x and y coordinates of the vertex.

By completing the square in Eq. (3-205) you should be able to obtain the form (3-207), where

$$p = a \tag{3-207}$$

$$h = -\frac{b}{2a} \tag{3-208}$$

$$k = \frac{4ac - b^2}{4a} \tag{3-209}$$

As an exercise, consider the following problem.

Problem

In a certain retail store, 50 items can be sold in one day when they are priced at $1. However, when the price is $1.25, the number sold drops to 49. In general, when the price is increased by 25 cents, the number sold in one day drops by one. If it costs 50 cents to manufacture one item, find the charge per item to achieve maximum profit in one day.

solution: On a per-item basis, the profit per item is given by

Profit per item = (selling price per item) − (manufacturing cost per item)
Thus, when the selling price is $1, we have
Profit per item = $1 − $0.50
or $.50 profit.

On a per-day basis, we have
Profit per day = (number of items sold per day) × (profit per item)
or
Profit per day = (50)($0.50)
That is, $25 will be the profit per day when items are priced at $1. But according to the problem statement, the following table can be constructed.

Number of items sold per day	*Selling price per item*
50	$1
50−1	$1 + $0.25
50−2	$1 + $0.50, or $1 + 2(0.25)
50−3	$1 + $0.75, or $1 + 3(0.25)
.	.
.	.
.	.
50−n	$1 + n(0.25)

Note that a relationship exists between the number of 25-cent increases and the decreases in the number of items sold per day. Sales for the day is obtained by multiplying the above two numbers. That is,

$$\text{Sales} = (50 - n)[1.00 + n(0.25)] \tag{3-210}$$

But we seek profit. Now profit is obtained by subtracting manufacturing cost from sales. In our case we have

$$\text{Manufacturing cost} = (50 - n)(0.50) \tag{3-211}$$

Then profit is given by

$$\text{Profit} = (\text{sales}) - (\text{manufacturing cost})$$

or

$$\text{Profit} = (50 - n)[1.00 + n(0.25)] - (50 - n)(0.50) \tag{3-212}$$

or

$$\text{Profit} = (50 - n)[1 - 0.50 + n(0.25)] \tag{3-213}$$

That is,

$$\text{Profit} = (50 - n)[0.50 + n(0.25)] \tag{3-214}$$

When Eq. (3-214) is expanded, we have

$$P(n) = -0.25n^2 + 12n + 12.50 \tag{3-215}$$

We have written profit in the form of a function P, where the independent variable n is the number of 25-cent increases.

We also note that Eq. (3-215) has the form of a quadratic equation in two unknowns. The graph of this equation is a parabola opening downward when n is scaled on the horizontal axis and $P(n)$ is scaled on the vertical axis (see Fig. 3-14). When Eq. (3-215) is compared with (3-205), we see that $a = -0.25$, $b = 12$, and $c = 12.50$.

From Eq. (3-208) the maximum $P(n)$ (that is, maximum profit) is obtained when the number of 25-cent increases is

$$n = -\frac{b}{2a} \tag{3-216}$$

or

$$n = -\frac{12}{-0.50} = 24 \tag{3-217}$$

and when $n = 24$,

$$P(24) = -0.25(24)^2 + 12(24) + 12.50 \tag{3-218}$$

or

$$P(24) = \$169 \tag{3-219}$$

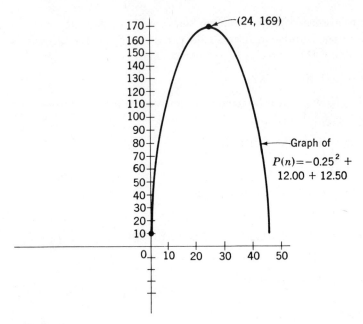

Fig. 3-14

The charge per item to achieve this maximum profit is (from the above table)

Charge per item = \$1 + (24)(\$0.25)   (3-220)

or

Charge per item = \$6   (3-221)

EXERCISES

3-1.   Find the products

        a. $(7x + 2)(x - 5)$
        b. $(6x^2 - 1)(6x^2 + 1)$
        c. $(x + 3ax + 4)(a + 2ax - 7)$
        d. $(a + b)(a + 2b)$
        e. $(c + d + e)(c + d)(d + e)$
        f. $(a + b)(a - b)$
        g. $(a + b)^2(a - b)^2$ (*Hint:* You should be able to do this with little work.)
        h. $(a - b)(a^2 + ab + b^2)$
        i. $(x + y)(x^2 - xy + y^2)$
        j. $(x - y)^3$
        k. $(x + y)^3$

Note: Parts f, h, i, j, and k are met often in mathematics and are true for all real values of the symbols. You will meet these in different form. As further practice, try part f when $a = 3x$, $b = 4y$.

3-2.   a. Write a polynomial with $A_4 = 5$, $A_3 = 0$, $A_2 = 1$, $A_1 = 3$, $A_0 = 0$.

   b. Write the polynomial from a as x times a polynomial of degree 3.

3-3.   a. $f(x) = 7x^2 - x + 2$. Find $f(0)$, $f(4)$.

   b. $f(x) = ax^2 + bx + c$. Find $f(a)$, $f(b)$, $f(c)$.

   c. $G(x) = \dfrac{x + 4}{x - 2}$. Find $G\left(\dfrac{1}{x}\right)$, $G(0)$, $G(4)$.

   d. $F(y) = y + 3$ and $H(x) = 7x + 4$. Find $F[H(x)]$.

   e. $y = f(x) = \dfrac{x + 1}{2x - 1}$. Show that $f(y) = x$.

   f. $f(x) = x^2 - x + 1$. Find $f(x + h) - f(x)$.

   g. $g(x) = \dfrac{x - 1}{x + 1}$. Find and simplify $g(x^2)$, $\dfrac{1}{g(x)}$, $g\left(\dfrac{1}{x}\right)$, $g(-x)$.

3-4. If the height h of a triangle is twice the base b, write the area A as a function of the base b only.

3-5. $g(x) = 2x + 3$. Find $g(x - 2)$, $g(x^2 + 1)$.

3-6. Formula 3-10 in the text for the difference of two squares is used to factor expressions that can be reduced to the difference of two squares.

   a. Thus

$$a^2x^2 - 2a^2xy - 9 + a^2y^2 = a^2(x^2 - 2xy + y^2) - 9$$

   Write this as the difference of two squares, and then write it in factored form.

   b. Factor

$$x^2 - y^2 - z^2 + 2yz$$

   c. $625x^4 - 4y^4z^4$

3-7. Factor

   a. $zx^2 - 2xyz + y^2z$

   b. $x^4 - (x + 2y)^4$

   c. $(x + 2b - 3z)^2 - (2x - y - 3z)^2$

   d. $\frac{1}{16} - b^4$

   e. $x^4 - 3x^2y^2 + y^4$ (*Hint:* Write this as $x^4 - 2x^2y^2 + y^4 - x^2y^2$.)

    f. $12b^3x^3 - 75bxz^2$

    g. $28ax^2 - 63ay^2$

    h. $4x^3y - 20x^2y^2 + 25xy^3$

3-8.   Within a computer, it is more costly to multiply than to add or subtract. For example, it is more costly to compute $ax^2 + bx + c$ than $x(ax + b) + c$, because the first takes three multiplications while the second takes two multiplications. You can see this when we indicate multiplication by an asterisk.

$$a * x * x + b * x + c = x * (a * x + b) + c$$

The equality sign is used to emphasize that they are algebraically equivalent.

Write the following in a "less costly" manner:

    a. $3x^3 - 4x^2 - 2x + 5$

    b. $5x^4 - 7x^3 + 3x^2 - 9x + 10$

    c. $x^2 + 2xy + y^2$

3-9.   Write the polynomial that has

    a.   Root 1 of multiplicity 2 and a root 5. What is the degree of the polynomial?

    b.   Roots equal to 2, 3, and -4. What is the degree of the polynomial?

3-10.   Solve

    a. $3 - (2 - x) = 3x + (4 - 9x)$

    b. $(x + 2)(x + 5) - (x - 5)(x - 2) = 14$

    c. $x = 2 + \dfrac{x}{2} + \dfrac{x}{2^2} + \dfrac{x}{2^3} + \dfrac{x}{2^4}$

    d. $x - 3[x - 2(x + 1) - 5] = 3\{3x - [x - 2(x - 4)]\} - 3$

    e. $\frac{1}{2}\{\frac{1}{3}[\frac{1}{4}(\frac{1}{5}x - 1) - 6] + 4\} = 1$

    f. $\dfrac{3x + 8}{3} = -\dfrac{x - 4}{6} + \dfrac{3x - 5}{4}$

    g. $3ax - 5b + c - 2a = 6c - (b + 3cx + 2a)$ a, b, and c assumed to be known quantities

3-11.   Perform the indicated operations.

    a. $\dfrac{x - y}{18} + \dfrac{3x + y}{12}$ b. $\dfrac{3}{x - 1} + \dfrac{2}{x + 1} - \dfrac{5x + 1}{x^2 - 1}$

    c. $\dfrac{3}{4 - 6a} - \dfrac{1 - 5a}{9a^2 - 4}$ d. $\dfrac{1}{a} + \dfrac{2}{a - 2} - \dfrac{2}{a + 2}$

3-12.   Find two successive positive integers whose squares differ by 33.

3-13.   The sum of a number and one-fourth of itself is 15.   Find the number.

3-14.   The sum of three consecutive whole numbers is 726.   Find the smallest.

3-15. A has twice as much money as B.   If A gives B $1, both would then have the same amount of money.   How much money did B start with?

3-16.   The sum of a number, one-third of itself, and one-fourth of itself is 2. Find the number.

3-17.   To write a quadratic equation in standard form means to write it in the form

$$ax^2 + bx + c = 0$$

Write these in standard form; then identify a, b, c.

  a. $6x = 6x^2 - 6$ b. $7x^2 - 5 = 5x^2 - 7$

  c. $(x + 1)^2 = 3x^2 - 1$ d. $(x - \sqrt{2})^2 = 0$

3-18.   A *pure quadratic* equation is one of the form

$$ax^2 + c = 0 \qquad a \neq 0$$

To solve for x we add $-c$ to both sides, then divide by a to obtain

$$x^2 = -\frac{c}{a}$$

From Chap. 2 we know that this means

$$x = \pm \sqrt{-\frac{c}{a}}$$

These two roots will be real when a and c are unlike in sign.

  Solve for x:

  a. $2x^2 - 9 = x^2 + 7$ b. $7x^2 - 4 = 60 - x^2$

  c. $x(9 + 2x) = 9(x + 2)$

3-19.   Complete the square.

  a. $x^2 + 8x$ b. $x^2 - 6x$ c. $3x^2 - 6x$

  [*Hint:*   Write part c as $3(x^2 - 2x)$; then complete the square on the parenthesized terms.]

3-20.   Solve by completing the square.

      a. $x^2 + 12x = 64$ b. $x^2 + 4x = 5$

      c. $x^2 - 10x = 24$ d. $x^2 - 10x = -24$

3-21.   Factor

      a. $x^2 - 10x + 24$ b. $6x^2 - 13x + 6$

      c. $14x^2 + x - 3$ d. $49x^2 + 105x + 44$

      e. $x^2 + 3x + 2$ f. $x^2 - 4x - 12$

3-22.   Solve by the quadratic formula.

      a. $6x^2 + x - 12 = 0$ b. $x^2 - 5x + 4 = 0$

      c. $x^2 - 6x - 16 = 0$ d. $lx^2 + kx + p = 0$

      e. $3x^2 + \sqrt{3}\,x - 2 = 0$ f. $\dfrac{y}{y - 2} - \dfrac{1 - y}{2} = y + 1$

      g. $12x^2 - 5ax - 3a^2 = 0$

3-23.   Solve the following equations for x.   Always check for extraneous roots.

      a. $x = \sqrt{12 - x}$ b. $\sqrt{3x - 2} = x$

      c. $\sqrt{5 - 2x} = 2x - 5$ d. $\sqrt{x - 2} = x - 2$

      e. $\sqrt{x} = 12 - 4$

3-24.   Examine the discriminant of these equations and thereby tell something about the roots.   If the roots are real, find them by any valid method.

      a. $3x^2 - x + 4 = 0$ b. $4x^2 - 5x + 1 = 0$

      c. $x^2 - 4x + 4 = 0$ d. $9x^2 + 6x + 1 = 0$

      e. $\dfrac{x}{x - 2} - \dfrac{1 - x}{2} = x + 1$

3-25.   Find two consecutive positive integers whose product is 210.

3-26.   Find two consecutive positive numbers whose product is 56.

3-27.   Find three consecutive positive even integers so that the sum of their squares is 440.

3-28.   Name the quadrant where each point lies: $(4,5)$, $(\frac{1}{2}, -\frac{1}{2})$, $(-3, -2)$.

3-29.   The relative-humidity readings for a 24-hour period (noon to noon) are as follows: 73, 75, 76, 80, 81, 81, 90, 89, 89, 87, 86, 86, 85, 83, 80, **79**, 78, 77, 76, 75, 73, 72, 73, 75, and 77.

      a. Construct a graph with hours and relative humidity as units, similar to the graph of Fig. 3-4.

    b.   Construct a horizontal and vertical axis as in Fig. 3-4. Let horizontal units be hours, and vertical units refer to degrees Fahrenheit and relative humidity simultaneously. Construct the graph of Fig. 3-4 and the graph of part a on the same set of axes.

3-30. Graph these functions. Use integral x values for simplicity. Select ten x values.

    a. $y = x + 5$ b. $y = x$ c. $y = x^2 + 2x$
    d. $y = 6 + x - x^2$ e. $y = x^2$ f. $y = -x^2$

3-31.   a. Find the x intercept and the y intercept of the graphs of these equations:

$$5x + 10y = 50 \qquad x + y + 1 = 0$$
$$3x + 4y = 12 \qquad -7x + 4y = 56$$

    b. Find the slope of each line given by the equations of part a.

3-32. Complete the square on $y = ax^2 + bx + c$ and write the equation in the form

$$y - k = p(x - h)^2$$

Thus verify that $h = -b/2a$, $k = (4ac - b^2)/4a$, and $p = a$.

3-33. Find the coordinates of the maximum or minimum of the following parabolas.

    a. $y = x^2 - 4x - 1$ b. $y = x^2 - 6x + 5$
    c. $4x - 2x^2 + 7 = y$ d. $y = 5 - 8x - x^2$

chapter four

SYSTEMS OF LINEAR EQUATIONS

INTRODUCTION

In many business applications, problems arise involving linear equations. When one problem leads to two or more linear equations with the same unknowns, we have a system of linear equations. An attempt is then made to find unknowns that will simultaneously satisfy all the linear equations that belong to the system. The methods used in attempts to solve systems of simultaneous equations usually involve operations of a repetitive nature. That is, certain arithmetic operations are performed repeatedly, each time using a different set of values. The computer is well suited as an aid in the solution of problems of this type, since it can perform repetitive operations at very high speed.

Introduction to systems of linear equations and methods used in their solution form the basis of this chapter.

4-1 SYSTEMS OF TWO LINEAR EQUATIONS

A simple problem will introduce a system of two simultaneous linear equations.

Problem

In a certain year a man invests a total of $15,000 in two savings accounts. The rates of interest are $4\frac{3}{4}$ and 5 percent per year, respectively. That year he gains a total of $725 in interest. Find the amounts deposited in each account.

solution: Let A_1 and A_2 be the amounts in dollars deposited in the two accounts. Then, from the problem statement,

$$A_1 + A_2 = \$15,000 \qquad (4\text{-}1)$$

This equation by itself will not yield unique solutions for A_1 and A_2. This is so because Eq. (4-1) is a linear equation in two unknowns (A_1 and A_2), and we know that the number of solutions of an equation such as (4-1) is infinite. Let us look further into the problem statement.

Annual interest rate for the two accounts is $4\frac{3}{4}$ and 5 percent respectively. The total interest gained in \$725. Let $4\frac{3}{4}$ percent be assigned to amount A_1 and 5 percent be assigned to amount A_2. (This is an arbitrary decision. We could just as well have reversed the assignments.) Then we have

$$0.0475A_1 + 0.05A_2 = \$725 \qquad\qquad (4\text{-}2)$$

Again we have a linear equation in two unknowns. No unique solution is possible. But note that Eqs. (4-1) and (4-2) involve the same unknowns, A_1 and A_2. These two equations form our system. A_1 and A_2 must be found so that Eqs. (4-1) and (4-2) are both satisfied simultaneously. In this problem we have constructed a system of two equations [(4-1) and (4-2)] in two unknowns, A_1 and A_2.

One method of solution for a system of this type is to eliminate one unknown by *substitution*. That is, from the two equations in two unknowns, we try to obtain one equation in one of the unknowns. This equation may then be solvable for the one unknown uniquely. This value is then substituted back in the first equation to obtain the remaining unknown.

From Eq. (4-1) we have

$$A_2 = \$15,000 - A_1 \qquad\qquad (4\text{-}3)$$

This expression for A_2 is substituted in Eq. (4-2).

$$0.0475A_1 + 0.05(\$15,000 - A_1) = \$725 \qquad\qquad (4\text{-}4)$$

or

$$0.0475A_1 + \$750 - 0.05A_1 = \$725 \qquad\qquad (4\text{-}5)$$

$$-0.0025A_1 = -25 \qquad\qquad (4\text{-}6)$$

Multiply by -1 and divide both sides by 0.0025 to obtain

$$A_1 = \$10,000 \qquad\qquad (4\text{-}7)$$

We substitute this value in Eq. (4-1) and find A_2.

$$A_2 = \$5,000 \qquad\qquad (4\text{-}8)$$

Thus the problem is solved.

The foregoing problem could have been solved by another method, the method of elimination by multiplication and addition. This method suggests that one equation be multiplied or divided by some real number. The two equations are then added. This operation should eliminate one of the unknowns. The result is a linear equation in one of the unknowns. This may then be solved, and the result substituted back into one of the original equations in order to obtain the other unknown. Let us pursue this idea by multiplying Eq. (4-1) by -0.05. The result is

$$-0.05A_1 - 0.05A_2 = -750 \tag{4-9}$$

Now, for ease in following, we rewrite Eq. (4-2).

$$0.0475A_1 + 0.05A_2 = 725 \tag{4-10}$$

Now add Eqs. (4-9) and (4-10).

$$(0.0475 - 0.05)A_1 + (0.05 - 0.05)A_2 = -25 \tag{4-11}$$

Note that the coefficient of A_2 becomes zero. Equation (4-11) then simplifies to

$$-0.0025A_1 = -25$$

or
$$\tag{4-12}$$

$$A_1 = \$10,000$$

This value is then substituted back in one of the original equations to obtain

$$A_2 = \$5,000 \tag{4-13}$$

As further practice, solve for x and y in Prob. 4-1, using both methods.

The following discussion will give some insight into the method used above.

First, we write two linear equations in their general form.

$$ax + by + c = 0 \tag{4-14}$$
$$dx + ey + f = 0 \tag{4-15}$$

If a solution exists which satisfies both simultaneously, that solution will of course satisfy each one individually. (This is what we mean by a solution of the system.) If Eqs. (4-14) and (4-15) are multiplied by nonzero numbers C and D, the resulting equations will be *equivalent* to the originals. That is,

$$C(ax + by + c) = 0 \tag{4-16}$$
$$D(dx + ey + f) = 0 \tag{4-17}$$

When Eqs. (4-16) and (4-17) are added and simplified, we have

$$(Ca + Dd)x + (Cb + De)y + (Cc + Df) = 0 \tag{4-18}$$

If a solution to the system (4-14) and (4-15) exists, that solution will satisfy Eq. (4-18).

Let us assume that C and D have been chosen so that the coefficient of

x in Eq. (4-18) is zero.   Then we would have

$$0x + (Cb + De)y + (Cc + Df) = 0 \tag{4-19}$$

with

$$Ca + Dd = 0 \tag{4-20}$$

If the coefficient of y in Eq. (4-19) is not zero, we may solve for y and obtain

$$y = -\frac{Cc + Df}{Cb + De} \tag{4-21}$$

This is a solution for y of Eq. (4-18).   We substitute this value into Eq. (4-14) or (4-15) to obtain the corresponding x.   We arbitrarily select Eq. (4-14) for this purpose and solve for x.

$$x = \frac{D(bf - ce)}{a(Cb + De)} \tag{4-22}$$

You should verify that this is indeed the proper result for x.

Thus we have found an x and y value which we claim is the solution to the system (4-14) and (4-15).   It should be clear that zero will be obtained when the right sides of Eqs. (4-22) and (4-21) are used in place of x and y on the left side of Eq. (4-14).   That is, Eqs. (4-22) and (4-21) are a solution to one equation of our system.   By direct substitution we find that the expression

$$dx + ey + f \tag{4-23}$$

is zero when the right sides of Eqs. (4-22) and (4-21) are used in place of x and y.   (You should verify this.)   This means that Eqs. (4-22) and (4-21) are a solution of (4-15).   Thus Eqs. (4-22) and (4-21) are indeed the solution of our system.

As an example, consider the system

$$3x + 4y - 24 = 0 \tag{4-24}$$

$$2x + 5y - 20 - 0 \tag{4-25}$$

We seek nonzero numbers C and D which will yield a zero coefficient of x *or* y when C times Eq. (4-24) is added to D times Eq. (4-25).   We choose to work with the coefficient of x as in the preceding discussion.   Then, by inspection, we find that $C = 2$ and $D = -3$ will accomplish what we desire.

Upon multiplying Eqs. (4-24) by 2 and Eq. (4-25) by -3, we obtain

$$6x + 8y - 48 = 0 \tag{4-26}$$

$$-6x - 15y + 60 = 0 \tag{4-27}$$

Note that when Eqs. (4-26) and (4-27) are added, the coefficient of x becomes zero, leaving us with

$$-7y + 12 = 0 \qquad\qquad (4\text{-}28)$$

This is readily solved for y, giving

$$y = {}^{12}\!/\!_7 \qquad\qquad (4\text{-}29)$$

This value is then substituted in one of the equations of our system. You should verify that in either case we will obtain

$$x = {}^{40}\!/\!_7 \qquad\qquad (4\text{-}30)$$

A pictorial representation of these results is obtained when we graph Eqs. (4-24) and (4-25). Note that a graphic interpretation of *solution*, if one exists, means a point (x,y) which simultaneously lies on both lines.

This can happen only when the lines intersect at that point (see Fig. 4-1). In the preceding discussion we pursued a solution *if one exists*. There are situations where no solution exists or many solutions may exist. Since the graph of every linear equation in two unknowns is a straight line, we can graphically interpret the discussion for these special cases.

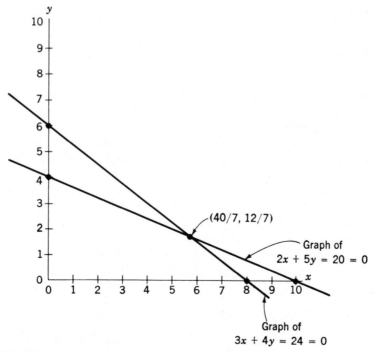

Fig. 4-1

Consider the following system:

$$2x - y = 1 \qquad (4\text{-}31)$$
$$-4x + 2y = -2 \qquad (4\text{-}32)$$

As before, we seek a single pair (x,y) which will satisfy both simultaneously. Let us graph these equations on different sets of axes (see Fig. 4-2).

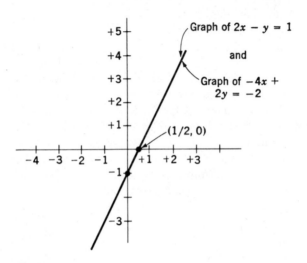

Fig. 4-2

Since these two lines both pass through the same set of points, the above equations actually represent the same line. Thus we may use one set of axes to display this as in Fig. 4-3.

Thus *any* pair of points (x,y) which lie on one line of this system will lie on the other line of the system. Algebraically, this means that *any* (x,y) pair satisfying one equation will satisfy the other. Thus there are *many solutions* to this system. In fact, every point on the line is a solution. Clearly, we cannot find one and only one pair (x,y), which satisfies both simultaneously.

Systems displaying the above property are called *dependent*. If we look back at Eqs. (4-31) and (4-32), we see that they are the same, except for a constant multiplier, -2. That is, Eq. (4-32) is (4-31) multiplied by -2. This is a characteristic of dependent systems. In the general case, we have

$$ax + by + c = 0 \qquad (4\text{-}33)$$
$$akx + bky + ck = 0 \qquad (4\text{-}34)$$

Here k is the constant multiplier. In systems like this, the method of substitution will not work. Let us try it in this general case. Let us solve Eq.

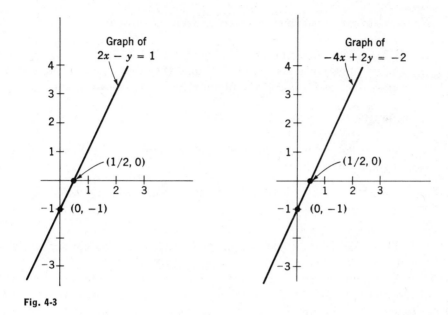

Fig. 4-3

(4-33) for y in terms of x. We obtain

$$y = -\frac{c + ax}{b} \tag{4-35}$$

Now substitute this expression for y in Eq. (4-34).

$$akx - bk\frac{(c + ax)}{b} + ck = 0 \tag{4-36}$$

Now simplify.

$$akx - kc - kax + ck = 0$$

or

$$0 \equiv 0 \tag{4-37}$$

In general, we will not be able to obtain a linear equation in *one* of the unknowns which is readily solvable for that unknown. Thus the method of substitution will not work for dependent systems.

The method of elimination by multiplication and addition will yield a similar zero identity. Let us consider again our dependent system (4-33) and (4-34).

$$ax + by + c = 0$$
$$akx + bky + ck = 0$$

Now recall that in this method these steps are followed:

1. By inspection, find nonzero numbers C and D.
2. Then C times one equation plus D times the other equation will result in a zero coefficient for *one* of the unknowns.

However, the only C's and D's available to us will yield zero for *all terms* when the two equations are added.

In particular, when k times the first equation is added to -1 times the second equation, we have

$$k(ax + by + c) - (akx + bky + ck) = 0$$

or

$$0 \equiv 0 \tag{4-38}$$

Thus, once again, we are stopped in an attempt to obtain one equation in one of the unknowns.

Dependent systems, then, are systems where one equation is a multiple of the other. Algebraically, this means that there are an *infinite number of solutions*. Graphically, this means that the two equations represent the same line. (See Exercise 4-3.)

We will now consider the case where there are *no solutions* to a system. For example, consider

$$3x - 12y = 9 \tag{4-39}$$
$$x - 4y = 8 \tag{4-40}$$

Let us try the method of substitution here. From Eq. (4-40),

$$x = 4y + 8 \tag{4-41}$$

Substitute this into Eq. (4-39).

$$3(4y + 8) - 12y = 9$$

or

$$24 = 9 \tag{4-42}$$

Clearly, something incorrect must have occurred. Before we explain, let us try the method of multiplication and addition. We multiply Eq. (4-40) by 3 and (4-39) by -1; then we add.

$$-1(3x - 12y - 9) + 3(x - 4y - 8) = 0 \tag{4-43}$$

or

$$-15 = 0 \tag{4-44}$$

Another incorrect statement.

The problem here is as follows. In the methods of elimination that we use, a solution is presumed to exist before we start. In the preceding discus-

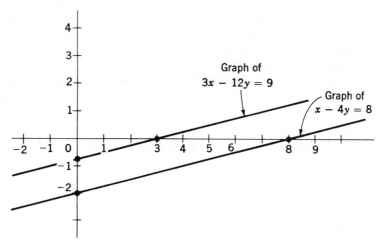

Fig. 4-4

sion, this assumption yielded incorrect results. We conclude from this that *no solution* exists. Let us now graphically interpret these results (see Fig. 4-4).

When the two equations are graphed, they seem to be parallel. This is indeed the case, for when the equations are rearranged in slope-intercept form, we see that the slopes are the same but the y intercepts are different.

$$y = \tfrac{1}{4}x - \tfrac{3}{4} \tag{4-45}$$
$$y = \tfrac{1}{4}x - 2 \tag{4-46}$$

This means that we have two distinct lines and these lines are parallel. Geometrically, two parallel lines never intersect. Algebraically, this means that the two equations have no common solution.

When a system has the above characteristics, we say the system is *inconsistent*. The general form of an inconsistent system of equations is

$$ax + by + c = 0 \tag{4-47}$$
$$akx + bky + d = 0 \tag{4-48}$$

Note that the coefficients of the unknowns in one equation are a multiple of the coefficients in the other equation.

When the above equations are rearranged in slope-intercept form, two equations with the same slope but different y intercepts result. You should verify this for yourself.

In general, when a system of two linear equations is to be solved, it should be examined for dependency and inconsistency. If the equations are neither dependent nor inconsistent, we may then attempt to solve the system. (See Exercise 4-4.)

As another application of solution of linear systems, consider the following problem. Tickets for a certain movie are 60 cents for adults and 30 cents for children. If 770 tickets were sold and $381 were taken in, how many adults' and how many children's tickets were sold?

In word problems such as this one, we should quickly introduce symbols and try to express the stated relationships symbolically. First, what do we seek? Clearly, we seek the number of adults' tickets sold and the number of children's tickets sold. We arbitrarily select x to represent the number of adults' tickets sold and y to represent the number of children's tickets sold. Then, from the problem statement,

$$x + y = 770 \qquad\qquad\qquad (4\text{-}49)$$

Also from the problem statement,

$$\$0.60x + \$0.30y = \$381. \qquad\qquad\qquad (4\text{-}50)$$

Note that we must express 60 cents, 30 cents, and $381 in the same units of currency (dollars). Hence 60 cents and 30 cents are expressed as $0.60 and $0.30, respectively.

Equations (4-49) and (4-50) comprise a system of two linear equations in two unknowns, x (the number of adults' tickets sold) and y (the number of children's tickets sold).

By inspection, we see that the system is neither dependent nor inconsistent.

Let us solve Eq. (4-49) for y and substitute the resulting expression into Eq. (4-50). We obtain

$$0.60x + 0.30(770 - x) = 381 \qquad\qquad (4\text{-}51)$$
$$0.60x + 231 - 0.30x = 381 \qquad\qquad (4\text{-}52)$$

or

$$0.30x = 150 \qquad\qquad\qquad (4\text{-}53)$$

We can readily solve this equation for x by dividing both sides by 0.30. We obtain a value for x, the number of adults' tickets sold.

$$x = 500 \qquad\qquad\qquad (4\text{-}54)$$

Substitute this value into Eq. (4-49) to obtain y, the number of children's tickets sold.

$$500 + y = 770 \qquad\qquad\qquad (4\text{-}55)$$

or

$$y = 270 \qquad (4\text{-}56)$$

Thus the problem is solved.

4-2 DETERMINANTS

We have seen how a simultaneous system of two equations may be solved by methods of elimination.   However, it was necessary first to inspect the equations for dependence and inconsistency.   Let us now develop a topic where dependence and inconsistency may be discovered algebraically.

We write a system of two equations in a slightly different but equivalent general form.

$$a_1 x + b_1 y = c_1 \qquad (4\text{-}57)$$
$$a_2 x + b_2 y = c_2 \qquad (4\text{-}58)$$

Let us multiply the first equation by b_2, the second equation by $-b_1$, and add.   It should be clear that the term containing y will be eliminated after adding.   We obtain

$$(a_1 b_2 - a_2 b_1)x = b_2 c_1 - b_1 c_2 \qquad (4\text{-}59)$$

If the coefficient of x is not zero in Eq. (4-59), we can solve for x.

$$x = \frac{b_2 c_1 - b_1 c_2}{a_1 b_2 - a_2 b_1} \qquad (4\text{-}60)$$

Now let us multiply the first equation of our system (4-57) by $-a_2$, the second by a_1, and add.   It should be clear that the term containing x will be eliminated after adding.   We obtain

$$(a_1 b_2 - a_2 b_1)y = a_1 c_2 - a_2 c_1 \qquad (4\text{-}61)$$

If the coefficient of y is not zero in Eq. (4-61), we can solve for y.

$$y = \frac{a_1 c_2 - a_2 c_1}{a_1 b_2 - a_2 b_1} \qquad (4\text{-}62)$$

One of the important things to note here is that we can now evaluate x and y through Eqs. (4-60) and (4-62).   This is so because all factors on the right of those equations are *known*.   Another important thing to note is the fact that *the denominators of both equations for x and y have the same expression*.

Before we speak further about this expression, we introduce the notion of *determinant.*   The symbol

$$\begin{vmatrix} m & n \\ p & q \end{vmatrix}$$

is called a 2 by 2 determinant.   The phrase "2 by 2" is used because there are two rows and two columns.   (Perhaps this suggests to you that determinants exist which are "3 by 3" and "4 by 4," etc.   This is indeed true, as we shall see later.)

The numbers m, n, p, q are called *elements* of the determinant.   The above symbol for determinant serves to define a certain relationship between these elements.   This definition is as follows:

$$\begin{vmatrix} m & n \\ p & q \end{vmatrix} = mq - np \tag{4-63}$$

The important thing to note here is that the determinant defines a real number when the elements are real numbers.   For example,

$$\begin{vmatrix} 2 & 3 \\ 4 & 5 \end{vmatrix} = 2 \times 5 - 3 \times 4 = -2$$

$$\begin{vmatrix} 1 & -2 \\ 7 & 3 \end{vmatrix} = 1 \times 3 - (-2) \times 7 = 3 - (-14) = 3 + 14 = 17$$

$$\begin{vmatrix} \sqrt{2} & \frac{1}{2} \\ 4 & 3\sqrt{2} \end{vmatrix} = \sqrt{2} \times 3\sqrt{2} - 4 \times \frac{1}{2} = 3 \times 2 - 2 = 6 - 2 = 4$$

The right side of Eq. (4-63) is called the expanded form of the determinant. Consider the following determinant:

$$\begin{vmatrix} a_1 & a_2 \\ b_1 & b_2 \end{vmatrix}$$

When the expanded form is written

$$\begin{vmatrix} a_1 & b_1 \\ a_2 & b_2 \end{vmatrix} = a_1 b_2 - a_2 b_1 \tag{4-64}$$

we see that it is the same expression that appears in the denominator of Eqs. (4-60) and (4-62).   For convenience, we rewrite the system and the solutions for x and y.

$$a_1 x + b_1 y = c_1$$
$$a_2 x + b_2 y = c_2$$

$$x = \frac{b_2 c_1 - b_1 c_2}{a_1 b_2 - a_2 b_1}$$

$$y = \frac{a_1 c_2 - a_2 c_1}{a_1 b_2 - a_2 b_1}$$

Note that the numerators in the solutions for x and y are the expanded forms of certain determinants.   For instance,

$$x \text{ numerator:} \quad b_2 c_1 - b_1 c_2 = \begin{vmatrix} c_1 & b_1 \\ c_2 & b_2 \end{vmatrix}$$

and

$$y \text{ numerator:} \quad a_1 c_2 - a_2 c_1 = \begin{vmatrix} a_1 & c_1 \\ a_2 & c_2 \end{vmatrix}$$

Now we rewrite Eq. (4-64)

$$\begin{vmatrix} a_1 & b_1 \\ a_2 & b_2 \end{vmatrix} = a_1 b_2 - a_2 b_1$$

Note that the elements in this determinant are the coefficients of x and y in our original system.   This is why the above determinant is called the *determinant of the coefficients*.   This must be checked for zero before Eqs. (4-60) and (4-62) are used.

Now recall that a system of equations may be dependent or inconsistent. In either case, the coefficients in one equation are a multiple of the coefficients in the other equation.   In general, the system

$$a_1 x + b_1 y = c_1$$
$$k a_1 x + k b_1 y = c_2$$

is dependent or inconsistent, according to how c_2 is related to c_1.

Let us write the determinant of the coefficients of the above system.

$$\begin{vmatrix} a_1 & b_1 \\ k a_1 & k b_1 \end{vmatrix} = a_1 k b_1 - k a_1 b_1 = k(a_1 b_1 - a_1 b_1) = k \cdot 0 = 0$$

That is,

$$\begin{vmatrix} a_1 & b_1 \\ k a_1 & k b_1 \end{vmatrix} = 0$$

Thus, when a system is dependent or inconsistent, the determinant of the coefficients is zero.   This determinant should be examined at the outset.   If this determinant is not zero, we can solve the system for x and y.   The following two problems are examples of the solution by determinants.

Problem 1

Solve

$$3x - 2y = 1$$
$$2x - \tfrac{4}{3}y = 5$$

solution: First we examine the determinant

$$\begin{vmatrix} 3 & -2 \\ 2 & -\tfrac{4}{3} \end{vmatrix} = (3)(-\tfrac{4}{3}) - (-2)(2) = -4 + 4 = 0$$

Thus the determinant of the coefficients is zero, and this means there is no unique solution.   We need go no further with this problem.

Problem 2

Solve

$$x + y = 5$$
$$3x - 2y = 12$$

First we have

$$\begin{vmatrix} 1 & 1 \\ 3 & -2 \end{vmatrix} = -2 - 3 = -5$$

Thus we may solve for x and y using Eqs. (4-60) and (4-62).   We note that the x numerator is a determinant.   Specifically, it is the determinant of the coefficients, with the coefficients of the unknown we seek replaced by the constants.   Thus

$$x = \frac{\begin{vmatrix} 5 & 1 \\ 12 & -2 \end{vmatrix}}{\begin{vmatrix} 1 & 1 \\ 3 & -2 \end{vmatrix}} = \frac{-10 - 12}{-5} = \frac{-22}{-5} = 4.4$$

For y we note that the y numerator is the determinant of the coefficients with the coefficients of y replaced by the constants.

$$y = \frac{\begin{vmatrix} 1 & 5 \\ 3 & 12 \end{vmatrix}}{\begin{vmatrix} 1 & 1 \\ 3 & -2 \end{vmatrix}} = \frac{12 - 15}{-5} = \frac{-3}{-5} = 0.60$$

Thus $x = 4.4$ and $y = 0.6$ is the solution to our system.   See Fig. 4-5 for a graphical interpretation of our results.

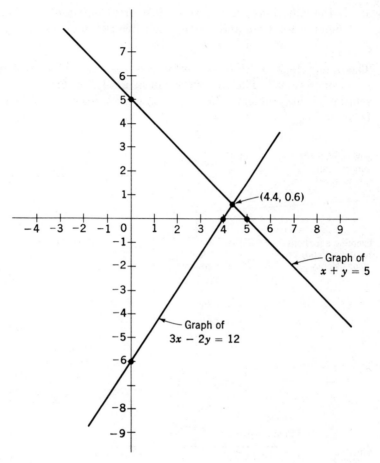

(4.4, 0.6)

Graph of
x + y = 5

Graph of
3x − 2y = 12

Fig. 4-5

Let us assume that we must solve many systems, each of the following form:

$$a_1x + b_1y = c_1$$
$$a_2x + b_2y = c_2$$

For each system, the coefficients and the constants will be different. That is, for each system:

1. Obtain new coefficients.
2. Examine the equations for dependency or inconsistency.
3. If the equations are dependent or inconsistent, we conclude there is no solution and attempt to solve the next system.

4. If the equations are not dependent or inconsistent, we find x and y, the common solution, and attempt to solve the next system.

These four steps are to be taken for each system.   Thus we have a repetitive set of operations.   The computer will fit nicely at this point as an aid in the solution of this problem.   Let us indicate the steps involved in a block-diagram fashion.

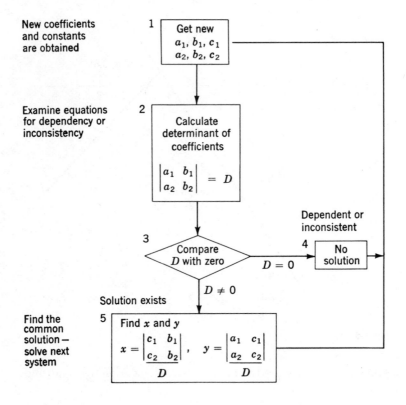

Note that the coefficients and the constants are of primary interest as far as the computer is concerned.   The original system is not of specific interest. This is so because only coefficients and constants are needed in the pursuit of a solution.

The mental work has been done by human beings; that is, realizing the importance of the determinant, constructing equations so that x and y may be found, etc.   It is in the repetitive operations that the computer will aid us.

4-3 SYSTEMS OF THREE OR MORE LINEAR EQUATIONS

When systems are made up of three or more equations in as many unknowns, a graphical interpretation, as we have seen, is impossible. Here we pursue the result in an entirely algebraic sense.

Solution by Determinants

The system we are concerned with is

$$a_1x + b_1y + c_1z = d_1 \tag{4-65}$$
$$a_2x + b_2y + c_2z = d_2 \tag{4-66}$$
$$a_3x + b_3y + c_3z = d_3 \tag{4-67}$$

The determinant of the coefficients in a system of three linear equations has meaning for us. Let us write it symbolically:

$$\begin{vmatrix} a_1 & b_1 & c_1 \\ a_2 & b_2 & c_2 \\ a_3 & b_3 & c_3 \end{vmatrix}$$

Its expanded form is slightly more complex than that of a 2 by 2. It is

$$a_1b_2c_3 + a_3b_1c_2 + a_2b_3c_1 - a_3b_2c_1 - a_1b_3c_2 - a_2b_1c_3 \tag{4-68}$$

The above expansion comes about in the following manner. Consider any row (or column). Take the first element in that row (or column). Draw a line through the row and column in which that element appears. Now let the remaining four elements form a 2 by 2 determinant. This determinant is called the *minor* of the first element. Precede the determinant by a plus or minus sign according to Fig. 4-6. The signed minor is called the cofactor of

$$\begin{vmatrix} + & - & + \\ - & + & - \\ + & - & + \end{vmatrix}$$

Fig. 4-6

the element. Now form the product of the element and its cofactor. Continue this process on the remaining elements in the row (or column), then add the results.

For example, if a_1 is the first element, its minor is preceded by a plus sign.

Problem 1

Expand the general 3 by 3 determinant by considering elements in the first row.

solution: Cross out the row and column in which a_1 appears.

$$\begin{vmatrix} a_1 & b_1 & c_1 \\ a_2 & b_2 & c_2 \\ a_3 & b_3 & c_3 \end{vmatrix}$$

The resulting 2 by 2 determinant is $\begin{vmatrix} b_2 & c_2 \\ b_3 & c_3 \end{vmatrix}$.

Now for b_1,

$$\begin{vmatrix} a_1 & b_1 & c_1 \\ a_2 & b_2 & c_2 \\ a_3 & b_3 & c_3 \end{vmatrix}$$

the resulting 2 by 2 determinant is $\begin{vmatrix} a_2 & c_2 \\ a_3 & c_3 \end{vmatrix}$.

Finally, for c_1 we have

$$\begin{vmatrix} a_1 & b_1 & c_1 \\ a_2 & b_2 & c_2 \\ a_3 & b_3 & c_3 \end{vmatrix}$$

and

$$\begin{vmatrix} a_2 & b_2 \\ a_3 & b_3 \end{vmatrix}$$

The 2 by 2 determinants above are called the cofactors of a_1, b_1, and c_1. Then, according to Fig. 4-6, we have

$$a_1 \begin{vmatrix} b_2 & c_2 \\ b_3 & c_3 \end{vmatrix} - b_1 \begin{vmatrix} a_2 & c_2 \\ a_3 & c_3 \end{vmatrix} + c_1 \begin{vmatrix} a_2 & b_2 \\ a_3 & b_3 \end{vmatrix}$$

or

$$a_1(b_2c_3 - c_2b_3) - b_1(a_2c_3 - a_3c_2) + c_1(a_2b_3 - a_3b_2)$$

When parentheses are removed the result is Eq. (4-68).

Problem 2

Expand the determinant according to column 1.
solution: You should obtain Eq. (4-68).
If the determinant of the coefficients is zero in a system of three simultaneous linear equations, that system is not solvable. In particular, the system is dependent or inconsistent.

Expanding the determinant of a system of three equations is a good way to find out if we should proceed further.

Now let D symbolize the determinant of the coefficients; let Dx be D when the coefficients of x are replaced by the constants. Similarly for Dy and Dz.

Then if D is not zero, x, y, and z may be found directly from the following equations.

$$x = \frac{Dx}{D} = \frac{\begin{vmatrix} d_1 & b_1 & c_1 \\ d_2 & b_2 & c_2 \\ d_3 & b_3 & c_3 \end{vmatrix}}{\begin{vmatrix} a_1 & b_1 & c_1 \\ a_2 & b_2 & c_2 \\ a_3 & b_3 & c_3 \end{vmatrix}} \qquad (4\text{-}69)$$

$$y = \frac{Dy}{D} = \frac{\begin{vmatrix} a_1 & d_1 & c_1 \\ a_2 & d_2 & c_2 \\ a_3 & d_3 & c_3 \end{vmatrix}}{\begin{vmatrix} a_1 & b_1 & c_1 \\ a_2 & b_2 & c_2 \\ a_3 & b_3 & c_3 \end{vmatrix}} \qquad (4\text{-}70)$$

$$z = \frac{Dz}{D} = \frac{\begin{vmatrix} a_1 & b_1 & d_1 \\ a_2 & b_2 & d_2 \\ a_3 & b_3 & d_3 \end{vmatrix}}{\begin{vmatrix} a_1 & b_1 & c_1 \\ a_2 & b_2 & c_2 \\ a_3 & b_3 & c_3 \end{vmatrix}} \qquad (4\text{-}71)$$

Some theorems (which we state without proof) about determinants follow:

1. If elements of one row (or one column) of a determinant are multiplied by some number v, the value of the entire determinant is multiplied by v. For example,

$$\begin{vmatrix} va_1 & vb_1 & vc_1 \\ a_2 & b_2 & c_2 \\ a_3 & b_3 & c_3 \end{vmatrix} = v \begin{vmatrix} a_1 & b_1 & c_1 \\ a_2 & b_2 & c_2 \\ a_3 & b_3 & c_3 \end{vmatrix}.$$

similarly for any other row or any column.

2. The value of a determinant does not change if

    a. Elements of some row (or column) are multiplied by a nonzero number p and added to corresponding elements in another row (or column), or
    b. Rows and columns are interchanged.

For example,

a. $\begin{vmatrix} a_1 & b_1 & c_1 \\ a_2 & b_2 & c_2 \\ a_3 & b_3 & c_3 \end{vmatrix} = \begin{vmatrix} a_1 & b_1 & c_1 \\ a_2 + pa_1 & b_2 + pb_1 & c_2 + pc_1 \\ a_3 & b_3 & c_3 \end{vmatrix}$

b. $\begin{vmatrix} a_1 & b_1 & c_1 \\ a_2 & b_2 & c_2 \\ a_3 & b_3 & c_3 \end{vmatrix} = \begin{vmatrix} a_1 & a_2 & a_3 \\ b_1 & b_2 & b_3 \\ c_1 & c_2 & c_3 \end{vmatrix}$

3. A determinant has a value of zero if

    a. All elements of one row (or column) are zero, or
    b. One row (or column) is a multiple of another row (or column), or
    c. Two rows (two columns) are the same.

For example,

a. $\begin{vmatrix} a_1 & b_1 & c_1 \\ 0 & 0 & 0 \\ a_3 & b_3 & c_3 \end{vmatrix} = 0$

b. $\begin{vmatrix} a_1 & b_1 & c_1 \\ ka_1 & kb_1 & kc_1 \\ a_3 & b_3 & c_3 \end{vmatrix} = 0$

c. $\begin{vmatrix} a_1 & b_1 & c_1 \\ a_1 & b_1 & c_1 \\ a_3 & b_3 & c_3 \end{vmatrix} = 0$

4. If two rows (two columns) of a determinant are interchanged, the value of the determinant changes sign. For example,

$$\begin{vmatrix} a_1 & b_1 & c_1 \\ a_2 & b_2 & c_2 \\ a_3 & b_3 & c_3 \end{vmatrix} = - \begin{vmatrix} a_2 & b_2 & c_2 \\ a_1 & b_1 & c_1 \\ a_3 & b_3 & c_3 \end{vmatrix}$$

Note that the illustrations given above for each theorem were for a 3 by 3 determinant. This was selected for simplicity. The results hold for determinants of any order (number of rows or colums).

Solution by Elimination

Consider again the system of three equations in three unknowns.

$$a_1x + b_1y + c_1z = d_1 \qquad\qquad (4\text{-}72)$$
$$a_2x + b_2y + c_2z = d_2 \qquad\qquad (4\text{-}73)$$
$$a_3x + b_3y + c_3z = d_3 \qquad\qquad (4\text{-}74)$$

If we proceed to eliminate unknowns as we did with a system of two unknowns, we would find similar things happening. For example, a system of two equations in two unknowns was manipulated to obtain one equation in one unknown. This we referred to as elimination. The elimination method that will be used here is due to a famous German mathematician, Karl Friedrich Gauss. The idea here is to combine the equations by multiplication and addition so as eventually to obtain an equivalent system that looks like the following:

$$a_1x + b_1y + c_1z = d_1 \tag{4-75}$$
$$\bar{b}_2y + \bar{c}_2z = \bar{d}_2 \tag{4-76}$$
$$\bar{c}_3z = \bar{d}_3 \tag{4-77}$$

We use $\bar{b}_2$, $\bar{c}_2$, $\bar{d}_2$, $\bar{c}_3$, and $\bar{d}_3$ to emphasize that these values are different from b_2, c_2, d_2, c_3, and d_3.

Now, by a process called back substitution, we merely solve the last equation for z. Substitute this value for z into the middle equation in order to find y. Finally, we substitute the computed values for y and z in the first equation, in order to find x.

Let us look at the steps involved in obtaining Eqs. (4-75) to (4-77).

First, multiply Eq. (4-72) by $-a_2/a_1$ and add the result to Eq. (4-73).

$$a_1x + b_1y + c_1z = d_1$$
$$0x + (a_1b_2 - a_2b_1)y + (a_1c_2 - a_2c_1)z = a_1d_2 - a_2d_1$$
$$a_3x + b_3y + c_3z = d_3$$

Now multiply Eq. (4-72) by $-a_3/a_1$ and add the result to Eq. (4-74). Our system becomes

$$a_1x + b_1y + c_1z = d_1 \tag{4-78}$$
$$(a_1b_2 - a_2b_1)y + (a_1c_2 - a_2c_1)z = a_1d_2 - a_2d_1 \tag{4-79}$$
$$(a_1b_3 - a_3b_1)y + (a_1c_3 - a_3c_1)z = a_1d_3 - a_3d_1 \tag{4-80}$$

Now multiply Eq. (4-79) by $-(a_1b_3 - a_3b_1)/(a_1b_2 - a_2b_1)$ and add the result to Eq. (4-80). The result is

$$a_1x + b_1y + c_1z = d_1 \tag{4-81}$$
$$(a_1b_2 - a_2b_1)y + (a_1c_2 - a_2c_1)z = a_1d_2 - a_2d_1 \tag{4-82}$$
$$[(a_1c_3 - a_3c_1)(a_1b_2 - a_2b_1) - (a_1b_3 - a_3b_1)(a_1c_3 - a_3c_1)]z$$
$$= [(a_1d_3 - a_3d_1)(a_1b_2 - a_2b_1) - (a_1d_2 - a_2d_1)(a_1b_3 - a_3b_1)] \tag{4-83}$$

Be assured that this system has the same form as the system (4-75) to (4-77), with

$$\bar{b}_2 = a_1b_2 - a_2b_1 \qquad \bar{c}_2 = a_1c_2 - a_2c_1 \qquad \bar{d}_2 = a_1d_2 - a_2d_1$$

and

$$\bar{c}_3 = (a_1c_3 - a_3c_1)(a_1b_2 - a_2b_1) - (a_1b_3 - a_3b_1)(a_1c_3 - a_3c_1)$$
$$\bar{d}_3 = (a_1d_3 - a_3d_1)(a_1b_2 - a_2b_1) - (a_1d_2 - a_2d_1)(a_1b_3 - a_3b_1)$$

Although this method seems tedious, it is the type of manipulation that is readily adaptable to a computer.

Let us solve a system of four linear equations by the Gauss method. The system is

$$a_1x + b_1y + c_1z + d_1w = v_1 \tag{4-84}$$
$$a_2x + b_2y + c_2z + d_2w = v_2 \tag{4-85}$$
$$a_3x + b_3y + c_3z + d_3w = v_3 \tag{4-86}$$
$$a_4x + b_4y + c_4z + d_4w = v_4 \tag{4-87}$$

Let us take a particular system

$$2x - 3y + z - w = 6$$
$$3x + 2y - 6z + w = 2$$
$$x - 7y + 3z + 2w = 1$$
$$-4x - y + 7z - 3w = 5$$

Now we attempt to make the coefficients of the x terms in the second, third, and fourth equations all zero. As you will recall, this is done by selecting an appropriate multiplier for the first equation. This multiplier is minus the coefficient of x in each of the remaining equations divided by a_1.

In order to facilitate our computations, it would be convenient if the denominator of our multiplier were 1. This can be accomplished if the equations are rearranged. To this end let us rearrange the system so that the third equation in the original set becomes the first. This makes $a_1 = 1$. Thus, when the first multiplier is formed from $-(a_2/a_1)$, we obtain $-(a_2/1)$, or merely $-a_2$.

For example, the coefficient of x in the second equation of the rearranged set is 2. So we take -2 and multiply the first equation by it and add the result to the second equation. The first equation *remains unchanged in our system*. It is the second equation that changes.

We have

$$x - 7y + 3z + 2w = 1$$
$$0x + 11y - 5z - 5w = 4$$

Note that the only things that changed in the second equation were the coefficients and the constant term on the right. We can take advantage of this fact by writing coefficients and constants only and working with them exclusively. For example, consider the first two equations of the rearranged system.

$$
\begin{array}{rrrrr}
1 & -7 & +3 & +2 & +1 \\
2 & -3 & +1 & -1 & +6
\end{array}
$$

When each element in the first row is multiplied by -2 and added to the corresponding element in the second row, we have

$$
\begin{array}{rrrrr}
1 & -7 & +3 & +2 & +1 \\
0 & +11 & -5 & -5 & +4
\end{array}
$$

Note that the second row consists of the coefficients and constant of the altered second equation.

We can continue this process on the third and fourth equations of our system. Let us first write the entire array consisting of coefficients and constants of our system, with the second equation altered.

$$
\begin{array}{rrrrr}
1 & -7 & +3 & +2 & +1 \\
0 & +11 & -5 & -5 & +4 \\
3 & +2 & -6 & +1 & +2 \\
-4 & -1 & +7 & -3 & +5
\end{array}
$$

Now multiply each element in the first row by -3 and add the result to the corresponding element in the third row. The third row becomes

$$
\begin{array}{rrrrr}
0 & +23 & -15 & -5 & -1
\end{array}
$$

Multiply each element in the first row by 4 and add the result to the corresponding element in the fourth row. The fourth row becomes

$$
\begin{array}{rrrrr}
0 & -29 & 19 & 5 & 9
\end{array}
$$

Thus the altered system is

$$
\begin{array}{rrrrr}
x - & 7y + & 3z + 2w & = 1 \\
& 11y - & 5z - 5w & = 4 \\
& +23y - & 15z - 5w & = -1 \\
& -29y + & 19z - 5w & = 9
\end{array}
$$

Our job now is to eliminate y from the third and fourth equations above. This is accomplished by making the coefficients of y in the last two equations above equal to zero.

Let us write down the coefficients and constants of the above system.

$$
\begin{array}{rrrrr}
1 & -7 & +3 & +2 & 1 \\
0 & 11 & -5 & -5 & 4 \\
0 & +23 & -15 & -5 & -1 \\
0 & -29 & 19 & -5 & 9
\end{array}
$$

Multiply each element in the second row by $-\frac{23}{11}$ and add to the corresponding element in the third row. The third row becomes

$$0 \quad 0 \quad -\frac{50}{11} \quad +\frac{60}{11} \quad -\frac{103}{11}$$

Multiply each element in the second row by $\frac{29}{11}$ and add to the corresponding element in the fourth row. The fourth row becomes

$$0 \quad 0 \quad \frac{64}{11} \quad -\frac{90}{11} \quad \frac{215}{11}$$

The altered system becomes

$$
\begin{aligned}
x - 7y + 3z + 2w &= 1 \\
11y - 5z - 5w &= 4 \\
-\tfrac{50}{11}z + \tfrac{60}{11}w &= -\tfrac{103}{11} \\
\tfrac{64}{11}z - \tfrac{90}{11}w &= \tfrac{215}{11}
\end{aligned}
$$

Now all that remains is to eliminate z from the last equation. Let us write down the coefficients thus far.

1	-7	$+3$	$+2$	1
0	11	-5	-5	4
0	0	$-\frac{50}{11}$	$+\frac{60}{11}$	$-\frac{103}{11}$
0	0	$\frac{64}{11}$	$-\frac{90}{11}$	$\frac{215}{11}$

Multiply the third row by $\frac{64}{50}$ and add the result to the fourth row. The result is

$$0 \quad 0 \quad 0 \quad -\frac{66}{55} \quad \frac{2{,}079}{11 \times 25}$$

The altered system becomes

$$
\begin{aligned}
x - 7y + 3z + 2w &= 1 \\
11y - 5z - 5w &= 4 \\
-\frac{50}{11}z + \frac{60}{11}w &= \frac{-103}{11} \\
-\frac{66}{55}w &= \frac{2{,}079}{11 \times 25}
\end{aligned}
$$

Note that the last equation contains only one unknown, w. This can be easily solved for w, and by substituting back in the remaining equations we can find z, y, and x.

You should verify for yourself that

$$
\begin{aligned}
w &= -\tfrac{63}{10} \\
z &= -11\tfrac{1}{2} \\
y &= -5 \\
x &= -\tfrac{49}{10}
\end{aligned}
$$

Thus the problem is solved.

You may have wondered how we can be sure our system is solvable. One way is to evaluate the determinant of the coefficients of our original system. This determinant is found in a manner similar to that of a 3 by 3. Expansion again is by a row *or* column, the resulting minors being 3 by 3 determinants instead of 2 by 2. These 3 by 3 determinants may then be evaluated by the method previously described.

If the determinant is found to be zero, the system is not solvable.

Evaluation of determinants beyond 3 by 3 becomes unwieldy, and this is not the approach usually taken in computer solution of systems of linear equations. The Gauss method just described is the type of approach used in an attempt to solve a linear system via computer. Why? Because certain operations (multiplication and addition) are done repeatedly, each time using a different multiplier.

We have not yet mentioned dependency and inconsistency when using the Gauss method. Let us symbolically discuss the method again. We began with a system

$$a_1 x + b_1 y + c_1 z + d_1 w = v_1$$
$$a_2 x + b_2 y + c_2 z + d_2 w = v_2$$
$$a_3 x + b_3 y + c_3 z + d_3 w = v_3$$
$$a_4 x + b_4 y + c_4 z + d_4 w = v_4$$

Our first effort was to make the coefficients of x zero in the second, third, and fourth equations. We obtain

$$a_1 x + b_1 y + c_1 z + d_1 w = v_1$$
$$0x + \bar{b}_2 y + \bar{c}_2 z + \bar{d}_2 w = \bar{v}_2$$
$$0x + \bar{b}_3 y + \bar{c}_3 z + \bar{d}_3 w = \bar{v}_3$$
$$0x + \bar{b}_4 y + \bar{c}_4 z + \bar{d}_4 w = \bar{v}_4$$

The bars appear over certain coefficients to indicate that, in general, they are different from the original coefficients. If it so happens that $\bar{b}_2$, $\bar{b}_3$, $\bar{b}_4$ are all zero, then the determinant of the coefficients will be zero. When this happens, the original system will be dependent or inconsistent.

If they are not all zero, our next effort is to make the coefficients of y zero in the third and fourth equations. We then have

$$a_1 x + b_1 y + c_1 z + d_1 w = v_1$$
$$0x + \bar{b}_2 y + \bar{c}_2 z + \bar{d}_2 w = \bar{v}_2$$
$$0x + 0y + \bar{\bar{c}}_3 z + \bar{\bar{d}}_3 w = \bar{\bar{v}}_3$$
$$0x + 0y + \bar{\bar{c}}_4 z + \bar{\bar{d}}_4 w = \bar{\bar{v}}_4$$

The double bars appear to indicate that, in general, these coefficients are different from the single-bar coefficients. Now if $\bar{\bar{c}}_3$ and $\bar{\bar{c}}_4$ are both zero, then the determinant of the coefficients of our original system will be zero. As before, the original system will be dependent or inconsistent. If they are not both zero, our next effort is to make the coefficient of z zero in the last equation. The result is

$$a_1x + b_1y + c_1z + d_1w = v_1$$
$$0x + \bar{b}_2y + \bar{c}_2z + \bar{d}_2w = \bar{v}_2$$
$$0x + 0y + \bar{\bar{c}}_3z + \bar{\bar{d}}_3w = \bar{\bar{v}}_3$$
$$0x + 0y + 0z + \bar{\bar{\bar{d}}}_4w = \bar{\bar{\bar{v}}}_4$$

We solve the last equation for w. Then, by back substitution, we find z, y, and x. (See Exercise 4-6.)

EXERCISES

4-1. Solve the system:

$$3x + 4y = 15$$
$$2x + y = 5$$

4-2. Solve the system:

$$\frac{x + y}{2} = 6$$
$$x - y = 5$$

4-3. Are the following systems dependent? If not, solve and graph; if so, graph only.

   a. $\frac{1}{2}x - 4y = -1$
       $-x + 8y = 2$
   b. $\frac{3}{4}x + \frac{9}{16}y = 1\frac{1}{3}$
       $x - \frac{3}{4}y = 1$
   c. $x + 4y = 12$
       $-x + 3y = -12$

4-4. Are the following systems inconsistent? If not, solve; if so, graph only.

   a. $3y = x + 2$
       $x = 3y + 7$
   b. $\frac{x}{m} + \frac{y}{n} = 1$

       $\frac{x}{n} + \frac{y}{m} = 1$

4-5. Examine the following system for solvability. If possible, find the solutions.

$$x + y = 7$$
$$3x + 2y - z = 1$$
$$x + 1 = y + 3 + 2$$

4-6. Solve the system

$$6x + y + z - 2w = 5$$
$$x + y + 1 = z + w + 2$$
$$3x + 2y + z = 3$$
$$z + x + 5 = w + y$$

Caution: Make sure you line up the equation according to general form.

4-7. An investment of $12,500 yielded $525 in interest. Part of the investment gained interest at 4 percent, the rest $4\frac{1}{2}$ percent. What was the amount invested for each part?

4-8. For a demonstration of the latest computer equipment, admission charges are 75 cents for adults and 25 cents for children. If 750 tickets were sold and the amount of money collected was $400, how many adults' and how many children's tickets were sold?

4-9. A men's apparel shop bought 540 shirts. Long-sleeve shirts cost $5, and short-sleeve shirts cost $3. The total cost for the shirts was $1,840. Find the number of long-sleeve and short-sleeve shirts bought.

4-10. Solve these systems by both elimination methods.

a. $5a - 3b = 12$ b. $15a + 7b = 37$
    $2a - 3b = 3$ $9a - 10b = 8$
c. $5a + 10b = 51$ d. $2\frac{2}{5}x + 2y = 11\frac{1}{10}$
    $3a - 15b = 28.5$ $x + y = 5$

4-11. Solve by the elimination method that is easier for you:

a. $\dfrac{2x + 5y}{10} = 4$ b. $0.04x + 0.02y = 5$
                                           $0.5x - 0.4y = 30$

$$\dfrac{x - 1}{3} - \dfrac{y + 2}{2} = 0$$

4-12. Solve graphically

a. $x + y - 1 = 0$ b. $y - 7 = 0$
    $2x - 3y + 4 = 0$ $x - 5 = 0$

c. $-5x + 8y = 40$ d. $10x - 8y = 8$
      $3x - 4y = 12$ $11x + 11 = 10y$
e. $3x - 2y = 4$ f. $4x + 7y - 3 = 20$
      $2x + 3y = 7$ $x - 7y - 1 = 20$

4-13. Graph the lines given by each system in Exercise 4-10. You should graph each system on a different set of axes. Identify the point of intersection for each. Compare these with the results you obtained algebraically in Exercise 4-10.

4-14. Graph each system on the same set of axes. Which are dependent or inconsistent?

a. $10x - 2y = 120$ b. $x - 0.2y = 11$
      $-x + 0.2y = 12$ $10x - 2y = 120$
c. $7x - 5y = 3$
      $3(7x - 5y - 3) = 3(3 + 5y - 7x)$
d. $\dfrac{x + y}{2} = 15$

      $2.5x + 2.5y = 12$

4-15. Answer the question of Exercise 4-14 by using determinants.

4-16. The equation $y = mx + b$ is the slope-intercept form of a straight line (see Chap. 3). Find m and b so that the points $(1,5)$ and $(5,10)$ are on the line.

4-17. The length of a rectangle is 7 feet greater than the width. Find the dimensions of the rectangle if the perimeter is 44 feet.

4-18. Evaluate these determinants

a. $\begin{vmatrix} 3 & 2 & 5 \\ 1 & 0 & -2 \\ 4 & 9 & 7 \end{vmatrix}$ b. $\begin{vmatrix} a & b \\ b & a \end{vmatrix}$ c. $\begin{vmatrix} 7 & 8 \\ 4 & 2 \end{vmatrix}$

d. $\begin{vmatrix} 6 & 4 & 1 & 2 \\ 7 & 2 & 0 & 5 \\ -8 & 3 & -5 & 0 \\ 4 & -9 & 6 & -2 \end{vmatrix}$ e. $\begin{vmatrix} 1 & -10 & -4 & 9 \\ 0 & 1 & 16 & 4 \\ 0 & 0 & 1 & 3 \\ 0 & 0 & 0 & -7 \end{vmatrix}$

(*Hint:* In 3e you can evaluate by doing very little work.)

4-19. Solve, if possible:

a. $5x - 2y = -33$ b. $y + z = 13$
      $x + 3y = -10$ $x + z = 12$
  $x + y - 7z = 13$ $x + y = 11$

c. $3x - 5 = 2(x - 2)$
$(x + 1)(y - 1) = (x + 2)(y - 2) + 5$
$2x + 3y + z = 6$

d. $x + 5y - z = 7$
$-2x + 3y + 2z = 5$
$3x + 7y - 3z = 4$

4-20. Consider the system

$$7x - 5y = 3$$
$$14x - 10y = k$$

Find a value for k so that the graphs of the equations (a) coincide, (b) are parallel.

4-21. In the system

$$x + 4y = 9$$
$$mx - 8y = n$$

find a value for m and n so that the graphs of the equations (a) coincide, (b) are parallel, (c) intersect.

4-22. Why are the determinants equal in part a?   In part b?

a.
$$\begin{vmatrix} 4 & 5 & 8 \\ 3 & 4 & -12 \\ -1 & 9 & 4 \end{vmatrix} = 4 \times \begin{vmatrix} 4 & 5 & 2 \\ 3 & 4 & -3 \\ -1 & 9 & 1 \end{vmatrix}$$

b.
$$\begin{vmatrix} 3 & 1 & 5 \\ 1 & 4 & 0 \\ -9 & 3 & 4 \end{vmatrix} = \begin{vmatrix} 3 & 1 & 5 \\ 7 & 6 & 10 \\ -9 & 3 & 4 \end{vmatrix}$$

(*Hint:* Use the theorems on determinants.)

4-23. Solve by the Gauss method

a. $x - y + 4z = 7$ b. $1.5x + y + 0.5z = 3$
$9x - 4y - z = 8$ $x + y - z = 1$
$-2x + y + 5z = 2$ $2x - 3y + 3z = 2$

4-24. Construct a flowchart, as in the text, for several three-equation systems.

4-25. Profits on a business amount to $50,000.   Net profits are defined to be profits minus income tax.   The president of this business receives a bonus amounting to 30 percent of net profits.   The tax on this business is 20 percent of the amount left after deducting bonus from profits. What is the tax and what is the bonus?

chapter five

MATRICES AND MATRIX METHODS

INTRODUCTION

First of all, let it be said that a matrix is merely an array of numbers. This array usually represents a set of numbers with which we are already familiar. For instance, the coefficients of the unknowns in a system of linear equations can be thought of as a matrix. The unknowns themselves can be thought of as elements of a matrix. Even the constants in a system can be thought of as a matrix. When the number of equations becomes large, the advantages offered by matrix description become evident. Arithmetic operations between these arrays are next in the pursuit of a solution for our system. These operations are repetitive in nature. That is, the same operations occur repeatedly, each time with different elements of our arrays. Thus we have repetitive operations with many different numbers. A computer is a welcome aid in this type of process.

5-1 THE MATRIX

We have described a matrix as an array of numbers. In particular, it is an array with rows and columns. Thus

$$\begin{bmatrix} a & b & c \\ d & e & f \end{bmatrix}$$

is an array of numbers with two rows and three columns. The letters symbolize real numbers, and the large brackets serve to enclose the array. When the number of rows and columns becomes large, you can see how rapidly we would run out of symbols to use as elements in our matrix. So another notation has been adopted which will readily describe any element in any matrix. Thus any matrix element is symbolized by

$$a_{ij}$$

where the subscript i is the *row* in which this element appears and the subscript j is the *column* in which this element appears. A capital letter is generally used to refer to a matrix. Thus

$$A = \begin{bmatrix} a_{11} & a_{12} & a_{13} \\ a_{21} & a_{22} & a_{23} \\ a_{31} & a_{32} & a_{33} \end{bmatrix}$$

serves as an example of the foregoing statements. The array above is also referred to as the matrix A. In general, a matrix A with n rows and m columns is written

$$A = \begin{bmatrix} a_{11} & a_{12} & \cdots & a_{1m} \\ a_{21} & a_{22} & \cdots & a_{2m} \\ \cdots & \cdots & \cdots & \cdots \\ a_{n1} & a_{n2} & \cdots & a_{nm} \end{bmatrix}$$

When $n = m$, we have a matrix with the same number of rows as columns. This is referred to as a *square matrix*. An imaginary line from upper left to lower right is called the *main diagonal* of the matrix. Note that elements a_{ij}, where $i = j$, are on the main diagonal. The number of rows (or columns) is called the *order* of the matrix.

Arrays with only one row or only one column also exist in a matrix sense. A one-row array is called a *row matrix*. A one-column array is called a *column matrix*. A row matrix or column matrix is also called a vector. It is important to emphasize at this point that a matrix does not have a *value*. It is merely a display, or table of numbers. The letter A (or any other symbol), as used above, is used only to name the array on the right side of the equal sign. This is quite similar to the convention of using a symbol, say P, to mean the point $(3,7)$ in the xy plane. Thus $P = (3,7)$ means that P is the name of the point $(3,7)$. However, P does not have an actual numerical value.

In the study of matrices we find that they become most useful in describing a system of linear equations when the number of equations is quite large. For example, consider the system

$$a_{11}x_1 + a_{12}x_2 + a_{13}x_3 + a_{14}x_4 + a_{15}x_5 = b_1$$
$$a_{21}x_1 + a_{22}x_2 + a_{23}x_3 + a_{24}x_4 + a_{25}x_5 = b_2$$
$$a_{31}x_1 + a_{32}x_2 + a_{33}x_3 + a_{34}x_4 + a_{35}x_5 = b_3$$
$$a_{41}x_1 + a_{42}x_2 + a_{43}x_3 + a_{44}x_4 + a_{45}x_5 = b_4$$
$$a_{51}x_1 + a_{52}x_2 + a_{53}x_3 + a_{54}x_4 + a_{55}x_5 = b_5$$

Here we have chosen to symbolize coefficients, unknowns, and constants with subscripts. This will make it convenient when matrices are introduced. For example, the coefficients can be set up in array form, with name A, as follows:

$$A = \begin{bmatrix} a_{11} & a_{12} & a_{13} & a_{14} & a_{15} \\ a_{21} & a_{22} & a_{23} & a_{24} & a_{25} \\ a_{31} & a_{32} & a_{33} & a_{34} & a_{35} \\ a_{41} & a_{42} & a_{43} & a_{44} & a_{45} \\ a_{51} & a_{52} & a_{53} & a_{54} & a_{55} \end{bmatrix}$$

Another shorthand notation for a matrix is (a_{ij}). Once we know the highest values of i and j, we know the size of the matrix.

The unknowns can also be set up in array form as a row matrix X:

$$X = (x_1 \quad x_2 \quad x_3 \quad x_4 \quad x_5)$$

or as a column matrix X:

$$X = \begin{pmatrix} x_1 \\ x_2 \\ x_3 \\ x_4 \\ x_5 \end{pmatrix}$$

Similarly, the constants can also be set up as a row matrix B:

$$B = (b_1 \quad b_2 \quad b_3 \quad b_4 \quad b_5)$$

or as a column matrix B:

$$B = \begin{pmatrix} b_1 \\ b_2 \\ b_3 \\ b_4 \\ b_5 \end{pmatrix}$$

We shall see later that the column matrix X and the column matrix B are the correct forms.

Thus we can describe our system with three symbols A, X, and B. So the matrix notion has helped us to *describe* a system of equations. Can the matrix notion help us to *solve* a system of equations? The answer is yes, but only after certain operations between matrices have been defined. When this is done, we will be able to manipulate matrix symbols arithmetically in a manner similar to operations between real numbers. In particular, we shall indicate how, under certain conditions, matrices can be added, subtracted, and multiplied.

5-2 RANK OF A MATRIX

Besides helping us solve our system, the matrix notion is helpful in telling us something about our system. To elaborate on this, two concepts are needed, the determinant of a matrix and the rank of a matrix.

The determinant of a matrix is found by considering each element of the matrix as being an element of a determinant, and then merely evaluating the determinant. Note that a determinant has the same number of rows as columns. That is, a determinant is constructed from a square array of numbers. Thus the determinant of a matrix exists *only if that matrix is square.* For example,

$$A = \begin{bmatrix} 3 & 4 & 2 \\ 1 & 2 & 3 \\ -1 & 2 & 1 \end{bmatrix} \tag{5-1}$$

Here A is a square matrix. The determinant of A, written $|A|$, is found by considering the elements of A to be elements of a determinant, thus:

$$|A| = \begin{vmatrix} 3 & 4 & 2 \\ 1 & 2 & 3 \\ -1 & 2 & 1 \end{vmatrix}$$

or

$$|A| = 3 \begin{vmatrix} 2 & 3 \\ 2 & 1 \end{vmatrix} - 4 \begin{vmatrix} 1 & 3 \\ -1 & 1 \end{vmatrix} + 2 \begin{vmatrix} 1 & 2 \\ -1 & 2 \end{vmatrix}$$
$$= 3(-4) - 4(4) + 2(4)$$
$$= -12 - 16 + 8$$
$$= -20 \tag{5-2}$$

Thus the determinant of the matrix A has a value of -20.

When a matrix is not square, we can speak of square matrices within. For example, the matrix

$$\begin{bmatrix} 2 & 3 & 4 \\ 5 & -1 & 6 \end{bmatrix}$$

is not square. However, if we consider columns 1 and 2 alone or columns 2 and 3 alone or columns 1 and 3 alone, we can consider those columns as making up three square matrices. That is,

$$\begin{bmatrix} 2 & 3 \\ 5 & -1 \end{bmatrix} \quad \begin{bmatrix} 3 & 6 \\ -1 & 6 \end{bmatrix} \quad \begin{bmatrix} 2 & 4 \\ 5 & 6 \end{bmatrix}$$

are the square matrices within. Note that, if desired, we could find the determinant for each matrix above.

A matrix constructed from elements of a larger matrix is called a submatrix. Constructing square submatrices from a larger square matrix can also be done by crossing off a row and column of the large matrix. Thus we obtain a square matrix of order one less than the original. For example, let A be a matrix of order 4.

$$A = \begin{bmatrix} -2 & 3 & 4 & 1 \\ 7 & 2 & 1 & 0 \\ 5 & 3 & 9 & 8 \\ 6 & 0 & 0 & 3 \end{bmatrix} \tag{5-3}$$

If the first row and the last column are not considered (are crossed out), we obtain a submatrix of order 3. Thus we have

$$\begin{bmatrix} 7 & 2 & 1 \\ 5 & 3 & 9 \\ 6 & 0 & 0 \end{bmatrix}$$

We are now in a position to define the term *rank* of a matrix. The *rank* of a matrix is the number of rows (or columns) of the *largest* nonzero determinant *contained in the matrix.*

The following theorems are useful in finding the rank of a matrix:

Theorem 1. *The rank of a matrix remains unchanged when a row (or column) is multiplied or divided by a nonzero real number.*

Theorem 2. *The rank of a matrix remains unchanged when a multiple of one row (column) is added to another row (column).*

Note that these theorems pertain to the rank. That is, the matrices themselves change, but the rank does not. For example, find the rank of A, where

$$A = \begin{bmatrix} 1 & 2 & 3 & 1 \\ 1 & 4 & 3 & 0 \\ 3 & 8 & 9 & 2 \end{bmatrix} \tag{5-4}$$

This is not a square matrix. To begin, there are four square submatrices of order 3 in A:

$$\begin{bmatrix} 1 & 2 & 3 \\ 1 & 4 & 3 \\ 3 & 8 & 9 \end{bmatrix} \quad \begin{bmatrix} 2 & 3 & 1 \\ 4 & 3 & 0 \\ 8 & 9 & 2 \end{bmatrix} \quad \begin{bmatrix} 1 & 3 & 1 \\ 1 & 3 & 0 \\ 3 & 9 & 2 \end{bmatrix} \quad \begin{bmatrix} 1 & 2 & 1 \\ 1 & 4 & 0 \\ 3 & 8 & 2 \end{bmatrix}$$

We must examine the determinant of each matrix.

The first is zero, since column 3 is a multiple (3) of column 1. The third is zero, since column 2 is a multiple of column 1.

Let us expand the determinant of the second one according to its third column.

$$\begin{vmatrix} 2 & 3 & 1 \\ 4 & 3 & 0 \\ 8 & 9 & 2 \end{vmatrix} = \begin{vmatrix} 4 & 3 \\ 8 & 9 \end{vmatrix} + 2 \begin{vmatrix} 2 & 3 \\ 4 & 3 \end{vmatrix} = 12 + (-12) = 0 \tag{5-5}$$

Thus the second is zero.

Now let us expand the determinant of the fourth according to its third column.

$$\begin{vmatrix} 1 & 2 & 1 \\ 1 & 4 & 0 \\ 3 & 8 & 2 \end{vmatrix} = \begin{vmatrix} 1 & 4 \\ 3 & 8 \end{vmatrix} + 2 \begin{vmatrix} 1 & 2 \\ 1 & 4 \end{vmatrix} = -4 + 4 = 0 \qquad (5\text{-}6)$$

Thus the fourth is zero.

All 3 by 3 determinants are zero. From this we can conclude that the rank of A in Eq. (5-4) is not 3. In fact, it must be less than 3, since only 2 by 2 determinants remain to be examined. If at least one of these is not zero, the rank is 2. If all the 2 by 2 determinants are zero, we examine the elements themselves. If at least one of these is not zero, the rank of the matrix is 1. If all elements are zero, the rank of the matrix is 0.

In our example at least one 2 by 2 determinant is not zero; hence the rank is 2. Sometimes direct application of one or both of the theorems mentioned above can help us.

Problem

Find the rank of

$$A = \begin{bmatrix} 1 & 5 & -2 \\ -3 & 8 & 6 \\ 2 & 7 & -4 \end{bmatrix}$$

solution: Add 2 times the first column to the third. The result is

$$\begin{bmatrix} 1 & 5 & 0 \\ -3 & 8 & 0 \\ 2 & 7 & 0 \end{bmatrix}$$

We immediately see that the rank is not 3 since the only 3 by 3 determinant contained in A is zero. This is so since elements of the third column are all zero.

Now at least one 2 by 2 determinant is not zero; in particular,

$$\begin{vmatrix} 1 & 5 \\ -3 & 8 \end{vmatrix} = 23$$

There are others. Hence the rank is 2.

As an aid in finding rank, it is convenient to form as many zero elements as we can. Then evaluation of determinants is easier.

We can elaborate now on the sentence that began this chapter. In particular, we can state that the matrix notion can help us tell something about a system of simultaneous equations.

Consider the system

$$a_{11}x_1 + a_{12}x_2 + a_{13}x_3 = b_1$$
$$a_{21}x_1 + a_{22}x_2 + a_{23}x_3 = b_2$$
$$a_{31}x_1 + a_{32}x_2 + a_{33}x_3 = b_3$$

The coefficient matrix, which we will call C, is

$$C = \begin{bmatrix} a_{11} & a_{12} & a_{13} \\ a_{21} & a_{22} & a_{23} \\ a_{31} & a_{32} & a_{33} \end{bmatrix}$$

The matrix formed by appending the column of constants to C is called the augmented matrix A.

$$A = \begin{bmatrix} a_{11} & a_{12} & a_{13} & b_1 \\ a_{21} & a_{22} & a_{23} & b_2 \\ a_{31} & a_{32} & a_{33} & b_3 \end{bmatrix}$$

When the ranks of these two matrices are found, we will know what to expect as far as a solution is concerned; in particular:

Rule 1. *If rank A is greater than rank C, the equations are inconsistent (no solution exists).*

Rule 2. *If rank A = rank C and this number equals the number of unknowns, there is one solution.*

Rule 3. *If rank A = rank C and this number is less than the number of unknowns, the equations are dependent (an infinite number of solutions exist).*

We introduce some examples to indicate that care must be used in applying the above rules.

Problem 1

Consider a system which has more equations than unknowns.

$$4x - 3y = 2$$
$$x - y = 3$$
$$2x - 2y = 6$$

Here

$$C = \begin{bmatrix} 4 & -3 \\ 1 & -1 \\ 2 & -2 \end{bmatrix}$$

$$A = \begin{bmatrix} 4 & -3 & 2 \\ 1 & -1 & 3 \\ 2 & -2 & 6 \end{bmatrix}$$

Now the determinant of A is zero. Why? Also rank A = rank C = 2, and this is the number of unknowns. So, by rule 2, there is one solution.

However, we cannot use the second and third equations to solve for x and y since the determinant of the coefficients is zero.   But using the first equation with either the second or third will yield the solution.

Using first and second, the determinant of the coefficients is

$$D = \begin{vmatrix} 4 & -3 \\ 1 & -1 \end{vmatrix} = -4 + 3 = -1$$

Then

$$x = \frac{Dx}{D} = \frac{\begin{vmatrix} 2 & -3 \\ 3 & -1 \end{vmatrix}}{-1} = \frac{7}{-1} = -7$$

$$y = \frac{Dy}{D} = \frac{\begin{vmatrix} 4 & 2 \\ 1 & 3 \end{vmatrix}}{-1} = \frac{10}{1} = -10$$

Solution: $x = -7$

$$y = -10$$

We will use the first and third equation to show that we arrive at the same solution.

First

$$D = \begin{vmatrix} 4 & -3 \\ 2 & -2 \end{vmatrix} = -8 + 6 = -2$$

Then

$$x = \frac{Dx}{D} = \frac{\begin{vmatrix} 2 & -3 \\ 6 & -2 \end{vmatrix}}{-2} = \frac{-4 + 8}{-2} = \frac{14}{-2} = -7$$

$$y = \frac{Dy}{D} = \frac{\begin{vmatrix} 4 & 2 \\ 2 & 6 \end{vmatrix}}{-2} = \frac{24 - 4}{-2} = \frac{20}{-2} = -10$$

In this case the solution is also

$x = -7$
$y = -10$

Problem 2

Examine for solvability, then solve:

$$2x - 3y + z = 1$$
$$x + 2y - z = 3$$
$$3x - y \qquad = 4$$

Here

$$C = \begin{bmatrix} 2 & -3 & 1 \\ 1 & 2 & -1 \\ 3 & -1 & 0 \end{bmatrix}$$

$$A = \begin{bmatrix} 2 & -3 & 1 & 1 \\ 1 & 2 & -1 & 3 \\ 3 & -1 & 0 & 4 \end{bmatrix}$$

Now, if -1 times the second row of C is added to the third row, we obtain a matrix with identical first and third rows.

The determinant of this new matrix is zero, since the first and third rows become identical when -1 times the second row is added to the third. Thus the rank of this new matrix, and hence the rank of C, is not 3 (see theorem 2).

Similarly, all 3 by 3 determinants in A are zero.

It is a simple matter to show that the rank of C is 2 and also that the rank of A is 2. Thus rank A = rank C = 2, and this is less than the number of unknowns. Here we fall under rule 3, and there are an infinite number of solutions. The term infinite comes about as follows: The rank of both matrices is 2. This means (since there are three unknowns) that we can solve for two unknowns in terms of the third. In our case, we can solve for x and z in terms of y or y *and z in terms of* x.

Since the third equation has no z term, we have

$$y = 3x - 4 \qquad y \text{ in terms of } x$$

and from the second equation,

$$x + 2(3x - 4) - z = 3$$

or

$$z = 7x - 11 \qquad z \text{ in terms of } x$$

So the solutions for x, y, and z are infinite in number.

The last system we will cover is called *homogeneous*. In this type the number of equations is the same as the number of unknowns. Also, the constant terms on the right-hand side are all zero. A system of three homogeneous equations is

$$a_{11}x_1 + a_{12}x_2 + a_{13}x_3 = 0$$
$$a_{21}x_1 + a_{22}x_2 + a_{23}x_3 = 0$$
$$a_{31}x_1 + a_{32}x_2 + a_{33}x_3 = 0$$

It should be clear that a solution to this system is

$$x_1 = 0 \qquad x_2 = 0 \qquad x_3 = 0$$

This solution is called the trivial solution. The next question you may ask is: Does a nontrivial solution exist? The answer is yes, under a certain condition.   We state that condition now:

A set of n homogeneous equations in n unknowns will have a nontrivial solution if the rank of the coefficient matrix is less than n.   Another way of stating this is: *The determinant of the coefficients must be zero.*

The above concepts enable us to solve problems such as the following.

Problem

For what values of e do the following set of homogeneous equations have nontrivial solutions for x, y, and z?

$$
\begin{aligned}
(1 + e)x - \quad\quad y - \quad\quad 3z &= 0 \\
-x - (2 - e)y \quad\quad\quad &= 0 \\
3x \quad\quad\quad\quad + (2 - e)z &= 0
\end{aligned}
$$

solution: In order for the system to have a nontrivial solution, the determinant of the coefficients must be zero.   That is,

$$
\begin{vmatrix}
(1 + e) & -1 & -3 \\
-1 & -(2 - e) & 0 \\
3 & 0 & (2 - e)
\end{vmatrix}
$$

must equal zero.   Let us expand the above determinant according to the elements in the last column and equate to zero.

$$
-3[3(2 - e)] + (2 - e)[-(2 - e)(1 + e) - 1] = 0
$$

or

$$
\begin{aligned}
(2 - e)[-9 - (2 - e)(1 + e) - 1] &= 0 \\
(2 - e)[-9 - (2 + e - e^2) - 1] &= 0 \\
(2 - e)[-9 - 2 - e + e^2 - 1] &= 0
\end{aligned}
$$

or

$$
\begin{aligned}
(2 - e)(e^2 - e - 12) &= 0 \\
(2 - e)(e - 4)(e + 3) &= 0
\end{aligned}
$$

Applying the product law to this equation, we obtain

$$
e = 2 \quad\quad e = -3 \quad\quad e = 4
$$

Thus our final answer is: The only values of e for which our homogeneous system has a nontrivial solution are

$$
e = 2 \quad\quad e = -3 \quad\quad e = 4
$$

These e's are called *latent roots*, or *eigenvalues*.

5-3 OPERATIONS WITH MATRICES

The term "operations" used in the title of this section refers to arithmetic operations.   In a manner similar to operations between real numbers, operations between matrices exist. In particular, sums, differences, products, and inverses of matrices exist. Since the notion of a matrix implies an array of real numbers, special care is needed when we define operations between matrices.

First of all, the notion of equality between matrices must be stated. Let A and B be two matrices, each *with the same number of rows and columns*. Equality is defined in the following way:

The matrix A is equal to the matrix B if and only if corresponding elements are equal. The phrase "if and only if" means that the reverse is true also. That is, when corresponding elements are equal between two matrices A and B, then those matrices are said to be equal.

Thus, if

$$\begin{bmatrix} a_1 & b_1 & c_1 \\ a_2 & b_2 & c_2 \\ a_3 & b_3 & c_3 \end{bmatrix} = \begin{bmatrix} 5 & 6 & 3 \\ -2 & 8 & 7 \\ \frac{1}{2} & 0.5 & -1 \end{bmatrix}$$

then

$$\begin{array}{lll} a_1 = 5 & b_1 = 6 & c_1 = 3 \\ a_2 = -2 & b_2 = 8 & c_2 = 7 \\ a_3 = \frac{1}{2} & b_3 = 0.5 & c_3 = -1 \end{array}$$

The matrices involved do not have to be square. The important thing is that the number of rows in each be the same, and the number of columns in each be the same.

As another example consider the following.

If

$$\begin{pmatrix} x_1 \\ x_2 \\ x_3 \end{pmatrix} = \begin{bmatrix} (5+6+a) \\ (7-5+3) \\ (4+0-1) \end{bmatrix} \tag{5-7}$$

then

$$\begin{array}{ll} x_1 = & 11 + a \\ x_2 = & 5 \\ x_3 = & 3 \end{array}$$

Finally, if

$$\begin{bmatrix} x_1 & y_1 \\ x_2 & y_2 \end{bmatrix} = \begin{bmatrix} a+b, & a-b \\ 2a & 3b \end{bmatrix} \tag{5-8}$$

then

$$\begin{array}{l} x_1 = a + b \\ y_1 = a - b \\ x_2 = 2a \\ y_2 = 3b \end{array}$$

When elements in a matrix are expressions, we find it convenient to separate these elements by commas.

Addition of matrices, as in equality, concerns corresponding elements. More specifically:

If A and B are two matrices with the same number of rows and the same number of columns, the sum of A and B is obtained by adding corresponding elements.

Symbolically, we can write this as follows:

Let matrices A and B be

$$A = (a_{ij})$$
$$B = (b_{ij})$$

Then the sum of A and B is a new matrix C, with elements c_{ij}.

$$C = A + B$$

where

$$C = (c_{ij}) = (a_{ij} + b_{ij})$$

Subtraction is defined similarly.

The difference $A - B$ is a new matrix D, with elements d_{ij}.

$$D = A - B$$

where

$$D = (d_{ij}) = (a_{ij} - b_{ij})$$

Thus the difference $A - B$ is obtained by subtracting corresponding elements. For example, if

$$A = \begin{bmatrix} 5 & \frac{1}{2} & 6 \\ 2 & -5 & 9 \\ 27 & 2 & 0 \\ -2 & 6 & -1 \end{bmatrix}$$

and

$$B = \begin{bmatrix} 2 & -\frac{1}{2} & -3 \\ 2 & 4 & -10 \\ -25 & 3 & 1 \\ 3 & -5 & 0 \end{bmatrix}$$

then the sum $A + B$ is a matrix C given by

$$C = A + B = \begin{bmatrix} 5+2, & \frac{1}{2}-\frac{1}{2}, & 6-3 \\ 2+2, & -5+4, & 9-10 \\ 27-25, & 2+3, & 0+1 \\ -2+3, & 6-5, & -1+0 \end{bmatrix}$$

or

$$C = A + B = \begin{bmatrix} 7 & 0 & 3 \\ 4 & -1 & -1 \\ 2 & 5 & 1 \\ 1 & 1 & -1 \end{bmatrix}$$

You should satisfy yourselves that

$$A + B = B + A$$

To discuss multiplication of matrices, we begin with the notion of a single real number, say, p, times a matrix A.

If A is a matrix (any size), then the product pA is a matrix with each element multiplied by p.

Thus, if

$$A = \begin{bmatrix} 3 & -2 & 1 \\ 7 & 5 & -\frac{1}{3} \end{bmatrix} \tag{5-9}$$

and

$$p = 3$$

then

$$pA = 3A = \begin{bmatrix} 9 & -6 & 3 \\ 21 & 15 & -1 \end{bmatrix}$$

When p is an integer, you will see that this is consistent with the notion of matrix addition. That is, p times a matrix A is the same as the sum of p identical matrices.

As an exercise, verify the above statement for $p = 4$ and A, matrix (5-9).

Problem

Let

$$A = \begin{bmatrix} 3 & 7 & 8 \\ 5 & 2 & 3 \\ -5 & 6 & -1 \end{bmatrix} \qquad B = \begin{bmatrix} \frac{1}{3} & 2 & 3 \\ -2 & -4 & 1 \\ 5 & 2 & \frac{1}{3} \end{bmatrix}$$

Find

$$A - 3B$$

solution: First, we find $3B$.

$$3B = \begin{bmatrix} 1 & 6 & 9 \\ -6 & -12 & 3 \\ 15 & 6 & 1 \end{bmatrix}$$

Now $A - 3B$ is found by subtracting corresponding elements.

$$A - 3B = \begin{bmatrix} 3 - 1, 7 - 6, 8 - 9 \\ 5 - (-6), 2 - (-12), 3 - 3 \\ -5 - 15, 6 - 6, -1 - 1 \end{bmatrix}$$

or

$$A - 3B = \begin{bmatrix} 2 & 1 & -1 \\ 11 & 14 & 0 \\ -20 & 0 & -2 \end{bmatrix}$$

To continue the discussion on matrix multiplication, we must point out that the *product* of two matrices *is not obtained* by forming the products of corresponding elements. The definition for multiplication follows:

Let A and B be two matrices, with A having the same number of columns as B has rows. (If A has n columns, then B has n rows.) *The product AB is a matrix C with number of rows equal to number of rows in A, number of columns equal to number of columns in B.*

To find the element in some row i and some column j of C, take the elements in row i of A, multiply each element by the corresponding element in column j of B. Now *add* these products to form some single real number. This real number is the element in row i, column j, of C.

If A is a 4 by 3 matrix and B is a 3 by 3 matrix, let us form the product matrix C.

$$\begin{bmatrix} a_{11} & a_{12} & a_{13} \\ a_{21} & a_{22} & a_{23} \\ a_{31} & a_{32} & a_{33} \\ a_{41} & a_{42} & a_{43} \end{bmatrix} \begin{bmatrix} b_{11} & b_{12} & b_{13} \\ b_{21} & b_{22} & b_{23} \\ b_{31} & b_{32} & b_{33} \end{bmatrix} = \begin{bmatrix} c_{11} & c_{12} & c_{13} \\ c_{21} & c_{22} & c_{23} \\ c_{31} & c_{32} & c_{33} \\ c_{41} & c_{42} & c_{43} \end{bmatrix}$$

From our definition of matrix multiplication we see that

$$c_{11} = a_{11}b_{11} + a_{12}b_{21} + a_{13}b_{31}$$
$$c_{12} = a_{11}b_{12} + a_{12}b_{22} + a_{13}b_{32}$$
$$c_{21} = a_{21}b_{11} + a_{22}b_{21} + a_{23}b_{31}$$
$$\cdot \cdot \cdot \cdot \cdot \cdot \cdot \cdot \cdot \cdot \cdot \cdot \cdot \cdot \cdot \cdot$$
$$c_{43} = a_{41}b_{13} + a_{42}b_{23} + a_{43}b_{33}$$

Keeping in mind that the first subscript refers to row and the second subscript refers to column, we can express any element of the product matrix as follows:

$$c_{ij} = a_{i1}b_{1j} + a_{i2}b_{2j} + a_{i3}b_{3j} \qquad (5\text{-}10)$$

In our case we know that i takes on values 1, 2, 3, 4 (the number of rows in A, and therefore the number of rows in C), and j takes on values 1, 2, 3 (the number of columns in B, and therefore the number of columns in C).

We can express c_{ij} in a more concise fashion by appealing to the summation symbol.

$$c_{ij} = \sum_{k=1}^{3} a_{ik}b_{kj} \tag{5-11}$$

Equation (5-10) is the expanded form of (5-11). The importance of the above notation becomes significant when we appeal to the computer as an aid in computation. In matrix multiplication there are repeated multiplications and additions. These operations are repetitive, with only the numbers for a_{ij} and b_{ij} changing for each evaluation of c_{ij}.

It happens that a computer language has rules of usage which are very compatible with the notation of Eq. (5-11), and except for rounding and truncation error (see Chap. 10), this problem of matrix multiplication is truly a trivial one for the computer.

For example, let

$$A = \begin{bmatrix} 3 & 4 & 2 \\ 1 & 2 & 5 \\ -1 & 7 & -3 \\ 9 & -2 & -6 \end{bmatrix} \qquad B = \begin{bmatrix} 7 & 0.5 & 0 \\ -1 & 6 & 2 \\ 3 & 1 & -8 \end{bmatrix}$$

Note that A has the same number of columns as B has rows. Then

$$AB = \begin{bmatrix} 3 \times 7 + 4(-1) + 2 \times 3, \ 3(0.5) + 4 \times 6 \\ \qquad + 2 \times 1, \ 3 \times 0 + 4 \times 2 + 2(-8) \\ 1 \times 7 + 2(-1) + 5 \times 3, \ 1(0.5) + 2 \times 6 \\ \qquad + 5 \times 1, \ 1 \times 0 + 2 \times 2 + 5(-8) \\ (-1)7 + 7(-1) + (-3)3, \ (-1)(0.5) + 7 \times 6 \\ \qquad + (-3)1, \ (-1)0 + 7 \times 2 + (-3)(-8) \\ 9 \times 7 + (-2)(-1) + (-6)3, \ 9(0.5) + (-2)6 \\ \qquad + (-6)1, \ 9 \times 0 + (-2)2 + (-6)(-8) \end{bmatrix}$$

Commas separate the elements in the above product.

$$AB = \begin{bmatrix} 23 & 27.5 & -8 \\ 20 & 17.5 & -36 \\ -23 & 38.5 & 38 \\ 47 & -13.5 & 44 \end{bmatrix}$$

It is possible to find the product AB (note that A is placed to the left of B) of two matrices *only* when the number of columns in A equals the number of *rows* in B. When the number of columns in A is not the same as the number of rows in B, we cannot find the product AB. In this case we say that B is *not conformable* with respect to A. However, we might be able to find the product BA.

For example, let

$$A = \begin{bmatrix} 2 & 3 \\ -7 & 6 \end{bmatrix} \qquad B = \begin{bmatrix} 2 & 9 \\ 1 & -5 \\ 4 & 3 \end{bmatrix}$$

We cannot find AB, since B is not conformable with respect to A. However, we can find the product BA, since the number of columns in B equals the number of rows in A.

$$BA = \begin{bmatrix} 2 & 9 \\ 1 & -5 \\ 4 & 3 \end{bmatrix} \begin{bmatrix} 2 & 3 \\ -7 & 6 \end{bmatrix}$$

$$= \begin{bmatrix} 2 \times 2 + 9(-7), \; 2 \times 3 + 9 \times 6 \\ 1 \times 2 + (-5)(-7), \; 1 \times 3 + (-5)6 \\ 4 \times 2 + 3(-7), \; 4 \times 3 + 3 \times 6 \end{bmatrix}$$

or

$$BA = \begin{bmatrix} -59 & 60 \\ 37 & -27 \\ -13 & 30 \end{bmatrix}$$

When two matrices are square and of the same order (same number of rows and columns in each), we can find both products AB and BA. But care must be exercised because, in general, the matrix AB is not the same as the matrix BA.

For example, let

$$A = \begin{bmatrix} 2 & -1 \\ 4 & 3 \end{bmatrix} \qquad B = \begin{bmatrix} 1 & 5 \\ 7 & 9 \end{bmatrix}$$

$$AB = \begin{bmatrix} 2 \times 1 + (-1)7, \; 2 \times 5 + (-1)9 \\ 4 \times 1 + 3 \times 7, \; 4 \times 5 + 3 \times 9 \end{bmatrix}$$

$$= \begin{bmatrix} -5 & 1 \\ 25 & 47 \end{bmatrix}$$

But

$$BA = \begin{bmatrix} 1 \times 2 + 5 \times 4, \; -1 + 5 \times 3 \\ 7 \times 2 + 9 \times 4, \; -7 + 9 \times 3 \end{bmatrix}$$

$$= \begin{bmatrix} 23 & 14 \\ 50 & 20 \end{bmatrix}$$

Thus $AB \neq BA$, and we see that in this case multiplication of matrices is not *commutative*.

For two particular matrices, it may happen that $AB = BA$. However, this is unlikely, and so we make the generalization

$$AB \neq BA$$

We are now able to show how matrix notation can be used to symbolize a system of linear equations. This notion was introduced in Sec. 5-1. In the following discussion we link the concepts together.

Let

$$A = \begin{bmatrix} a_{11} & a_{12} & a_{13} \\ a_{21} & a_{22} & a_{23} \\ a_{31} & a_{32} & a_{33} \end{bmatrix}$$

$$X = \begin{pmatrix} x_1 \\ x_2 \\ x_3 \end{pmatrix}$$

$$B = \begin{pmatrix} b_1 \\ b_2 \\ b_3 \end{pmatrix}$$

Form the matrix product AX.

$$AX = \begin{bmatrix} a_{11} & a_{12} & a_{13} \\ a_{21} & a_{22} & a_{23} \\ a_{31} & a_{32} & a_{33} \end{bmatrix} \begin{pmatrix} x_1 \\ x_2 \\ x_3 \end{pmatrix}$$

$$= \begin{bmatrix} a_{11}x_1 + a_{12}x_2 + a_{13}x_3 \\ a_{21}x_1 + a_{22}x_2 + a_{23}x_3 \\ a_{31}x_1 + a_{32}x_3 + a_{33}x_3 \end{bmatrix} \tag{5-12}$$

When we write

$$AX = B \tag{5-13}$$

or

$$\begin{bmatrix} a_{11}x_1 + a_{12}x_2 + a_{13}x_3 \\ a_{21}x_1 + a_{22}x_2 + a_{23}x_3 \\ a_{31}x_1 + a_{32}x_2 + a_{33}x_3 \end{bmatrix} = B \tag{5-14}$$

we recall the notion of matrix equality. Equation (5-14) really means

$$a_{11}x_1 + a_{12}x_2 + a_{13}x_3 = b_1 \tag{5-15}$$
$$a_{21}x_1 + a_{22}x_2 + a_{23}x_3 = b_2 \tag{5-16}$$
$$a_{31}x_1 + a_{32}x_2 + a_{33}x_3 = b_3 \tag{5-17}$$

Thus we see how Eq. (5-13) is matrix notation for the system of three simultaneous equations (5-15) to (5-17).

Problem

Set up the system of equations when

$$A = \begin{bmatrix} 5 & 0 & 1 \\ -3 & 1 & 0 \\ 7 & 3 & -2 \end{bmatrix}$$

$$X = \begin{pmatrix} x \\ y \\ z \end{pmatrix}$$

$$B = \begin{pmatrix} -7.5 \\ 6 \\ 9 \end{pmatrix}$$

solution:

$$AX = B$$

or

$$\begin{bmatrix} 5 & 0 & 1 \\ -3 & 1 & 0 \\ 7 & 3 & -2 \end{bmatrix} \begin{pmatrix} x \\ y \\ z \end{pmatrix} = \begin{pmatrix} -75 \\ 6 \\ 9 \end{pmatrix}$$

The system is

$$\begin{aligned} 5x + z &= -7.5 \\ -3x + y &= 6 \\ 7x + 3y - 2z &= 9 \end{aligned}$$

Note that, in general, A and B are matrices whose elements are known. It would be helpful to us if we could isolate the column matrix X from the equation

$$AX = B$$

and somehow make it equal to a combination of our known matrices A and B. Once this is done, we can equate corresponding elements (because of matrix equality), and thereby solve the corresponding system of equations.

Under certain conditions this is possible. It is taken up in the next section, on inverse of a matrix.

5-4   INVERSE OF A MATRIX

When A and B are two matrices, the expression A/B has no meaning; that is, matrices cannot be divided. However, the notion of inverse exists analogous to the notion of inverse for real numbers (recall that every nonzero real number a has a multiplicative inverse a^{-1}, with the property $aa^{-1} = 1$). We will pursue this notion, but first a few definitions.

Unit Matrix of Order n

A square matrix of n rows and n columns with 1's down the main diagonal and 0's everywhere else. The unit matrix is usually symbolized by I. It is also called *identity matrix*.

Example 1

A unit matrix of order 3 is

$$I = \begin{bmatrix} 1 & 0 & 0 \\ 0 & 1 & 0 \\ 0 & 0 & 1 \end{bmatrix}$$

The identity matrix has the unique property $AI = IA = A$, when A and I are conformable.

Singular Matrix

A square matrix whose determinant is zero. Sometimes nonsquare matrices are also called singular. A square matrix whose determinant is not zero is called nonsingular.

Example 2

If

$$A = \begin{bmatrix} 3 & 2 \\ 9 & 6 \end{bmatrix} \qquad B = \begin{bmatrix} 4 & 7 \\ 5 & 8 \end{bmatrix}$$

then A is singular, since

$$\det A = 18 - 18 = 0$$

and B is nonsingular since

$$\det B = 32 - 35 = -3 \qquad \text{(not zero)}$$

(In the preceding example we have used the symbolism det A to mean "determinant of the matrix A." Sometimes the notation $|A|$ is also used. Both mean the same thing.)

Transpose of a Matrix A

A matrix formed from the matrix A by interchanging the rows and columns of A. We will use the symbol A' to mean the transpose of a matrix A, or merely "A transpose."

Example 3

If

$$A = \begin{bmatrix} 4 & 7 \\ -3 & 5 \\ 1 & 0 \end{bmatrix}$$

then A' (A transpose) is

$$A' = \begin{bmatrix} 4 & -3 & 1 \\ 7 & 5 & 0 \end{bmatrix}$$

In this new matrix A', row 1 of A is now column 1 of A'; row 2 of A is column 2 of A'; and so on.

The notion of cofactor, first mentioned in the discussion on determinants, also exists when we discuss matrices. [Recall that the cofactor of an element in a determinant of order n is a determinant of order $n - 1$. It is formed by disregarding the row and column in which the element appears and forming a determinant with the remaining elements. If the element appears in row i and column j, then the sign preceding the determinant of order $n - 1$ is $(-1)^{i+j}$.] We can speak of the cofactor of an element in a matrix, but only if that matrix is square. Under this condition, the definition of cofactor of an element in a matrix is the same as the definition of the cofactor of an element in a determinant.

Example 4

Let

$$A = \begin{bmatrix} 5 & 3 & 2 \\ 4 & 1 & 0 \\ 7 & -9 & 8 \end{bmatrix}$$

The cofactor of the element in the second row and first column is

$$(-1)^{2+1} \begin{vmatrix} 3 & 2 \\ -9 & 8 \end{vmatrix} = -1 \begin{vmatrix} 3 & 2 \\ -9 & 8 \end{vmatrix} = -1(24 + 18) = -42$$

Now we can introduce another special matrix, which is formed from a given square matrix A. This special matrix is called the adjoint of A.

Adjoint of A (or Symbolically, $adj\ A$)

A matrix formed by replacing each element of A by its cofactor and then transposing the result. A is a square matrix.

Example 5

Let A be the matrix of the preceding example.

$$A = \begin{bmatrix} 5 & 3 & 2 \\ 4 & 1 & 0 \\ 7 & -9 & 8 \end{bmatrix}$$

Now we replace each element by its cofactor. (Note that we obtain a different matrix.)

$$\begin{bmatrix} \begin{vmatrix} 1 & 0 \\ -9 & 8 \end{vmatrix} & -\begin{vmatrix} 4 & 0 \\ 7 & 8 \end{vmatrix} & \begin{vmatrix} 4 & 1 \\ 7 & -9 \end{vmatrix} \\ -\begin{vmatrix} -3 & 2 \\ -9 & 8 \end{vmatrix} & \begin{vmatrix} 5 & 2 \\ 7 & 8 \end{vmatrix} & -\begin{vmatrix} 5 & 3 \\ 7 & -9 \end{vmatrix} \\ \begin{vmatrix} 3 & 2 \\ 1 & 0 \end{vmatrix} & -\begin{vmatrix} 5 & 2 \\ 4 & 0 \end{vmatrix} & \begin{vmatrix} 5 & 3 \\ 4 & 1 \end{vmatrix} \end{bmatrix}$$

or when the determinants are evaluated,

$$\begin{bmatrix} 8 & -32 & -43 \\ -42 & 26 & 66 \\ -2 & 8 & -7 \end{bmatrix}$$

We transpose this result to obtain the adjoint of A.

$$adj\ A = \begin{bmatrix} 8 & -42 & -2 \\ -32 & 26 & 8 \\ -43 & 66 & -7 \end{bmatrix}$$

Now we are in a position to define the inverse of a matrix A.

Inverse of a Matrix A

The matrix obtained by dividing each element of the adjoint of A by the determinant of A. This inverse matrix is symbolically written A^{-1}, or inv A. In symbols, we have

$$A^{-1} = \text{inv } A = \frac{1}{|A|}\ adj\ A$$

Note that since we divide by the real number $|A|$, we must be certain that the determinant of the matrix A is not zero. If this determinant is zero, we say that the inverse of A does not exist. Another way of stating this is: The inverse of a matrix exists only if that matrix is nonsingular.

The inverse matrix has the property

$$A \cdot \text{inv } A = \text{inv } A \cdot A = I$$

Example 6

Let A be the matrix of Example 4. Find the inverse of A.
We must find

$$A^{-1} = \frac{1}{|A|}\ adj\ A$$

Note that *adj A* was found in Example 5.   All we need now is $|A|$ in order to divide each element of the adjoint by $|A|$.   It should be clear that

$$\frac{1}{|A|} \, adj \, A = \begin{bmatrix} \dfrac{8}{|A|} & \dfrac{-42}{|A|} & \dfrac{-2}{|A|} \\ \dfrac{-32}{|A|} & \dfrac{26}{|A|} & \dfrac{8}{|A|} \\ \dfrac{-43}{|A|} & \dfrac{66}{|A|} & \dfrac{-7}{|A|} \end{bmatrix}$$

Now

$$|A| = \begin{vmatrix} 5 & 3 & 2 \\ 4 & 1 & 0 \\ 7 & -9 & 8 \end{vmatrix}$$

We will use the second row to expand this determinant.

$$\begin{aligned} |A| &= -4 \begin{vmatrix} 3 & 2 \\ -9 & 8 \end{vmatrix} + \begin{vmatrix} 5 & 2 \\ 7 & 8 \end{vmatrix} \\ &= -4(24 + 18) + (40 - 14) \\ &= -168 + 26 \\ &= -142 \end{aligned}$$

Thus

$$A^{-1} = \begin{bmatrix} \dfrac{-8}{142} & \dfrac{42}{142} & \dfrac{2}{142} \\ \dfrac{32}{142} & \dfrac{-26}{142} & \dfrac{-8}{142} \\ \dfrac{43}{142} & \dfrac{-66}{142} & \dfrac{7}{142} \end{bmatrix}$$

At the conclusion of Sec. 5-3 we suggested the possibility of perhaps isolating the column matrix X of unknowns in the matrix equation $AX = B$, that is, solving the matrix equation for X.   We are now in a position where it may be possible to execute this suggestion.   Once we are satisfied that the coefficient matrix A is nonsingular, then A^{-1} exists.   Now we multiply both sides of our matrix equation on the left by A^{-1}.   Thus

$$AX = B$$
$$A^{-1}AX = A^{-1}B$$

But

$$A^{-1}A = I$$

and

$$IX = X$$

So we obtain

$$X = A^{-1}B$$

Thus, when our matrix equation represents a system of simultaneous equations, one way of solving the system is to calculate the inverse of the coefficient matrix. In this section we have described what an inverse matrix is and how it is obtained from the original matrix. However, the methods described are not suited to the problem-solving capabilities of the computer. We do not imply that it cannot be done on a computer; we only wish to point out that other methods have been devised that take better advantage of the computer's repetitive, high-speed arithmetic capabilities.

One excellent method will be described below. We will not rigorously investigate *why* it works. It is sufficient to say that this method has been tested and has proved to be satisfactory.

It will be convenient for us to discuss the method using a 3 by 3 coefficient matrix.

$$A = \begin{bmatrix} a_{11} & a_{12} & a_{13} \\ a_{21} & a_{22} & a_{23} \\ a_{31} & a_{32} & a_{33} \end{bmatrix} \tag{5-18}$$

In this method we will perform certain repetitive operations on each of the elements in A. After a certain number of operations have been performed, the matrix A will become a different matrix. This new matrix will be the inverse A^{-1}. Thus, if A is the coefficient matrix of the system

$$AX = B \tag{5-19}$$

all we need do is multiply each side of the above matrix equation by A^{-1} to obtain

$$X = A^{-1}B \tag{5-20}$$

The method follows.

First, make sure that a_{11} is not zero. If it is, rearrange the equations given by (5-19) so that the element in the first row and first column is not zero.

Step 1

We augment a fourth column on the right of the last column in which the first element is 1 and the remaining elements are 0. In order to take advantage of the subscript notation of A, we will refer to the elements of this fourth column as a_{14}, a_{24}, a_{34}. So far we have

$$\begin{matrix} a_{11} & a_{12} & a_{13} & a_{14} \\ a_{21} & a_{22} & a_{23} & a_{24} \\ a_{31} & a_{32} & a_{33} & a_{34} \end{matrix}$$

where

$$a_{14} = 1 \qquad a_{24} = 0 \qquad a_{34} = 0$$

Step 2

Now we construct a fourth row of elements from the elements in the first as follows:

$$a_{41} = \frac{a_{12}}{a_{11}} \qquad a_{42} = \frac{a_{13}}{a_{11}} \qquad a_{43} = \frac{a_{14}}{a_{11}}$$

Since the second subscript is the only one that changes, we can express the above three equations with one equation.

$$a_{4j} = \frac{a_{1,(j+1)}}{a_{11}} \tag{5-21}$$

where $j = 1, 2, 3$. The parentheses around $j + 1$ indicate that the entire expression $j + 1$ is the subscript.

Note that there are three elements in this fourth row.

Step 3

Now we compute a new value for each element as follows: The subscripts still refer to row and column in which that element appears.

$$\bar{a}_{11} = a_{12} - a_{11}(a_{41})$$
$$\bar{a}_{12} = a_{13} - a_{11}(a_{42})$$
$$\bar{a}_{13} = a_{14} - a_{11}(a_{43})$$

Note that, because of the way a_{41}, a_{42}, a_{43} were constructed, the above equations yield 0 for $\bar{a}_{11}$, $\bar{a}_{12}$, $\bar{a}_{13}$.

We can describe the above three equations by one equation:

$$\bar{a}_{1j} = a_{1,(j+1)} - a_{11}(a_{4j}) \tag{5-22}$$

where $j = 1, 2, 3$.

Constructing new elements for row 2 we have

$$\bar{a}_{21} = a_{22} - a_{21}(a_{41})$$
$$\bar{a}_{22} = a_{23} - a_{21}(a_{42})$$
$$\bar{a}_{23} = a_{24} - a_{21}(a_{43})$$

The above equations give us three new elements for row 2. The above three equations can be described by one equation.

$$\bar{a}_{2j} = a_{2,(j+1)} - a_{21}(a_{4j}) \tag{5-23}$$

where $j = 1, 2, 3$.

Finally, we compute three new elements for row 3 as follows:

$$\bar{a}_{3j} = a_{3,(j+1)} - a_{31}(a_{4j}) \tag{5-24}$$

where $j = 1, 2, 3$.

The subscript notation allows us to write *one* equation that describes the three equations (5-22) to (5-24).

$$\bar{a}_{ij} = a_{i,(j+1)} - a_{i1}(a_{4j}) \tag{5-25}$$

where $i = 1, 2, 3$, $j = 1, 2, 3$. i is the row subscript, and j is the column subscript.

Let us write in array form what we have so far.

$$
\begin{array}{cccc}
\bar{a}_{11} & \bar{a}_{12} & \bar{a}_{13} & a_{14} \\
\bar{a}_{21} & \bar{a}_{22} & \bar{a}_{23} & a_{24} \\
\bar{a}_{31} & \bar{a}_{32} & \bar{a}_{33} & a_{34} \\
a_{41} & a_{42} & a_{43} &
\end{array}
$$

We know that $\bar{a}_{11}, \bar{a}_{12}, \bar{a}_{13}$ are all zero and $a_{14} = 1$, $a_{24} = 0$, $a_{34} = 0$. Now delete the entire first row and the last column. We are left with

$$
\begin{array}{ccc}
\bar{a}_{21} & \bar{a}_{22} & \bar{a}_{23} \\
\bar{a}_{31} & \bar{a}_{32} & \bar{a}_{33} \\
a_{41} & a_{42} & a_{43}
\end{array}
$$

Note that this can be considered a matrix of the same order as the one we started with. Next we perform a very important step.

Step 4

The subscripts are adjusted so as to correspond to the row-and-column position of the element in the *above matrix*. For example,

$$
\begin{array}{lll}
\bar{a}_{21} & \text{becomes} & \bar{a}_{11} \\
\bar{a}_{22} & \text{becomes} & \bar{a}_{12} \\
\bar{a}_{31} & \text{becomes} & \bar{a}_{21} \\
\end{array}
$$

. . . .

For the last row

$$
\begin{array}{lll}
a_{41} & \text{becomes} & \bar{a}_{31} \\
a_{42} & \text{becomes} & \bar{a}_{32} \\
a_{43} & \text{becomes} & \bar{a}_{33}
\end{array}
$$

Now we have a new matrix.

$$
\begin{array}{ccc}
\bar{a}_{11} & \bar{a}_{12} & \bar{a}_{13} \\
\bar{a}_{21} & \bar{a}_{22} & \bar{a}_{23} \\
\bar{a}_{31} & \bar{a}_{32} & \bar{a}_{33}
\end{array}
$$

As long as we are aware of the fact that the above is a matrix different from our original matrix, we can delete the bars over the a's. This gives us

$$
\begin{matrix}
a_{11} & a_{12} & a_{13} \\
a_{21} & a_{22} & a_{23} \\
a_{31} & a_{32} & a_{33}
\end{matrix}
$$

Step 5

If a_{11} is zero, the method breaks down at this point. If a_{11} is not zero, we go back and repeat steps 1, 2, 3, and 4 on the above new matrix. When steps 1, 2, 3, and 4 are performed a total of three times, the new matrix obtained in step 4 is the inverse A^{-1} of the original matrix A.

Now we merely perform a matrix multiplication as indicated in Eq. (5-20). The product $A^{-1}B$ is a column matrix. We equate each element in this product matrix to the elements in the column matrix X. The result is the solution to our system of linear equations.

We have discussed the method for a square matrix of order 3. We selected 3 for simplicity and convenience in discussion. The method is applicable to square matrices of any order n. Hence the method works for solving a system of n linear equations.

Let us compute the inverse of the following matrix.

$$
A = \begin{bmatrix}
3 & 1 & 6 \\
2 & -4 & 5 \\
-1 & 7 & 3
\end{bmatrix}
$$

Step 1

$$
\begin{array}{rrr|r}
3 & 1 & 6 & 1 \\
2 & -4 & 5 & 0 \\
-1 & 7 & 3 & 0
\end{array}
$$

Step 2

Here we construct a fourth row from the elements in the first row.

$$
a_{41} = \frac{a_{12}}{a_{11}} = \frac{1}{3} \qquad a_{42} = \frac{a_{13}}{a_{11}} = \frac{6}{3} = 2 \qquad a_{43} = \frac{a_{14}}{a_{11}} = \frac{1}{3}
$$

So far we have

$$
\begin{array}{rrr|r}
3 & 1 & 6 & 1 \\
2 & -4 & 5 & 0 \\
-1 & 7 & 3 & 0 \\
\hline
\frac{1}{3} & 2 & \frac{1}{3} &
\end{array}
$$

Step 3

Now we compute a new value for each element.

$$\bar{a}_{11} = a_{12} - a_{11}(a_{41}) = 1 - 3(\tfrac{1}{3}) = 0$$
$$\bar{a}_{12} = a_{13} - a_{11}(a_{42}) = 6 - 3(2) = 0$$
$$\bar{a}_{13} = a_{14} - a_{11}(a_{43}) = 1 - 3(\tfrac{1}{3}) = 0$$
$$\bar{a}_{21} = a_{22} - a_{21}(a_{41}) = -4 - 2(\tfrac{1}{3}) = -14\tfrac{2}{3}$$
$$\bar{a}_{22} = a_{23} - a_{21}(a_{42}) = 5 - 2(2) = 1$$
$$\bar{a}_{23} = a_{24} - a_{21}(a_{43}) = 0 - 2(\tfrac{1}{3}) = -\tfrac{2}{3}$$
$$\bar{a}_{31} = a_{32} - a_{31}(a_{41}) = 7 + 1(\tfrac{1}{3}) = 22\tfrac{2}{3}$$
$$\bar{a}_{32} = a_{33} - a_{31}(a_{42}) = 3 + 1(2) = 5$$
$$\bar{a}_{33} = a_{34} - a_{31}(a_{43}) = 0 + 1(\tfrac{1}{3}) = \tfrac{1}{3}$$

Step 4

A new array is obtained.

$$
\begin{array}{ccc}
-14\tfrac{2}{3} & 1 & -\tfrac{2}{3} \\
22\tfrac{2}{3} & 5 & \tfrac{1}{3} \\
\tfrac{1}{3} & 2 & \tfrac{1}{3}
\end{array}
$$

Step 5

The new a_{11} is not zero (it is $-14\tfrac{2}{3}$); so we repeat steps 1, 2, 3, and 4 twice more.

Step 1 (First Repeat)

$$
\begin{array}{ccc|c}
-14\tfrac{2}{3} & 1 & \tfrac{2}{3} & 1 \\
22\tfrac{2}{3} & 5 & \tfrac{1}{3} & 0 \\
\tfrac{1}{3} & 2 & \tfrac{1}{3} & 0
\end{array}
$$

Step 2 (First Repeat)

$$a_{41} = \frac{a_{12}}{a_{11}} = \frac{1}{-14\tfrac{2}{3}} = -\frac{3}{14}$$

$$a_{42} = \frac{a_{13}}{a_{11}} = \frac{-\tfrac{2}{3}}{-14\tfrac{2}{3}} = \frac{2}{14} = \frac{1}{7}$$

$$a_{43} = \frac{a_{14}}{a_{11}} = \frac{1}{-14\tfrac{2}{3}} = -\frac{3}{14}$$

So we have

$$
\begin{array}{ccc|c}
-14\tfrac{2}{3} & 1 & -\tfrac{2}{3} & 1 \\
22\tfrac{2}{3} & 5 & \tfrac{1}{3} & 0 \\
\tfrac{1}{3} & 2 & \tfrac{1}{3} & 0 \\
\hline
-\tfrac{3}{14} & \tfrac{1}{7} & -\tfrac{3}{14} &
\end{array}
$$

Step 3 (First Repeat)

$$\bar{a}_{11} = a_{12} - a_{11}(a_{41}) = 1 + \frac{14}{3}\left(-\frac{3}{14}\right) = 1 - 1 = 0$$

$$\bar{a}_{12} = a_{13} - a_{11}(a_{42}) = -\frac{2}{3} + \frac{14}{3}\left(\frac{1}{7}\right) = -\frac{2}{3} + \frac{2}{3} = 0$$

$$\bar{a}_{13} = a_{14} - a_{11}(a_{43}) = 1 + \frac{14}{3}\left(-\frac{3}{14}\right) = 1 - 1 = 0$$

$$\bar{a}_{21} = a_{22} - a_{21}(a_{41}) = 5 - \frac{22}{3}\left(-\frac{3}{14}\right) = \frac{70 + 22}{14} = \frac{92}{14} = \frac{46}{7}$$

$$\bar{a}_{22} = a_{23} - a_{21}(a_{42}) = \frac{1}{3} - \frac{22}{3}\left(\frac{1}{7}\right) = \frac{7 - 22}{21} = -\frac{15}{21} = -\frac{5}{7}$$

$$\bar{a}_{23} = a_{24} - a_{21}(a_{43}) = 0 - \frac{22}{3}\left(-\frac{3}{14}\right) = \frac{11}{7}$$

$$\bar{a}_{31} = a_{32} - a_{31}(a_{41}) = 2 - \frac{1}{3}\left(-\frac{3}{14}\right) = \frac{29}{14}$$

$$\bar{a}_{32} = a_{33} - a_{31}(a_{42}) = \frac{1}{3} - \frac{1}{3}\left(\frac{1}{7}\right) = \frac{7 - 1}{21} = \frac{6}{21} = \frac{2}{7}$$

$$\bar{a}_{33} = a_{34} - a_{31}(a_{42}) = 0 - \frac{1}{3}\left(-\frac{3}{14}\right) = \frac{1}{14}$$

Step 4 (First Repeat)

A new array is obtained.

$$
\begin{array}{ccc}
{}^{46}\!/_{7} & -{}^{5}\!/_{7} & {}^{11}\!/_{7} \\
{}^{29}\!/_{14} & {}^{2}\!/_{7} & {}^{1}\!/_{14} \\
-{}^{3}\!/_{14} & {}^{1}\!/_{7} & -{}^{3}\!/_{14}
\end{array}
$$

Step 5 (First Repeat)

The new a_{11} is not zero (it is ${}^{46}\!/_{7}$); so we repeat steps 1, 2, 3, and 4 once more.

Step 1 (Second Repeat)

$$
\begin{array}{ccc|c}
{}^{46}\!/_{7} & -{}^{5}\!/_{7} & {}^{11}\!/_{7} & 1 \\
{}^{29}\!/_{14} & {}^{2}\!/_{7} & {}^{1}\!/_{14} & 0 \\
-{}^{3}\!/_{14} & {}^{1}\!/_{7} & -{}^{3}\!/_{14} & 0
\end{array}
$$

Step 2 (Second Repeat)

$$a_{41} = -\tfrac{5}{46} \qquad a_{42} = \tfrac{11}{46} \qquad a_{43} = \tfrac{7}{46}$$

So far we have

$$
\begin{array}{ccc|c}
\tfrac{46}{7} & -\tfrac{5}{7} & \tfrac{11}{7} & 1 \\
\tfrac{29}{14} & \tfrac{2}{7} & \tfrac{1}{14} & 0 \\
-\tfrac{3}{14} & \tfrac{1}{7} & -\tfrac{3}{14} & 0 \\
\hline
-\tfrac{5}{46} & \tfrac{11}{46} & \tfrac{7}{46} &
\end{array}
$$

Step 3 (Second Repeat)

$$\bar{a}_{11} = 0 \qquad \bar{a}_{12} = 0 \qquad \bar{a}_{13} = 0$$
$$\bar{a}_{21} = \tfrac{2}{7} - \tfrac{29}{14}(-\tfrac{5}{46}) = \tfrac{329}{644}$$
$$\bar{a}_{22} = \tfrac{1}{14} - \tfrac{29}{14}(\tfrac{11}{46}) = -\tfrac{273}{644}$$
$$\bar{a}_{23} = 0 - \tfrac{29}{14}(\tfrac{7}{46}) = -\tfrac{29}{92}$$
$$\bar{a}_{31} = \tfrac{1}{7} + \tfrac{3}{14}(\tfrac{5}{46}) = \tfrac{77}{644}$$
$$\bar{a}_{32} = -\tfrac{3}{14} + \tfrac{3}{14}(\tfrac{11}{46}) = -\tfrac{105}{644}$$
$$\bar{a}_{33} = 0 + \tfrac{3}{14}(\tfrac{7}{46}) = \tfrac{21}{644}$$

Step 4 (Second Repeat)

The new array obtained is

$$
\begin{array}{ccc}
\tfrac{329}{644} & -\tfrac{273}{644} & -\tfrac{29}{92} \\
\tfrac{77}{644} & -\tfrac{105}{644} & \tfrac{21}{644} \\
-\tfrac{5}{46} & \tfrac{11}{46} & \tfrac{7}{46}
\end{array}
$$

Step 5 (Second Repeat)

Since we have performed steps 1, 2, 3, and 4 a total of *three times* (the first time plus two repeats), the matrix obtained in the above step is the inverse A^{-1} of A.

Thus, when

$$
A = \begin{bmatrix} 3 & 1 & 6 \\ 2 & -4 & 5 \\ -1 & 7 & 3 \end{bmatrix}
$$

then

$$
A^{-1} = \begin{bmatrix} \tfrac{329}{644} & -\tfrac{273}{644} & -\tfrac{29}{92} \\ \tfrac{77}{644} & -\tfrac{105}{644} & \tfrac{21}{644} \\ -\tfrac{5}{46} & \tfrac{11}{46} & \tfrac{7}{46} \end{bmatrix}
$$

You may wish to verify that

$$AA^{-1} = I$$

where I is the identity matrix of order 3.

Now let A be the coefficient matrix of a system of three linear equations

$$\begin{aligned}
3x_1 + x_2 + 6x_3 &= b_1 \\
2x_1 - 4x_2 + 5x_3 &= b_2 \\
-x_1 + 7x_2 + 3x_3 &= b_3
\end{aligned}$$

That is,

$$AX = B$$

where

$$X = \begin{pmatrix} x_1 \\ x_2 \\ x_3 \end{pmatrix}$$

$$B = \begin{pmatrix} b_1 \\ b_2 \\ b_3 \end{pmatrix}$$

(The b's are known real numbers.) The solutions are found by multiplying the column matrix of constants B on the left by A^{-1}. When we equate corresponding elements with the elements of X, the solutions are found.

The method for finding the inverse of a matrix is indeed tedious when done by hand. It becomes useful *only* when we are able to use a high-speed computing device as an aid in computation. The use of subscripts in identifying elements of a matrix affords great advantages when we look to the computer as an aid in computation. This is because a mere change in subscript identifies another element of our array. The computer is able to keep track of these changing subscripts, and thus it can identify any elements of our array when we command it to do so. Now we can instruct the computer to perform certain arithmetic operations on these elements. When the operations are performed a certain number of times, we can instruct the computer to halt operations. In general, this is the procedure involved in forming the inverse matrix.

We have shown the method in detail for a 3 by 3 matrix. It is applicable to square matrices of any order.

The five steps can easily be described with a flowchart. Let us construct this flowchart to describe the method for a square matrix of order n.

In the following discussion, we assume the matrix elements are described by symbols a_{11}, a_{12}, . . . , a_{nn}. Also, the matrix elements are assumed to be stored in the memory unit of some computer.

Step 1 tells us to augment a new column in which the first element is 1 and the remaining elements are 0. This step is described by

0

$$a_{1,\,(n+1)} = 1$$
$$a_{i,\,(n+1)} = 0$$
$$i = 1, 2, \ldots n$$

Let us introduce an integer M. This M will correspond to the number of times we have performed the steps described below in the boxes. We first set it to an initial value $M = 0$.

1

$$M = M + 1$$

Now we construct a new row of elements.

2

$$a_{(n+1),\,j} = \frac{a_{1,\,(j+1)}}{a_{11}}$$
$$j = 1, 2, 3, \ldots, n$$

Compute a new element for each previous element.

3

$$\bar{a}_{ij} = a_{i,\,(j+i)} - (a_{i1})\,(a_{(n+1),\,j})$$
$$i = 1, 2, 3, \ldots n$$
$$j = 1, 2, 3, \ldots n$$

Remember, the preceding step causes all new elements in the first row to be zero. Now we rename these newly computed elements. (Note that in a computer-language context, the equal sign means replacement.)

4

$$a_{ij} = \bar{a}_{(i+1),j}$$
$$i = 1, 2, 3, \ldots, n-1$$
$$j = 1, 2, 3, \ldots n$$

Thus we have a new matrix with $n - 1$ rows and n columns. The nth row consists of elements we have already created in box 2.

5

$$a_{nj} = a_{(n+1),j}$$
$$j = 1, 2, \ldots n$$

At this point we ask: How many times have we performed the above steps? When we have been through n times, these new elements a_{ij} will be elements of the inverse matrix. The number M tells us how many times we have been through. So we compare M with n. We use a decision box for this.

6

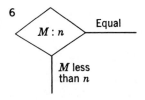

$M : n$ — Equal

M less than n

At this point (or at the end of box 4), we could examine a_{11} for a zero value. If it is zero, we must stop the method. For this examination a decision

7

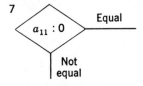

$a_{11} : 0$ — Equal

Not equal

box is used. The colon means "compared with." If a_{11} is not zero, we go back to box 1 and repeat the process.

The boxes in a flowchart are usually connected by arrows directing the sequence of steps.

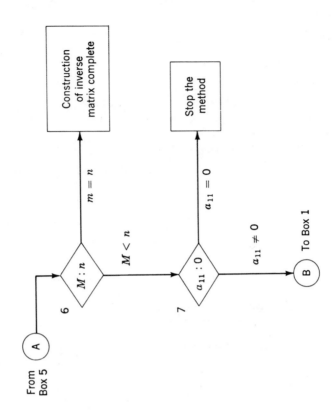
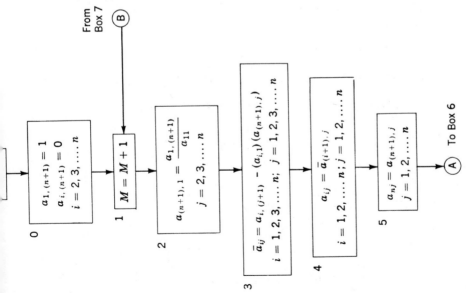

EXERCISES

5-1. In the following sets of equations write
   a. The matrix of coefficients.
   b. The matrix of constants.
   c. Part a with rows and columns interchanged.

$$6x - 4y + 3z = 7 \qquad w + 2x + 3y = 1$$
$$x + 0.5y - 10z = 1 \qquad x + 2y + 3z = -1$$
$$13x - \tfrac{3}{2}y + z = 0 \qquad w + 2y + 3z = 1$$
$$y - 2x + 3w = 1$$

5-2. a. Construct a matrix A with the following elements:

$$a_{11} = 5 \qquad a_{23} = 0.7 \qquad a_{21} = -3 \qquad a_{12} = 10 \qquad a_{13} = \tfrac{1}{2}$$
$$a_{22} = 16 \qquad a_{31} = 0 \qquad a_{32} = 0 \qquad a_{33} = \tfrac{1}{4}$$

   b. Find the determinant of A.
   c. Find the rank of A.

5-3. Find the rank of

$$A = \begin{bmatrix} 2 & -5 & 1 \\ -6 & 15 & -3 \end{bmatrix} \qquad B = \begin{bmatrix} 3 & 6 & 2 \\ -1 & 5 & 7 \end{bmatrix}$$

$$C = \begin{bmatrix} 7 & 5 & -63 \\ -3 & 1 & 27 \\ 2 & 6 & -18 \end{bmatrix}$$

5-4. What can you tell about the solutions of the following sets of equations?
   [*Hint:* Find the ranks of C (coefficient matrix) and A (augmented matrix).]

$$-x + y - z = 4 \qquad x + 2y = 2$$
$$x - y + 2z = 3 \qquad 2x + 3y = 1$$
$$2x - 2y + 4z = 6 \qquad x + 3y = 5$$

5-5. Find the eigenvalues in the following problem:

$$(1 + e)x - 9y = 0$$
$$-x + (1 + e)y = 0$$

5-6. Let

$$A = \begin{bmatrix} 3 & 2 \\ -1 & 5 \\ 6 & 1 \end{bmatrix} \qquad B = \begin{bmatrix} -2 & 7 \\ 3 & 1 \\ 9 & -9 \end{bmatrix}$$

   Find
   a. $A + B$ b. $A - B$ c. $B + A$ d. $B - A$
   e. $3(A + B)$ f. $3A + 3B$ g. $B - B$ h. $5(B - B)$

5-7. Let

$$A = \begin{bmatrix} -1 & 3 & 2 \\ 4 & 7 & 8 \\ 1 & 0 & 9 \end{bmatrix} \qquad B = \begin{bmatrix} 2 & 4 \\ 1 & 8 \\ 5 & -9 \end{bmatrix} \qquad C = \begin{bmatrix} 0 & 2 & 3 \\ -1 & 5 & 4 \end{bmatrix}$$

Find *if possible*

    a. $A + B$ b. $A + C$ c. AB d. AC
    e. BC f. CA g. CB h. BA

5-8. Let

$$A = \begin{pmatrix} x \\ y \\ z \end{pmatrix} \qquad B = \begin{pmatrix} y \\ z \\ 5 \end{pmatrix} \qquad C = \begin{pmatrix} 20 \\ 15 \\ 10 \end{pmatrix}$$

Then if $A + B = C$, find x, y, and z.

5-9. Let

$$A = \begin{bmatrix} 6 & -2 & 1 \\ 4 & 7 & 9 \\ -5 & 17 & 33 \end{bmatrix} \qquad B = \begin{bmatrix} 5 & -2 & -1 \\ 4 & 6 & 9 \\ -5 & 17 & 32 \end{bmatrix}$$

Find

    a. $A + B$ b. $A - B$ c. det $(A - B)$
    d. $(A + B)(A - B)$ (*Hint:* You should be able to answer part d with very little work.)

5-10. If D is a 3 by 2 matrix with elements d_{ij} and if E is a square matrix of order 2 with elements e_{kl}, write the expression for any element in the product matrix F, where

$$F = DE$$

5-11. Write: (a) the unit matrix of order 5; (b) identity matrix of order 4; (c) a singular matrix of order 3; (d) det I, where I is your result from part a; (e) the transpose of

$$C = \begin{bmatrix} 2 & -3 & 4 \\ -5 & 6 & -8 \end{bmatrix}$$

$$D = \begin{bmatrix} 1 & 5 & 4 \\ -3 & 2 & 7 \\ 10 & 15 & 1 \end{bmatrix} \qquad E = (4 \quad -5 \quad 9)$$

5-12.   In both matrices, replace each element by its cofactor.

$$A = \begin{bmatrix} 1 & 4 & 3 \\ -1 & 5 & 2 \\ 1 & 6 & -7 \end{bmatrix} \qquad B = \begin{bmatrix} 4 & -2 & 10 \\ -6 & 3 & -15 \\ 1 & -1 & 8 \end{bmatrix}$$

5-13.   Find the inverse of each matrix in Exercise 5-12.

5-14.   Verify that

$$A^{-1}A = I$$

and also

$$AA^{-1} = I$$

where I is the identity matrix of order 3, and A^{-1}, A are taken from Examples 5 and 6 in the text.

5-15.   A theorem on matrices states that matrix multiplication is associative when results are conformable; that is, $A(BC) = (AB)C$.

  a.   Find BC first; then find $A(BC)$.

$$A = \begin{bmatrix} 1 & -2 & 4 \\ -3 & -1 & 6 \end{bmatrix}$$

$$B = \begin{bmatrix} 3 & 1 \\ 6 & 4 \\ 2 & -5 \end{bmatrix} \qquad C = \begin{bmatrix} 2 & 3 & 5 \\ -1 & -2 & 7 \end{bmatrix}$$

  b.   Find AB first; then find $(AB)C$.   Compare your result with part a.

5-16.   If E is a 4 by 5 matrix and if F is a 5 by 3 matrix, what is the size of the product EF?   Can you generalize?

5-17.   a.   Construct a square matrix A of order 3 consisting of elements a_{ij}, where

$$a_{ij} = \frac{1}{i + j - 1}$$

  b.   Find the inverse A^{-1} of A by methods of this chapter.
  c.   The following expression will give the elements b_{ij} of the inverse of the matrix A:

$$b_{ij} = (-1)^{i+j} \frac{(3 + i - 1)!(3 + j - 1)!}{(i + j - 1)[(i - 1)!(j - 1)!]^2(3 - i)!(3 - j)!}$$

  (Compare your results with part b.)

Note: The symbol ! used here is called the factorial symbol.   Its meaning is

$$0! = 1, \qquad 1! = 1, \qquad 2! = 1 \times 2 = 2, \ 3! = 1 \times 2 \times 3 = 6$$
$$4! = 1 \times 2 \times 3 \times 4 = 24, \ \ldots, \ n! = 1 \times 2 \times 3 \times \cdots$$
$$\times (n - 2)(n - 1)n$$

5-18.   A matrix A is said to be *symmetric* if A equals its transpose A'.

  a.   Which matrices are symmetric?   (Recall definition of matrix equality.)

$$A = \begin{bmatrix} 3 & 2 & 4 \\ 2 & 5 & 3 \\ 4 & 3 & -1 \end{bmatrix}$$

$$B = \begin{bmatrix} 2 & 3 & 7 \\ 1 & -5 & 6 \end{bmatrix} \qquad C = \begin{pmatrix} 4 \\ 0 \\ 2 \end{pmatrix}$$

  b.   Use the elements off the main diagonal to describe the conditions for a matrix A to be symmetric.

5-19.   Find the inverse of these matrices using the five-step technique described in the text.

  a. $A = \begin{bmatrix} 1 & 2 & -1 \\ 1 & 3 & -2 \\ 2 & 1 & 3 \end{bmatrix}$ b. $B = \begin{bmatrix} 1 & -2 & 4 \\ 2 & -5 & 8 \\ 7 & 0 & 9 \end{bmatrix}$

5-20.   A man buys 100 cubic feet of corn, wheat, and oats.   Twice the difference between wheat and oats will fit into a 60-cubic-foot bin. Also, half the sum of corn and oats will fit into a 25-cubic-foot bin. Find the volume of corn, wheat, and oats the man has purchased.

chapter six

SEQUENCES, SERIES, AND NUMBER BASES

INTRODUCTION

In this chapter we try to build a foundation for the study of certain numerical techniques that can aid in solving linear systems of equations and finding roots of certain equations. These techniques are *iterative* in nature; that is, they have their basis in certain repetitive arithmetic procedures. With the help of a computer we are able to examine our results after each repetition. When these results satisfy predetermined criteria, we can stop our iterations and form certain conclusions. Sometimes these conclusions are close approximations to the solutions of a linear system. Sometimes they are approximations to the roots of certain equations.

To begin, we must introduce the notions of sequence, series, and progression.

6-1 SEQUENCE

First of all, consider a set of numbers, say,

$$1, \frac{1}{2}, \frac{1}{3}, \frac{1}{4}, \frac{1}{5} \cdot \cdot \cdot , \frac{1}{k}, \frac{1}{k+1}, \cdot \cdot \cdot$$

The dots (ellipsis) mean that the set of numbers continues in a regular fashion. Note that the denominator increases by one for each successive number. We could describe this entire set of numbers symbolically by writing

$$a_n = \frac{1}{n} \quad \text{where } n = 1, 2, 3, \ldots \tag{6-1}$$

A sequence is a set of numbers written in some order.

Then

$$a_1 = 1 \qquad a_2 = \tfrac{1}{2} \qquad a_3 = \tfrac{1}{3}$$

and so on. n is called the index of the sequence.

Each number in a sequence is called a member of the sequence. Note that the members in a sequence are not added to each other or subtracted.

A sequence can consist of a finite number of members or an infinite number of members. We can tell whether a sequence is finite or infinite when we specify the values n can take. From Eq. (6-1), for example, we can write a finite sequence in the following way:

$$a_n = \frac{1}{n} \qquad \text{where } n = 1, 2, 3 \tag{6-2}$$

Here the sequence consists of three members: 1, $\tfrac{1}{2}$, $\tfrac{1}{3}$. We can also write an infinite sequence.

$$a_n = \frac{1}{n} \qquad \text{where } n = 1, 2, 3, \ldots \tag{6-3}$$

The dots following 3 indicate that n continues indefinitely, and thus we have an infinite sequence.

An equation such as any of the above is called the *general term*, or *general member*, of a sequence. From it all other members of the sequence can be obtained.

Sometimes we will meet sequences in which only a few members appear. We may then be asked: What is the general term? We should be able to construct it once a certain pattern is observed in the few terms that we see.

For example, find the general member of the infinite sequence whose first four terms are

$$\tfrac{2}{3}, \ \tfrac{4}{5}, \ \tfrac{6}{7}, \ \tfrac{8}{9}$$

The first thing we notice is that the numerators are positive even numbers and the denominators are positive odd numbers. As we know, any positive even number can be written $2n$, where n is a positive integer. Also, any positive odd member starting with 3 can be written $2n + 1$, where n is a positive integer. Therefore the general term of the above sequence is

$$a_n = \frac{2n}{2n + 1} \qquad \text{where } n = 1, 2, 3, \ldots \tag{6-4}$$

It is easy to write several members of a sequence once the general member is known. Frequently, it is not so easy to write the general member when we see only a few members. This will depend on our ability to detect a pattern among the members.

We can construct sequences in which all members are negative. For example,

$$a_n = -\frac{3n}{2n+1} \qquad \text{where } n = 1, 2, 3, \ldots \qquad (6\text{-}5)$$

Then

$$a_1 = -\tfrac{3}{3} = -1$$
$$a_2 = -\tfrac{6}{5}$$
$$a_3 = -\tfrac{9}{7}$$

We can also construct sequences in which the signs of the members alternate. For example,

$$a_n = \frac{(-1)^n}{2n} \qquad \text{where } n = 1, 2, 3 \qquad (6\text{-}6)$$

Then

$$a_1 = \frac{(-1)^1}{2} = -\frac{1}{2}$$
$$a_2 = \frac{(-1)^2}{2 \times 2} = \frac{1}{4}$$
$$a_3 = \frac{(-1)^3}{2 \times 3} = -\frac{1}{6}$$
$$a_4 = \frac{(-1)^4}{2 \times 4} = \frac{1}{8}$$
$$\cdot \; \cdot \; \cdot \; \cdot \; \cdot \; \cdot \; \cdot \; \cdot \; \cdot \; \cdot$$

Sequences of this type are called *alternating sequences*.

Sometimes sequences will begin with an index of zero. An example of this is the sequence which gives all positive odd integers.

$$a_n = 2n + 1 \qquad \text{where } n = 0, 1, 2, 3, \ldots \qquad (6\text{-}7)$$

Here

$$a_0 = 1 \qquad a_1 = 3 \qquad a_2 = 5 \qquad \ldots$$

Problem

An employer wishes to hire you for a month of summer work. As part of the work agreement you ask if he will pay one penny for the first day's work, two pennies for the second, four pennies for the third, and in general twice the previous day's pennies for a given day. The employer is in a hurry, and he agrees. How much pay will you receive at the end of 30 days?

solution: Let us write down pay received at the end of several days' work.

At the end of the first day 1 penny

At the end of the second day $\quad 2 \times 1$, or 2 pennies

At the end of the third day $\quad 2 \times 2$, or $2^2 = 4$ pennies

At the end of the fourth day $\quad 2 \times 2^2$, or $2^3 = 8$ pennies

At the end of the fifth day $\quad 2 \times 2^3$, or $2^4 = 16$ pennies

We see a pattern forming which tells us that the power of 2 is one less than the number of the day involved. The payments at the end of each day are members of a finite sequence which can be described by a general formula. Let P_n be the pay in pennies at the end of the nth day.

Then

$$P_n = 2^{n-1}$$

where n is the day involved. Thus n takes on values 1, 2, 3, . . . , 30. P_{30} is the pay at the end of the thirtieth day. Thus

$$P_{30} = 2^{30-1} = 2^{29}$$

Now

$$2^{29} = 536,870,912$$

This is the number of pennies you will receive. We can divide by 100 to arrive at pay in dollars. It is

$5,368,709.12$

Sometimes we come across sequences where the first few terms are defined to be certain real numbers and the remaining terms are expressed as some arithmetic combination of the previous few terms. As an example, consider the sequence whose first two terms are both 1. That is,

$$a_0 = 1 \qquad a_1 = 1$$

Now let

$$a_2 = a_1 + a_0 \tag{6-8}$$
$$a_2 = 2 \tag{6-9}$$
$$a_3 = a_2 + a_1 \tag{6-10a}$$

or

$$a_3 = 3 \tag{6-10b}$$
$$a_4 = a_3 + a_2 \tag{6-11a}$$

or

$$a_4 = 5 \tag{6-11b}$$

In general,

$$a_n = a_{n-1} + a_{n-2} \tag{6-12}$$

where $n = 2, 3, 4, 5, ...$

Sequences in which the general member is defined in terms of previous members are called *recursive sequences,* or *recursive relations.*

We can think of sequences as functions if we like. From this point of view we can graph a sequence. A function is symbolized by

$$y = f(x) \tag{6-13}$$

where x and y are real members, x being the independent variable and y the dependent variable. In the case of a sequence, the independent variable is in general a positive integer or zero. Thus a sequence may be symbolized by

$$y = f(n) \tag{6-14}$$

In previous examples we have used a_n to denote the form of the general member of a sequence. The form (6-14) is used to indicate that in general a sequence is a function. We emphasize that although the independent variable n is a positive integer or zero, the dependent variable can be any real number.

We can easily graph a sequence if we are careful not to connect the points that are obtained.

For example, the graph of

$$y = a_n = \frac{1}{n} \tag{6-15}$$

(see Fig. 6-1) consists of points, some of which are given in the following table.

n	1	2	3	4
y	1	½	⅓	¼

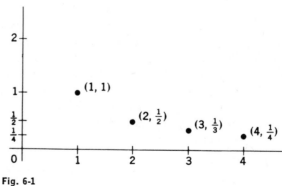

Fig. 6-1

One important thing to remember is that the points must not be connected.

As another example, consider

$$y = a_n = \frac{n}{n+1} \qquad n = 0, 1, 2, \ldots \tag{6-16}$$

This graph is given in Fig. 6-2.

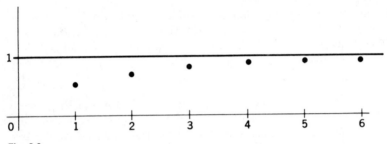

Fig. 6-2

The graphs of Figs. 6-1 and 6-2 have been introduced to provide some insight into the notion of *convergence*. From Eq. (6-15) and Fig. 6-1 we note that, with each succeeding value of n, the resulting member of the sequence becomes smaller. We also note that since n is restricted to positive values, the resulting member will always be positive. Graphically, this means that no point will be below the x axis. So, as n gets larger, $1/n$ gets smaller. Another way of saying this is: The sequence given by Eq. (6-15) approaches zero as n approaches infinity.

Symbolically,

$$\frac{1}{n} \to 0 \; as \; n \to \infty \qquad \text{or} \qquad \lim_{n \to \infty} \frac{1}{n} = 0$$

Now let us look at Eq. (6-16). From the way the sequence is defined, we see that the numerator is always less then the denominator. Hence all terms of the sequence are less than 1. Graphically, this means that no point will be above the line $y = 1$. However, with each succeeding value of n, the resulting term is always slightly larger than its predecessor. So, as n gets larger, $n/(n+1)$ gets closer and closer to 1. Another way of saying this is: The sequence given by Eq. (6-16) approaches 1 as n approaches infinity.

Symbolically,

$$\frac{n}{n+1} \to 1 \; as \; n \to \infty \qquad \text{or} \qquad \lim_{n \to \infty} \frac{n}{n+1} = 1$$

The sequences given by (6-15) and (6-16) are two examples of sequences that converge to some finite real number. A sequence which has this property is said to have a limit L. In (6-15) L is zero. In (6-16) L is 1.

Mathematically, this means that when the index n is large enough, we can find a term of the sequence as close as we please to the limit L. This notion of closeness is defined rigorously by using absolute value and a number understood to be very small, which we refer to as ϵ (read epsilon). Thus, if a_n is a sequence and

$$\lim_{n \to \infty} a_n = L$$

then for a given $\epsilon > 0$, we can find a value N for n so that

$$|a_n - L| < \epsilon \text{ when } n > N$$

As an example, consider the sequence given by (6-16).

$$a_n = \frac{n}{n + 1}$$

The limit of this sequence is 1. Let us see if we can find a value for n so that the absolute value of the difference between the term involving n and the limit will be less than 0.01. This 0.01 is the ϵ mentioned above. We must find a value N for the index n so that

$$|a_n - 1| < 0.01 \tag{6-17}$$

Now any term of a_n is less than 1. This means that the expression $a_n - 1$ is negative. From the definition of absolute value we have

$$|a_n - 1| = -(a_n - 1) = 1 - a_n$$

Thus (6-17) becomes

$$1 - a_n < 0.01 \tag{6-18}$$

or

$$1 - \frac{n}{n + 1} < 0.01 \tag{6-19}$$

Let us try to solve this inequality for n. First we obtain

$$\frac{1}{n + 1} < 0.01 \tag{6-20}$$

or since

$$0.01 = \frac{1}{100}$$

then

$$100 < n + 1$$

That is,

$$n > 99 \tag{6-21}$$

Now (6-21) was obtained from our original inequality (6-17).   Another way of saying this is: *Inequality (6-17) will be true when (6-21) is true.* From (6-21) we have found a value for n that we seek.

We can interpret this graphically.   Inequalities (6-21) and (6-17) tell us that a term a_n of the sequence will be within 0.01 of the limit 1 when n is greater than 99.   In particular, let n be 100.   See Fig. 6-3.

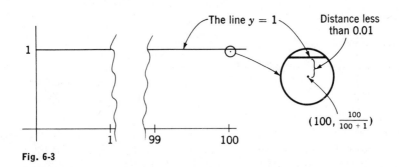

Fig. 6-3

Since every term is larger than its predecessor, the terms are getting closer to the limit 1.   This means that all terms beyond $n = 99$ will satisfy (6-17).

As further practice, you should try to follow through the above example using the sequence given by Eq. (6-15), with

$$a_n = \frac{1}{n} \qquad \epsilon = 0.001$$

In the preceding examples we have attempted to bring two quantities together to some prescribed degree of closeness.   The first quantity was fixed (this is the limit L); the second quantity (a term of the sequence) varied. The degree of closeness was determined by a given value for ϵ.

We solved the inequality (6-19) algebraically and found a value for n which made the inequality true.   We proceeded algebraically because the sequence was not very complex, and hence the inequality was simple to solve.

Situations may arise where the resulting inequality is difficult to solve. At this point we can look to the computer for aid, not to solve the inequality, but to evaluate terms of the sequence for each succeeding value of n.   At each step we calculate the absolute value and compare it with the given ϵ. If the absolute value is less than ϵ, we calculate and compare for the next value of n.   When the absolute value is equal to or greater than ϵ, we are done, and the current value of n is the one we seek.

A flowchart follows to describe these steps.

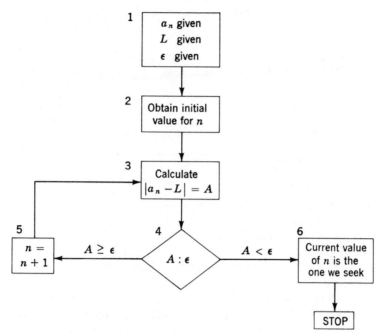

Let us use the flowchart with the sequence

$$\frac{n}{n+1} \qquad n = 0, 1, 2, \ldots \tag{6-22}$$

This sequence has a limit of 1. Let ϵ be 0.01. Then, in box 1, we have

$$a_n = \frac{n}{n+1}$$
$$L = 1$$
$$\epsilon = 0.01$$

The initial value for n is the one which begins the sequence. This is usually obtained from the line that defines the sequence. Thus, from Eq. (6-22), the initial value for n is (in box 2)

$$n = 0 \tag{6-23}$$

Box 3 computes an absolute value. First, when $n = 0$,

$$|a_0 - 1| = |0 - 1| = 1$$

Thus

$$A = 1$$

Now

$$1 > \epsilon$$

So we enter box 5. Now n becomes 1 since $0 + 1 = 1$.

Now we enter box 3 again, and continue the process until A becomes less than ϵ.

Let us see what happens for a few large values of n.

n	A	Box 4	Path taken
95	0.05	$A > \epsilon$	Box 5
96	0.04	$A > \epsilon$	Box 5
97	0.03	$A > \epsilon$	Box 5
98	0.02	$A > \epsilon$	Box 5
99	0.01	$A = \epsilon$	Box 6

The current value of n is 99. This is the same n as obtained when we solved the problem algebraically.

In the discussion thus far we have been assuming that the sequences have a limit; that is, the sequences converge to some finite real number. Many sequences do not demonstrate this property; that is, they do not get closer and closer to some finite real number as n gets larger and larger. Sequences of this type are said to *diverge*. The notions of convergence and divergence are important in other mathematical discussions, as well as sequences. We will meet these topics again.

6-2 SUMMATIONS AND SERIES

The notion of series logically follows a discussion of sequences. One characteristic of a computer which makes it such an important tool in man's problem-solving process is its ability, once directed to do so, of performing repetitive operations. In some instances these repetitions number in the thousands, sometimes millions. A common repetitive operation that might occur is the operation of addition. This introduces the notion of a repeated sum.

As an example, consider the problem of finding the sum of four fractions whose numerators are all 1 and whose denominators begin with 1 and thereafter increase by 1. If s is the sum, this problem may be written

$$s = 1 + \tfrac{1}{2} + \tfrac{1}{3} + \tfrac{1}{4} \tag{6-24}$$

It is an easy task to find s.

$$s = \frac{12 + 6 + 4 + 3}{12} = \frac{25}{12} \tag{6-25}$$

If the problem required us to find the sum of 10 fractions, it is obvious that the expression for s might become very unwieldy. Fortunately, symbolisms exist which allow us to express certain repeated sums, such as Eq. (6-24), in a very simple manner.

We use Eq. (6-24) to introduce it.

$$s = \sum_{i=1}^{4} \frac{1}{i} = \frac{1}{1} + \frac{1}{2} + \frac{1}{3} + \frac{1}{4} \qquad (6\text{-}26)$$

The symbol Σ is the Greek capital letter sigma. In its use here, it means a sum is to be found; that is, a summation is to occur. This is why Σ is referred to as the *summation* symbol. The symbol i is called the *index* of the sum. It is understood to be an integer. i takes on all integral values beginning at 1 (indicated by the 1 below Σ) and ending at 4 (indicated by the 4 above Σ). The symbol $1/i$ is called the *term* of the sum. This term assumes a value when i assumes a value. Thus, when $i = 1$, $1/i$ becomes $\frac{1}{1}$; when $i = 2$, $1/i$ becomes $\frac{1}{2}$, and so on. The right side of Eq. (6-26) is called the *expanded form* of the sum. Equation (6-26) is also called a *finite series*.

So, when we know what the symbols mean, we can write

$$\frac{25}{12} = \sum_{i=1}^{4} \frac{1}{i} \qquad (6\text{-}27)$$

More examples of finite series are introduced below.

$$\sum_{k=2}^{4} k = 2 + 3 + 4 = 9 \qquad (6\text{-}28)$$

$$\sum_{i=0}^{5} 2i = 2 \times 0 + 2 \times 1 + 2 \times 2 + 2 \times 3 + 2 \times 4 + 2 \times 5 = 30$$
$$\qquad (6\text{-}29)$$

$$\sum_{l=0}^{3} 3^l = 3^0 + 3^1 + 3^2 + 3^3 = 40 \qquad (6\text{-}30)$$

$$\sum_{k=0}^{4} \frac{2^k}{2k+1} = \frac{2^0}{2 \times 0 + 1} + \frac{2^1}{2 \times 1 + 1} + \frac{2^2}{2 \times 2 + 1}$$
$$+ \frac{2^3}{2 \times 3 + 1} + \frac{2^4}{2 \times 4 + 1}$$
$$= \frac{1}{1} + \frac{2}{3} + \frac{4}{5} + \frac{8}{7} + \frac{16}{9} = \frac{1{,}697}{315} \qquad (6\text{-}31)$$

As you can see, the term of a sum can take on many different forms. Also, the index of the sum can be any integral set of values that we wish.

As a final example, we introduce a finite series where some terms may be negative.

$$\sum_{i=0}^{3} (-1)^i(i+1)^2 = (-1)^0(0+1)^2 + (-1)^1(1+1)^2 + (-1)^2(2+1)^2$$
$$+ (-1)^3(3+1)^2$$
$$= 1(1)^2 - (2)^2 + (3)^2 - (4)^2$$
$$= 1 - 4 + 9 - 16$$
$$= -10 \tag{6-32}$$

Series in which the signs of succeeding terms are different are called *alternating series*.

The general form of a series is

$$\sum_{k=0}^{n} a_k \tag{6-33}$$

where a_k is the term of the series, and k is used here as a subscript. As you have seen in Eqs. (6-27) to (6-32), the term and the subscript can take many forms.

In (6-27) $a_k = \dfrac{1}{k}$ and k starts at 1

In (6-28) $a_k = k$ and k starts at 2

In (6-29) $a_k = 2k$ and k starts at 0

In (6-30) $a_k = 3^k$ and k starts at 0

In (6-31) $a_k = \dfrac{2^k}{2k+1}$ and k starts at 0

In (6-32) $a_k = (-1)^k(k+1)^2$ and k starts at 0

When we discussed sequences, the symbol a_n was used to denote the general term of the sequence. We could easily have chosen n to be the subscript in the general terms for the series above. The main point is that each succeeding term of the series changes as the subscript (index) changes. But this is the way we described the succeeding terms of a sequence. By this reasoning we can say that a series is merely the sum of the terms in a sequence. Keeping this in mind, consider the following problem.

Problem

Find the general term of the series and write it using summation symbol

$$\frac{1}{1 \times 2} + \frac{2}{2 \times 3} + \frac{4}{3 \times 4} + \frac{8}{4 \times 5} + \cdots$$

solution: We first observe that the numerators are powers of 2. The first numerator is 2^0, the second 2^1, and so on. The denominators are products which change in a pattern.   The *first* denominator is $1 \times (1 + 1)$; the *second* is $2 \times (2 + 1)$; and so on.

Thus the general term is

$$\frac{2^{n-1}}{n(n + 1)} \tag{6-34}$$

In summation notation,

$$\sum_{n=1}^{\infty} \frac{2^{n-1}}{n(n + 1)} \tag{6-35}$$

The symbol ∞ (infinity) is used above the summation symbol to indicate that this series continues indefinitely, with n getting larger and larger.   This is another way of saying that Eq. (6-35) is an *infinite series*.   Summations where that last value of n is some fixed number are called *finite series*.

Adding the first n terms of an *arithmetic progression* yields a finite series. Another finite series is obtained when the first n terms of a *geometric progression* are added together.   (See Exercises 6-3 to 6-8.)

Simple interest, compound interest, and annuities are topics in which the notion of progressions is very important.

As an example consider the following problem.

Problem

A man borrows $1,000.   He agrees to pay it back over a period of 3 years.   If the interest is 6 percent per year computed on the original $1,000, find the total amount paid over 3 years.   (Interest computed this way is called simple interest.)

solution: In this problem, the $1,000 is called the principal P, and 6 percent is called the rate of interest i.   Interest is usually defined as the fraction of the principal paid at the end of a unit period of time.   (The period is usually 1 year; the fraction is expressed in hundredths.)   So at the end of the first year the man owes $P + Pi$, that is, the principal plus the interest.   At the end of the second year the man owes another year's interest, or Pi.   Similarly, at the end of the third year, the man owes another Pi dollars in interest. The following table will assist us.

Amount owed

At end of zeroth year (start of loan)	$P = \$1,000$
At end of first year	$P + Pi$, or $\$1,000 + \$60$
At end of second year	$(P + Pi) + Pi$, or $P + 2Pi$ or $\$1,000 + \$120$
At end of third year	$[(P + Pi) + Pi] + Pi$, or $P + 3Pi$, or $\$1,000 + \$180$

Thus the total amount owed is \$1180. Note that the terms P, $P + Pi$, $P + 2Pi$ are terms of an arithmetic progression, with a common difference of Pi (see Exercise 6-3). An expression for the nth term is

$$P + (n - 1)Pi \tag{6-36}$$

At the end of n years, the total amount A owed is

$$A = P + nPi \tag{6-37}$$

The total interest I paid is the difference between the total amount A and original principal P. Thus

$$I = A - P \tag{6-38}$$

or

$$I = nPi \tag{6-39}$$

Here n is the number of years, and i is the simple interest rate per year (expressed in percents, but computed using hundredths). When the period of time is less than a year, say, 9 months, we express n in the form of a fraction, $n = \frac{9}{12}$ (since 9 months is $\frac{9}{12}$ of a year).

Compound interest is found in a different way. Let P be the principal, i the interest. The amount at the end of the first time period is, as before, $P + Pi$. But now the interest is calculated on this new principal. At the end of the second period the amount is

$$(P + Pi) + (P + Pi)i \tag{6-40}$$

This can be written

$$P(1 + i)^2 \tag{6-41}$$

In general, at the end of the nth period, the amount A_n is

$$A_n = P(1 + i)^n \tag{6-42}$$

Here A_n is called the *compound amount*. The difference between the original P and the compound A_n is called *compound interest*.

As an example consider the following problem.

Problem

How much money would accumulate in a savings account after 15 years if the interest rate is 5 percent, the period is 1 year (this means the interest is compounded or calculated yearly), and the principal is \$100?

Here

$$P = \$100 \qquad i = 0.05 \qquad n = 15$$

We seek

$$A_{15} = 100(1 + 0.05)^{15} \tag{6-43}$$

solution: It is easy to calculate the result on the right because tables exist where we can find $(1 + i)^n$ for many values of i and n. We find that

$$(1 + 0.05)^{15} = 2.0789 \tag{6-44}$$

Hence the solution is

$$A_{15} = \$207.89 \tag{6-45}$$

Every finite series has a sum. But not every infinite series has a sum. One infinite series we can examine is the infinite geometric series. This is given by the expression

$$\sum_{i=0}^{\infty} a_1 r^i \tag{6-46}$$

Another way of writing this is

$$\lim_{n \to \infty} S_n \tag{6-47}$$

where (see Exercise 6-7)

$$S_n = a_1 \frac{1 - r^n}{1 - r} = \sum_{i=0}^{n-1} a_1 r^i \tag{6-48}$$

is a single real number representing the sum of the first n terms in a geometric progression. As the subscript of S changes, we get a sequence of numbers, $S_0, S_1, S_2, S_3, \ldots, S_n, S_{n+1}, \ldots$. An attempt to find the limit of this sequence is equivalent to finding the sum of the infinite series (6-46). Thus

$$\lim_{n \to \infty} S_n = \lim_{n \to \infty} \sum_{i=0}^{n-1} a_1 r^i \tag{6-49}$$

You may ask: How can an expression with an infinite number of terms yield a finite number? This question is properly answered in higher-mathematics courses. All we will say here is that the sequence (6-48) does converge when the absolute value of the common ratio is less than 1. When this happens, the term r^n becomes zero as n gets larger and larger. Thus

$$\lim_{n \to \infty} S_n = a_1 \frac{1 - 0}{1 - r}$$

or

$$\lim_{n \to \infty} S_n = \frac{a_1}{1 - r} \qquad \text{when } |r| < 1 \tag{6-50}$$

or

$$\sum_{i=0}^{\infty} a_1 r^i = \frac{a_1}{1 - r} \qquad \text{when } |r| < 1 \tag{6-51}$$

As an application, consider the never-ending decimal number

0.6666 . . .

As we know, this decimal number really represents an infinite series.   Thus

$$0.6666 \ldots = \frac{6}{10} + \frac{6}{10^2} + \frac{6}{10^3} + \frac{6}{10^4} + \cdots \tag{6-52}$$

We note that the right side of Eq. (6-52) is a geometric series with first term a_1 equal to $6/10$ and common ratio r equal to $1/10$.   From Eq. (6-51) we have

$$\sum_{i=0}^{\infty} \frac{6}{10}\left(\frac{1}{10}\right)^i = \frac{6/10}{1 - 1/10} \tag{6-53}$$

or

$$0.6666 \ldots = 2/3 \tag{6-54}$$

This is one example which demonstrates that every repeating decimal number can be represented in the form a/b.   In other words, every repeating decimal number is a rational.

As another example, consider the repeating decimal number

2.57777 . . .

This can be written

$$2.57777 \ldots = 2 + \frac{5}{10} + \frac{7}{10^2} + \frac{7}{10^3} + \frac{7}{10^4} + \frac{7}{10^5} + \cdots \tag{6-55}$$

After the first two terms on the right we have a geometric series with

$$a_1 = \frac{7}{10^2} \tag{6-56}$$

and

$$r = \frac{1}{10} \tag{6-57}$$

Thus

$$2.57777 \ldots = 2 + \frac{5}{10} + \sum_{i=0}^{\infty} \frac{7}{10^2}\left(\frac{1}{10}\right)^i \tag{6-58}$$

or

$$2.57777 \ldots = 2 + \frac{5}{10} + \frac{7/10^2}{1 - \frac{1}{10}} = 2 + \frac{5}{10} + \frac{7}{10^2} \times \frac{10}{9} \qquad (6\text{-}59)$$

You should verify by simplifying the right side that Eq. (6-59) becomes

$$2.57777 \ldots = {}^{116}\!/_{45} \qquad (6\text{-}60)$$

An application of finite series will be discussed in the next section.

We were introduced to a positional numbering system in Chap. 2. This was the most familiar base 10 system. At that time we suggested that other positive integers could be used as a base (or radix). We will study three systems in use today.

6-3 THE BINARY NUMBER SYSTEM

The positional number system using a base of 2 is called the binary number system. Numbers expressed in this system are called binary numbers. Just as the base 10 system allows us to express a number using 10 digits, the binary system allows us to express a binary number with a combination of the digits 0 and 1. Thus only two digits are allowed in the base 2 system. This two-digit system is quite compatible with computer circuitry since most electronic devices have two possible states. A common example of a two-state device is the light bulb. It can be on or off. Another two-state device is a small doughnut-shaped piece of metal called a core. This core has the capability of being magnetized in a clockwise or counterclockwise direction. Cores are the main elements of most computer memory units. So if we agree that one direction of magnetization is to be associated with 0 and the other with 1, then we can use these cores to represent binary numbers. This association is what makes the binary number system so important.

Since each position in a binary number represents a power of 2, the following table will be handy.

2^7	2^6	2^5	2^4	2^3	2^2	2^1	2^0	2^{-1}	2^{-2}	2^{-3}	2^{-4}	2^{-5}	2^{-6}	2^{-7}
128	64	32	16	8	4	2	1	$\frac{1}{2}$	$\frac{1}{4}$	$\frac{1}{8}$	$\frac{1}{16}$	$\frac{1}{32}$	$\frac{1}{64}$	$\frac{1}{128}$
								.5	.25	.125	.0625	.03125	.015625	.0078125

An example of a binary number is

11011

When no decimal point appears, this is understood to be a positive integer. Since this is a positional numbering system, each binary digit is meant to be multiplied by a certain power of the base. We can actually carry out this multiplication to obtain the *base* 10 *equivalent of our binary number*. With binary integers, the rightmost binary digit is multiplied by the zeroth power of 2, the next left digit by the first power of 2, and so on.

In the example above we have

$$11011 = 1 \times 2^4 + 1 \times 2^3 + 0 \times 2^2 + 1 \times 2^1 + 1 \times 2^0 \qquad (6\text{-}61)$$

or

$$11011_2 = 27_{10} \qquad (6\text{-}62)$$

The subscripts 2 and 10 are used to designate to which number system the number belongs. Thus 11011 in base 2 is equivalent to 27 in base 10.

A binary number less than 1 is written with a point called a radix point. Thus

.1011

is a binary number less than 1. This is also called a binary fraction. Its base 10 equivalent is found in a similar manner. The radix point tells us we are dealing with negative powers of 2.

$$.1011 = 1 \times 2^{-1} + 0 \times 2^{-2} + 1 \times 2^{-3} + 1 \times 2^{-4} \qquad (6\text{-}63)$$
$$.1011 = \tfrac{1}{2} + 0 + \tfrac{1}{8} + \tfrac{1}{16} \qquad (6\text{-}64)$$
$$.1011_2 = .5 + .125 + .0625 \qquad (6\text{-}65)$$
$$.1011_2 = .6875_{10} \qquad (6\text{-}66)$$

Note that we refer to a digit in a binary number as a *binary digit*. These two words have been shortened to the term *bit*, and we shall refer to a binary digit as a bit.

We can easily convert any positive base 10 integer into its equivalent binary representation by repeatedly dividing the base 10 number by 2 until we obtain a quotient of zero. We make note of the remainders at each step. The first remainder is the rightmost bit. The final remainder is the leftmost bit.

As an example, convert 22_{10} to its binary equivalent.

$$\dfrac{11}{2\,)\,22} \quad \text{remainder 0}$$

$$\dfrac{5}{2\,)\,11} \quad \text{remainder 1}$$

$$\dfrac{2}{2\,)\,5} \quad \text{remainder 1}$$

$$\dfrac{1}{2\,)\,2} \quad \text{remainder 0}$$

$$\dfrac{0}{2\,)\,1} \quad \text{remainder 1}$$

Thus

$$22_{10} = 10110_2 \tag{6-67}$$

Addition of Binary Numbers

We add binary numbers using a notion that is used in our familiar base 10 system, the notion of a carry. For instance, when we add in base 10 the numbers 17 and 18, we first add the units digits 7 and 8. The result is 15, but instead of writing 15, we merely write the 5 and carry the 1 over to the tens position and add these digits. The result is 3. This is how we obtain our final result of 35.

How did we know that 7 plus 8 equaled 15? Most of us probably memorized the base 10 addition table long ago. For similar reasons you should commit the following examples to memory.

$$
\begin{array}{cccc}
0 & 1 & 0 & {}^{①}1 \\
\underline{+0} & \underline{+0} & \underline{+1} & \underline{+1} \\
0 & 1 & 1 & 0
\end{array}
$$

The circled 1 in the last sum indicates that we have a carry of 1.

Problem 1

Add the binary numbers 1001 and 11.

solution: Since no radix point appears, we assume these are positive integers. In that case we line up the rightmost digits in each number under each other. The others will fall in place. Thus we have

$$
\begin{array}{r}
1001 \\
+\ \ 11
\end{array}
$$

Starting on the right, we add

$$
\begin{array}{r}
{}^{①}\ \ \ \\
1001 \\
+\ \ 11 \\
\hline
0
\end{array}
$$

Note that the rightmost digit in the sum is zero. We have a carry as a result of this first addition. Going to the next left position, we add the carry digit and the other digits in that position. We obtain

$$
\begin{array}{r}
{}^{①①}\ \ \\
1001 \\
+\ \ 11 \\
\hline
00
\end{array}
$$

Now, in a binary number such as 11, leading zeros are understood if needed. So we augment two zeros to 11. We have, after adding a third time,

$$\begin{array}{r} {\scriptstyle ①①} \\ 1001 \\ +0011 \\ \hline 100 \end{array}$$

This third addition yields no carry, and hence our final result is

$$\begin{array}{r} 1001 \\ +0011 \\ \hline 1100 \end{array}$$

To check our results we could convert to base 10.

$$1001_2 = 9_{10} \tag{6-68}$$
$$11_2 = 3_{10} \tag{6-69}$$
$$1100_2 = 12_{10} \tag{6-70}$$

The binary sum obtained is consistent with the base 10 sum. Hence our addition is correct. These concepts hold for binary fractions also.

Problem 2

Add binary $\frac{3}{8}$ and binary $\frac{1}{4}$.

solution: A glance at the table that began this section tells us

$$(\tfrac{1}{4})_{10} = .010_2 = .25_{10}$$
$$(\tfrac{3}{8})_{10} = (\tfrac{2}{8} + \tfrac{1}{8})_{10} = .011_2 = .375_{10}$$

Now we add

$$\begin{array}{r} .010 \\ +.011 \\ \hline .101 \end{array}$$

You should satisfy yourself that a conversion to base 10 will verify these results.

If a column generates more than one carry digit, we indicate ① for each carry.

Example

$$\begin{array}{r r} {\scriptstyle ①} \\ {\scriptstyle ①①①} \\ 1101_2 = 13_{10} \\ 11_2 \quad\ 3_{10} \\ 101_2 \quad\ 5_{10} \\ 1_2 \quad\ 1_{10} \\ \hline 10110_2 \quad 22_{10} \end{array}$$

Subtraction of Binary Numbers

One of two methods might be used in the arithmetic unit of a computer to accomplish binary subtraction. Both these methods require the notion of complement. For the sake of completeness, we will define the two types of complements.

One's Complement

The one's complement of a binary number B is another binary number obtained from the expression $2^n - 1 - B$, where 2^n is expressed in binary form and n is the number of bit positions in B. If B is a binary fraction, the expression becomes $1 - 2^{-n} - B$.

Two's Complement

The two's complement of a binary number B is another binary number obtained from the expression $2^n - B$, where 2^n is expressed in binary form and n is the number of bit positions in B. If B is a binary fraction, then n becomes 1, and zeros are augmented to the right of the radix point in the binary form of 2^1, equal in number to the positions in B. Here the binary fraction is written with a zero to the left of the radix point.

These definitions require a knowledge of binary subtraction using the notion of borrow if needed. This notion is applied when we subtract in base 10. We can avoid the entire notion of borrow by using the following rule.

To form the one's complement of a binary number B, change all zeros to ones and ones to zeros. The resulting binary number is the one's complement of B.

For example,
The one's complement of 1101 is 0010
The one's complement of .101 is .010
The one's complement of 111.001 is 000.110

The notion of complement is used in the arithmetic unit of the computer when subtraction is desired. It is easier to carry out an addition than a subtraction between binary numbers. For this reason the complement of the number to be subtracted (the subtrahend) is formed. This number is then added to the minuend. We will investigate this idea more deeply first with one's complement.

The One's Complement, End-around Carry Method

In this method we wish to form the difference $M - S$ of two binary numbers M and S. We form the one's complement of S, calling it $\bar{S}$. Now we form the binary sum $M + \bar{S}$. *If a carry digit occurs* beyond the high-order (left-most) position of the sum, we take this digit and add it to the low-order (right-most) position of the sum. The result is the binary difference $M - S$. It will be positive. *If no carry digit occurs*, we form the one's complement of the sum $M + \bar{S}$. The result is the binary difference $M - S$. It is understood to be negative.

Example

Find the difference

$$\begin{array}{r} 1101 \\ -101 \\ \hline \end{array}$$

We add zeros to make the number of digits in the minuend and subtrahend the same.

$$\begin{array}{r} 1101 \\ -0101 \\ \hline \end{array}$$

Now we form the one's complement of the subtrahend and add. We obtain

$$\begin{array}{r} ① \\ 1101 \\ +1010 \\ \hline 0111 \end{array}$$

Note that a carry digit occurs. We take this digit and add it to the rightmost position of our sum.

$$\begin{array}{r} ↻ \\ 1101 \\ 1010 \\ \hline 0111 \\ +1 \\ \hline 1000 \end{array}$$

This final result is the difference. Thus

$$1101 - 101 = 1000 \tag{6-71}$$

We can convert to base 10 and check our results.

$$1101_2 = 13_{10} \tag{6-72}$$
$$101_2 = 5_{10} \tag{6-73}$$

Now

$$13_{10} - 5_{10} = 8_{10} \tag{6-74}$$
$$8_{10} = 1000_2 \tag{6-75}$$

Let us take an example where no carry digit occurs.

Example

Find

10100
−11000

We form the one's complement of the subtrahend and add.

10100
+00111
11011

Note that no carry digit occurs beyond the high-order position. This means two things: the difference will be a negative number, and we are to form the one's complement of our above sum. This binary number will be the difference that we seek. Now the one's complement of 11011 is 00100. Thus our final result is

10100	20_{10}
−11000	-24_{10}
−00100	$- 4_{10}$

As a check on our answer the base 10 equivalent numbers appear on the right.

Consider this next example using binary fractions.

Subtract

.10110
−.00101

As before, we form the one's complement of the subtrahend and add.

①
.10110
+.11010
.10000

We perform the end-around carry to form the final result.

.10110	$.68750_{10}$
−.00101	$-.15625_{10}$
.10001	$.53125_{10}$

As a check, base 10 equivalent numbers appear on the right.

Example

Perform the subtraction

.00111
−.01101

As in the previous example, we form the one's complement of the subtrahend and add.

.00111
+.10010
.11001

No carry occurs. This means the result of the subtraction will be a negative
number. To form the actual result, we form the one's complement of the
above sum. The one's complement of .11001 is .00110. Thus

.00111	$.21875_{10}$
−.01101	$-.40625_{10}$
−.00110	$-.18750_{10}$

is our final result. Base 10 equivalent numbers appear on the right.

As a final example we consider binary numbers which have an integer
part and a fractional part.

Subtract

11.01
− 1.11

Form the one's-complement of the subtrahend and add. We augment zeros
on the left and right when needed.

①
11.01
+10.00
01.01

After performing the end-around carry we obtain as a final result

11.01	3.25_{10}
− 1.11	-1.75_{10}
1.10	1.50_{10}

The Two's-complement Method

Before we can describe the two's-complement method of subtraction, we must
know how to form the two's complement of a binary number.

To form the two's complement of a binary number, first form its one's complement (change zeros to ones and ones to zeros), *then add one to the right-most (low-order) position.*

Example

Binary number	Two's complement
1101	0011
1.001	0.111
.101	.011
01100	10100

Now we will make use of the fact that subtraction is really addition of numbers with unlike signs.

When the two's-complement method is used in the arithmetic unit of a computer, certain assumptions are made.

1. Fixed-length binary representations are implied.
2. Negative numbers are held in two's-complement form.
3. The high-order bit in a binary representation is used to indicate the sign: 0 if positive, 1 if negative.

Example

A fixed-length binary representation means that a binary number cannot exceed n bit positions.

When $n = 8$, 00110111 is a valid binary number. The decimal equivalent of this binary number is 55. Note that the high-order bit is zero. This indicates a positive number.

The two's complement of the above binary number is 11001001. Note that the high-order bit is 1. This is the binary representation for -55. A few more examples follow. We assume $n = 8$.

+3	00000011
−3	11111101
+15	00001111
−15	11110001
+32	00100000
−32	11100000

So the "negative of a number" is found by forming the two's complement of its positive binary representation.

Description of the two's-complement method for subtraction follows. A fixed length of n bit positions is assumed, and M is positive (its high-order bit is zero).

We seek the difference $M - S$ of two binary numbers M and S. Form the two's complement of S, calling it $\bar{S}$. Now form the binary sum $M + \bar{S}$. If the high-order digit is zero, the sum is positive and it is the binary representation of the difference $M - S$. If the high-order digit is 1, this sum is negative. Furthermore, it is in two's-complement form.

We assume 8-bit fixed-length binary numbers in the examples.

Example

Find the difference between 00001101 (binary 13) and 00000101 (binary 5). Note that this means to add positive binary 13 and negative binary 5. Form the two's complement of the subtrahend and add.

$$
\begin{array}{r}
^{①}00001101 \\
+11111011 \\
\hline
00001000
\end{array}
$$

Note that a carry digit occurs in the ninth bit position, but it is lost since we are limited to eight bit positions. Also, the result is positive, since the high-order bit position is zero. Thus

$$
\begin{array}{r}
00001101 \\
+11111011 \\
\hline
00001000
\end{array}
\qquad
\begin{array}{r}
13_{10} \\
+(-5)_{10} \\
\hline
8_{10}
\end{array}
$$

The numbers 13_{10} and 8_{10} on the right are the base 10 equivalents of the binary minuend and difference. *However, -5 is not the base 10 equivalent of the binary subtrahend. As a matter of fact, the base 10 equivalent of 11111011_2 is 127_{10}. But 11111011_2 is the two's complement of positive binary 5. This is what we have agreed is to represent negative 5.*

As another example, find the sum of positive binary 15 and negative binary 21. First, we write positive binary 15.

00001111

In order to write negative binary 21, we must form the two's complement of positive binary 21.

Positive binary 21 is

00010101

The two's complement of this is

11101011

This is what we have agreed to call negative 21.

Now we add.

$$
\begin{array}{ll}
00001111 & 15_{10} \\
+11101011 & +(-21)_{10} \\
\hline
11111010 &
\end{array}
$$

As you can see from the sum on the right the result should be negative. (In fact, it should be -6.) Is the binary result a negative number?

As you can see, the high-order bit in the sum is one. This tells us that we have a negative number. But in this system negative numbers are to be held in two's-complement form. The next question is, "Is our binary sum the two's-complement form of positive binary 6?"

Positive binary 6 is

00000110.

The two's complement of this is

11111010.

Note that this is the same as our binary sum. Thus our sum is indeed the binary representation for -6. Hence

$$
\begin{array}{ll}
00001111 & 15_{10} \\
+11101011 & +(-21) \\
\hline
11111010 & -6
\end{array}
$$

When the binary sum that we obtain is a negative member (high-order bit is one), we must answer the question, "Of what number is this the two's complement?" We can answer this question by merely forming the two's complement of the sum. In the above example we wished to find out, "Of what positive binary number is 11111010 the two's complement?"

We form the two's complement of 11111010. It is

00000110.

This is positive binary 6.

Thus, to find the positive-binary representation of a negative number, form its two's complement.

As another example consider

$$
\begin{array}{l}
00110010 \\
+11000111 \\
\hline
11111001
\end{array}
$$

We can tell quickly that the positive number in the above sum is 50_{10}.

What is the negative number that we are adding to it? We find out by forming its two's complement.

The two's complement of 11000111 is 00111001.

But $00111001 = 57_{10}$.

Thus 11000111 is the representation for -57.

You should verify for yourself that 11111001 is the representation for -7 by forming its two's complement.

Example

Add in 8-bit two's-complement binary notation 67_{10}, -70_{10}.

We know the result will be -3_{10}, but we are to perform the operations in two's-complement binary.

Now

$$67_{10} = 01000011$$

-70_{10} is formed by taking the two's complement of 70_{10}.

$$70_{10} = 01000110$$

so -70_{10} has the form 10111010.

Now form the sum

$$
\begin{array}{r}
01000011 \\
+10111010 \\
\hline
11111101
\end{array}
$$

The result is negative (why?). We can, if we wish, find its positive binary form by taking its two's complement. Thus the two's complement of 11111101 is 00000011.

Our result is -3_{10}

We may attempt to add binary numbers whose sum cannot be held in eight bit positions. This condition is called an overflow. Erroneous results will occur. (See Exercise 6-21.)

The two's-complement method works as well with binary fractions as with binary integers. As with integers, *the leftmost position is the sign position.* The next left position is needed in case the sum of the fractions is greater than 1. See examples below.

Example

00.11_2 is positive binary $\frac{1}{2} + \frac{1}{4}$

or

$$00.11_2 = +.75_{10}$$

But 11.1101 is representation for some negative binary fraction (since the high-order position is 1). Form its two's complement.

The two's complement of 11.1101 is 00.0011.

Now $00.0011_2 = +.1875_{10}$.

Thus 11.1101 is the representation for $-.1875$.

Some operations with binary fractions using two's-complement representations follow below. The base 10 representations appear alongside.

$$
\begin{array}{ll}
00.1011 & +.6875 \\
+11.0001 & +(-.9375) \\
\hline
11.1100 & -.25 \\
11.00001 & -.96875 \\
+11.00010 & +(-.9375) \\
\hline
10.00011 & -1.90625
\end{array}
$$

Here is an example where we see why two bit positions are needed to the left of the radix point.

$$
\begin{array}{ll}
00.111111 & +.984375 \\
+00.101111 & +.734375 \\
\hline
01.101110 & 1.718750
\end{array}
$$

You may ask: Why does this two's-complement method work? The following discussions will serve as an answer.

We seek the difference

$$D = M - S \tag{6-76}$$

where M and S are two positive binary integers with a fixed number n of bit positions. We claim that the difference D will be obtained when we add the two's complement of the subtrahend S to M. Furthermore, we claim D will be positive if $M - S$ is positive; D will be the two's-complement form of $S - M$ if $M - S$ is negative.

First, form the two's complement of S.

$$2^n - S \tag{6-77}$$

Now add this to M.

$$M + (2^n - S) \tag{6-78}$$
$$2^n + (M - S) \tag{6-79}$$

Let $M - S > 0$.

Since M and S are restricted to n bit positions, adding 2^n will have no effect on the ultimate result. (Try this for yourself. Add 2^n to any n-bit-position number, using binary notation.) Thus D has n bit positions, and

$$D = 2^n + (M - S) = M - S \tag{6-80}$$

Now let $M - S < 0$. Then $S - M > 0$. We see that Eq (6-79) can be written

$$2^n - (S - M) \tag{6-81}$$

But this is the two's-complement form of $S - M$.

Although it is similar, we omit the discussion for S and M as binary fractions.

No radically new ideas are necessary to achieve division and multiplication. For instance, the product ab means: Take a, b times. This could be obtained by repeatedly adding a.

Similarly, a/b means: Find the number of times b is contained in a. This could be found by subtracting b repeatedly.

6-4 BASE 8 (OCTAL) NUMBER SYSTEM

The binary numbers we have dealt with so far are easy to write down and work with. This is because we have been dealing with binary numbers with relatively few bit positions. Many computer manufacturers represent binary numbers internally, with 12, 24, 32, and sometimes more bit positions. The more bit positions used, the more difficult it becomes for the computer to communicate these binary numbers to us. (Try writing out a 36-bit binary integer.) Other positional numbering systems are used to permit communication of binary numbers without resorting to a series of zeros and ones. Two positional numbering systems used to accomplish this are the base 8 (octal) and base 16 (hexadecimal) numbering systems. We will discuss integer representation, base 8 first.

In order to see how the octal system is used to communicate binary information, it is necessary to know how an octal number is formed.

The following table on powers of 8 will be helpful.

8^7	8^6	8^5	8^4	8^3	8^2	8^0
2097152	262144	32768	4096	512	64	1

The digits permitted in this system are 0, 1, 2, 3, 4, 5, 6, 7. An octal number is made up of a combination of these, each digital position being a different power of the base 8.

Thus a typical octal number would be

765

We can find its base 10 equivalent by writing it as a sum of powers of the radix 8.

$$765_8 = 7 \times 8^2 + 6 \times 8^1 + 5 \times 8^0 = 448_{10} + 48_{10} + 5_{10}$$
$$= 501_{10} \qquad (6\text{-}82)$$

We find the octal equivalent of any base 10 integer by repeatedly dividing the integer by 8 and making note of the remainders at each step. The last remainder is the high-order digit of the equivalent octal number.

For example, consider the base 10 number 501.

$$\begin{array}{r} 62 \\ 8\overline{)501} \\ 48 \\ \hline 21 \\ 16 \\ \hline 5 \end{array}$$ The first remainder is 5; now divide 62 by 8.

$$\begin{array}{r} 7 \\ 8\overline{)62} \\ 56 \\ \hline 6 \end{array}$$ The second remainder is 6.

$$\begin{array}{r} 0 \\ 8\overline{)7} \\ 0 \\ \hline 7 \end{array}$$ The final remainder is 7.

Thus

$$502_{10} = 765_8$$

To continue, we write the eight octal digits and their binary equivalents.

Octal digit	Binary equivalent
0	000
1	001
2	010
3	011
4	100
5	101
6	110
7	111

We need, at most, three binary digits to represent any octal digit. We can represent any two octal digits side by side with at most six binary digits. For example,

57_8 is represented by 101111_2

The question arises: Are these two representations equivalent? To answer, let us find the base 10 equivalent for each.

$$57_8 = 5 \times 8^1 + 7 \times 8^0 = 47_{10} \tag{6-83}$$

and

$$101111_2 = 2^5 + 2^3 + 2^2 + 2^1 + 2^0 = 32 + 8 + 4 + 2 + 1 \qquad (6\text{-}84)$$

or

$$101111_2 = 47_{10} \qquad (6\text{-}85)$$

Thus they are equivalent, and we can write

$$101111_2 = 57_8 \qquad (6\text{-}86)$$

This will be true for any binary integer that we write. That is, given any binary integer, its octal equivalent is found by separating the binary number into groups of 3 bits each, starting on the right. Augment zeros on the left to make a 3-bit group. Now convert each 3-bit group to an octal digit. The result will be the octal equivalent of the binary number.

Example

Convert 1110010101001_2 to its octal equivalent.
We will separate each 3-bit group by a slash, thus:

001/110/010/101/001

We have augmented two zeros on the left to make a 3-bit group. Now we can easily convert each group to an octal digit. From left to right we have 1, 6, 2, 5, 1. Thus

$$1110010101001_2 = 16251_8 \qquad (6\text{-}87)$$

You should verify for yourself that the base 10 equivalents for each number are the same.

If we are given an octal number, we find its binary equivalent by reversing the above process. Thus, to find the binary equivalent of 6762_8, we convert each octal digit into a 3-bit representation.

$$6762_8 = 110111110010_2 \qquad (6\text{-}88)$$

Verify, as before, that this is true.

This convenient method of conversion is not by accident. It is valid because of a certain interrelationship between *successive powers of* 8 and each *third higher power of* 2. The table below will give some insight into this interrelationship. (See also Exercise 6-28.)

8^5			8^4			8^3			8^2			8^1			8^0
2^{15}	2^{14}	2^{13}	2^{12}	2^{11}	2^{10}	2^9	2^8	2^7	2^6	2^5	2^4	2^3	2^2	2^1	2^0
32,768			4096			512			64			8			1

Two's-complement binary notation becomes very easy to interpret when octal representation is used. For example, we write positive binary 22 and the equivalent octal representation using nine bit positions.

000010110_2 $\qquad$ 026_8

Now we write negative 22 and its octal representation.

111101010_2 $\qquad$ 752_8

Note that if we are limited to nine bit positions, we are necessarily limited to three octal positions.

You should satisfy yourself that positive numbers will have 0, 1, 2, or 3 in the high-order octal position. Also, negative numbers (which are in two's-complement binary) will have 4, 5, 6, or 7 in the high-order octal position.

The following addition table for base 8 will prove useful.

	0	1	2	3	4	5	6	7
0	0	1	2	3	4	5	6	7
1	1	2	3	4	5	6	7	①0
2	2	3	4	5	6	7	①0	①1
3	3	4	5	6	7	①0	①1	①2
4	4	5	6	7	①0	①1	①2	①3
5	5	6	7	①0	①1	①2	①3	①4
6	6	7	①0	①1	①2	①3	①4	①5
7	7	①0	①1	①2	①3	①4	①5	①6

The circled 1 in some boxes indicates that a carry of 1 occurs. It is to be carried to the next left octal position. For example, intersection of the row headed 4 and the column headed 5 yields 1 with a 1 carry.

Example

$$
\begin{array}{ccc}
^① & ^① & ^① \\
1_8 & 7_8 & 25_8 \\
+\ 7_8 & +\ 6_8 & +14_8 \\
\hline
10_8 & 15_8 & 41_8
\end{array}
$$

Convert all the above numbers to decimal in order to verify the results for yourself.

We have seen how two's-complement binary numbers are added. Their equivalent octal representations will obey the laws of octal addition (see table).

Example

Add positive binary 20 and negative binary 22. Then add the octal representations and check that the results are equivalent.

000010100
111101010
‾‾‾‾‾‾‾‾‾‾
111111110

Now we write the octal representations and add in octal.

024_8
752_8
‾‾‾‾‾
776_8

The results are equivalent.

We know immediately from the above that the sum is a negative number. The above are both representations for negative 2. So we shall obtain zero if positive 2 is added. Now positive binary 2 and positive octal 2 are

000000010_2 002_8

Adding the above corresponding binary and octal numbers, we have

000000010_2 002_8
111111110_2 776_8
‾‾‾‾‾‾‾‾‾   ‾‾‾‾‾
000000000 000

Thus zero is obtained in both cases.

You can now see how conveniently we can describe a long series of zeros and ones using octal representation. For similar reasons the hexadecimal number system will be studied.

6-5 BASE 16 (HEXADECIMAL) NUMBERING SYSTEM

In base 16 we need 16 digits, with each digit signifying a value. These values begin at zero and proceed upward up to a value one less than the base. Now each digit must be a single symbol. We represent 10 of these symbols with the digits 0 to 9, but we need 6 more. Any symbols could be used, but the letters A, B, C, D, E, F have been adopted. Thus the 16 digits that we use in the base 16 number system are

0, 1, 2, 3, 4, 5, 6, 7, 8, 9, A, B, C, D, E, F

Any hexadecimal (for short, we say *hex*) number is written as a combination of the above digits. For example,

5AB6

is a hexadecimal number.

Since base 16 is a positional numbering system, each position in a hexadecimal number represents a certain power of the base 16.

We list some powers of 16:

16^4	16^3	16^2	16^1	16^0
65536	4096	256	16	1

As an aid in writing the base 10 equivalent of any hexadecimal number, we list the base 10 equivalents of the base 16 digits. Binary equivalents appear for later reference.

Base 16	Base 10	Base 2
0	0	0000
1	1	0001
2	2	0010
3	3	0011
4	4	0100
5	5	0101
6	6	0110
7	7	0111
8	8	1000
9	9	1001
A	10	1010
B	11	1011
C	12	1100
D	13	1101
E	14	1110
F	15	1111

Fig. 6-4

Now we can convert any hex number into its base 10 equivalent.

$$5AB6_{16} = (5 \times 16^3 + 10 \times 16^2 + 11 \times 16^1 + 6 \times 16^0)_{10}$$
$$= (20480 + 2560 + 176 + 6)_{10} = 23222_{10} \qquad (6\text{-}89)$$

or

$$5AB6_{10} = 23222_{10} \qquad (6\text{-}90)$$

When a positive base 10 integer is given, we can find its hexadecimal equivalent by the method of repeated divisions. This time we divide by 16 and note the remainder at each step.

Now each remainder will be no greater than 15. We convert each remainder to a hexadecimal digit. These remainders make up the hexadecimal equivalent of our base 10 number, with the final remainder the high-order digit. An example follows.

Example

   Convert 431_{10} to its hex equivalent.

$$
\begin{array}{r}
26 \\
16)\overline{431} \\
32 \\
\hline
111 \\
96 \\
\hline
15
\end{array}
$$ The first remainder is 15, and the equivalent hex digit is E.

$$
\begin{array}{r}
1 \\
16)\overline{26} \\
16 \\
\hline
10
\end{array}
$$ The second remainder is 10, and the equivalent hex digit is A.

$$
\begin{array}{r}
0 \\
16)\overline{1} \\
0 \\
\hline
1
\end{array}
$$ The final remainder is 1, and its equivalent hex digit is 1.

Thus

   $431_{10} = 1AE_{16}$

   From Fig. 6-4 we can see that any hex digit can be represented with at most four binary digits; any two hex digits, with at most eight binary digits; and so on.

   For example,

   $AE_{16} = 10101110_2$ (6-91)

   In general, we can find the hex equivalent of any binary integer by separating the integer into groups of 4 bits, starting on the right. We augment zeros on the left, if needed, to make a 4-bit group.

   Conversely, we find the binary equivalent of any hex integer by converting each integer into its 4-bit equivalent.

Example

   Convert

   $10101100101101101111100001_2$

to its hex equivalent.

   We separate each 4-bit group by a slash.

   1010/1100/1011/0110/1111/0001

Now convert each 4-bit group to a hex digit.   We obtain

ACB6F1

Thus

$$101011001011011011110001_2 = ACB6F1_{16}$$

You can see how conveniently we can represent long strings of zeros and ones (binary numbers) by using hex representation.

The conversion method between binary and hexadecimal that we have been using is valid because of a certain interrelationship that exists between powers of 16 and each 4th higher power of 2.   It is similar to the relationship which exists between powers of 8 and powers of 2.

EXERCISES

6-1. Find the general member of the infinite sequence whose first five terms are

a. $1, \dfrac{3}{2}, \dfrac{5}{4}, \dfrac{7}{8}, \dfrac{9}{16}, \dfrac{11}{32}$

b. $1, \dfrac{\sqrt{2}}{4}, \dfrac{\sqrt{3}}{9}, \dfrac{\sqrt{4}}{16}, \dfrac{\sqrt{5}}{25}, \dfrac{\sqrt{6}}{36}$

c. $2, -\dfrac{3}{2}, \dfrac{4}{3}, -\dfrac{5}{4}, \dfrac{6}{5}, -\dfrac{7}{6}$

6-2. Write the first six terms of

$$a_{n+2} = 2\,(a_{n+1} + a_n) \qquad \text{where } a_0 = 1, a_1 = 2$$

6-3. An example of a sequence which you have probably met before is an arithmetic progression.   This is a sequence where each term is obtained from the preceding one by adding to it a fixed *common difference*.

If b is the first term and d is the common difference, then

$b + $d is the second term
$b + 2d$ is the third term
$b + 3d$ is the fourth term
. . . .
$b + (n - 1)d$ is the nth term

Thus a sequence that has the general form

$$a_n = b + (n - 1)d$$

with b and d known, is an arithmetic progression.

    a. Write the general form of an arithmetic progression whose first five terms are

$$10,\ 6,\ 2,\ -2,\ -6$$

    b. Write the general form of an arithmetic progression as a recursive relation. (*Hint:* Let the first term be a_1, the second term a_2, the third term a_3, etc. Now try to express a_2 in terms of a_1, a_3 in terms of a_2, etc.)

6-4. Another example of a sequence which you have probably met before is a geometric progression. This is a sequence where each term is obtained from the preceding one by multiplying it by a fixed number called a *common ratio*.

If a_1 is the first term and r is the common ratio, then

a_1r is the second term
a_1r^2 is the third term
a_1r^3 is the fourth term
. . . .
a_1r^{n-1} is the nth term

Thus a sequence that has the general form

$$a_n = a_1r^{n-1}$$

with a_1 and r known, is called a geometric progression.

    a. Write the general form of a geometric progression whose first five terms are

$$50,\ 25,\ 12\tfrac{1}{2},\ 6\tfrac{1}{4},\ 3\tfrac{1}{8}$$

    b. 1, 2, 4, 8, 16

    c. 1, 10, 100, 1000, 10,000

    d. Write the general form of a geometric progression as a recursive relation. (*Hint:* Let the first term be a_1, the second term a_2, the third term a_3, etc. Now try to express a_2 in terms of a_1 and r, a_3 in terms of a_2 and a_1 etc.)

6-5. Let the first term of an arithmetic progression be a_1. If a_n is the nth term, show that

    a. The $(n-1)$st term a_{n-1} is

$$a_{n-1} = a_n - d$$

    b. Also show that

$$a_{n-2} = a_n - 2d$$

Thus you have verified that the series S_n associated with the first n terms of an arithmetic progression is

$$S_n = a_1 + (a_1 + d) + (a_1 + 2d) + \cdots$$
$$+ (a_n - 2d) + (a_n - d) + a_n$$

c. Write S_n in reverse order [that is, a_n first, then $(a_n - d)$, then $(a_n - 2d)$, ending with a_1]. Now add S_n, given in Exercise 6-5b to the form of S_n you have just written, and obtain an expression for the sum of the first n terms of an arithmetic progression. Verify that

$$S_n = \frac{n(a_1 + a_n)}{2}$$

6-6. a. Find the sum of the first 11 positive integers. (*Hint:* These form an arithmetic progression.)

b. Find the sum of the first k positive even integers, starting with 2. (*Hint:* Here $a_1 = 2 \times 1$, $a_2 = 2 \times 2$.)

c. Show that the sum S_k of the first k positive odd integers is

$$S_k = k^2$$

6-7. Form the sum S_n of the first n terms in a geometric progression. From Exercise 6-4

$$S_n = a_1 + a_1r + a_1r^2 + \cdots + a_1r^{n-2} + a_1r^{n-1}$$

Now multiply both sides of this by r. We obtain

$$rS_n = a_1r + a_1r^2 + \cdots + a_1r^{n-2} + a_1r^{n-1} + ar^n$$

Now subtract this expression from the original expression S_n. You should obtain a simplified form for the sum of the first n terms in a geometric progression.

$$S_n = a_1 \frac{1 - r^n}{1 - r}$$

This expression is true when $r \neq 1$. What is the sum S_n when $r = 1$?

6-8. a. Find the sum of

$$1 + (1.01) + (1.01)^2 + \cdots + (1.01)^{10}$$

[*Hint:* $(1.01)^{10} = 1.10462$.]

b. Find the sum of

$$1 + (1 + r) + (1 + r)^2 + \cdots + (1 + r)^{n-1}$$

6-9.   What principal will amount to $4,000 in 20 years at 4 percent interest compounded yearly?

6-10. Convert the following repeating decimals to the form a/b.

      a.   1.5555. . .   b.   .21212121. . .

      c.   .33333. . .   d.   .0333. . .

6-11. a.   Write the base 10 equivalent of the following binary numbers.

      101   1111   .1111   1000
      10101   110011   101100110 10

      b.   Write the binary equivalent of the following base 10 numbers.

      10 2 29 31 100 1

6-12. A convergence condition in wide use today is based on a theorem called the Cauchy criterion for convergence (after Augustin Louis Cauchy, 1759–1857).   The theorem states:

    A sequence a_n of real numbers has a finite limit L if and only if, for every $\epsilon > 0$, there exists some integer N so that

$$|s_n - s_m| < \epsilon \text{ when } n, m > N$$

The theorem is modified in the following way:

    Let s_m and s_{m+1} be succeeding terms of the sequence s_m.   Now select a sufficiently small number, calling it ϵ.

    If

$$(A) \quad |s_m - s_{m+1}| < \epsilon$$

then the sequence is *assumed* to obey the Cauchy criterion.   However, at this point we do not know the actual limit L.   So we make another assumption: The term s_{m+1} is taken as the limit.

    We demonstrate with the sequence

$$s_n = \frac{2(n + 1)}{n}$$

For illustrative purposes, we give the actual limit L.   It is 2.
As an example, we select $\epsilon = 10^{-6}$.
Now let $m = 100$; then $m + 1 = 101$, and

$$s_m = 2(101/100) = 2(1.01) = 2.02$$
$$s_{m+1} = 2(102/101) = 2.01980$$

Then

$$|s_m - s_{m+1}| = |2.02 - 2.01980|$$

or

$$|s_m - s_{m+1}| = .00020$$

This value is greater than ϵ, so our condition is not obeyed. We continue to increase m until condition (A) is obeyed.

    a.   Show that condition (A) is not obeyed when $m = 1,000$.

    b.   Show that condition (A) is obeyed when $m = 2,000$.

    c.   Let $\epsilon = 0.01$. Find an m so that condition (A) is obeyed for the sequence

$$s_n = \frac{n + 3}{n}$$

(*Hint:* Try $m = 10$; then $m = 20$; then $m = 30$.)

6-13. a. Add the following binary numbers.

1111	1010	11
101	111	1111

    b.   Convert the above to base 10 numbers and make sure your binary sums convert to the base 10 sum.

6-14. a. Do the same as in Exercise 6-13a.

.010	.111	.111
.001	.1	.111

    b.   Do the same as in Exercise 6-13b.

6-15. a. Add

110110	111101
10010	111111
111011	

    b.   Add the following numbers, first using base 10 arithmetic, then using binary arithmetic.

$$(25)_{10}$$
$$(11)_{10}$$
$$(10)_{2}$$
$$(1110)_{2}$$

6-16. Perform the following subtractions, using the one's-complement and end-around carry method. Augment zeros where needed.

a. 11010   b. 11101110   c. .011011
   −10001   −01011010   −.1

d. 1101.1101   e. 110.110
   − 10.0010   −110.110

Verify your results by using base 10 arithmetic.

6-17. Perform the following operations, using the two's-complement method.
       Assume 8 positions as fixed length. Change the minus numbers first.

a. 00011011   b. −01010101   c. 00011111
   −00101010   01111010   −   010

d. 11110101   e. 11011011   f. 00.1001
   +10010010   +01110000   −00.1100

6-18. a. What is the highest positive number which can be represented in
           8-bit two's-complement binary notation? The lowest negative
           number?
       b. Answer part a for fixed-length binary representation of n bits.

6-19. Perform the following operations using the two's-complement method.
       Assume 6 positions as fixed length. Change the minus numbers first.

a. 00.0001   b. 00.1000   c. 00.1010
   −00.1000   −00.0001   +11.1110

6-20. Some computers hold floating-point numbers in two's-complement form
       in the following format:

$$F \times 2^{\pm E}$$

where F is the fractional part of this binary number, with $-1 < F < 1$,
and E is the appropriate power of 2. F is held in a certain fixed number
of bit positions, and also E is a binary integer held in a certain lesser
number of bit positions. The leading bit position of F and E is the
sign position. The second leftmost bit position is not zero in F, for
positive F's. For example, let F be held in eight positions and E be held
in four positions. Then

```
     1 2 3 4 5 6 7 8     1 2 3 4
    |±| | | | | | | |   |±| | | |
           F                 E
```

The radix point is assumed to be between the sign position and the bit position labeled 2 in F. Thus, since the binary representation for $\frac{3}{4}$ is .11, in floating-point notation this is

$+.1100000 \times 2°$

Within the computer we would have

1 2 3 4 5 6 7 8   1 2 3 4
|0|1|1|0|0|0|0|0| |0|0|0|0|

Since $(\frac{1}{4})_{10}$ is $.01_2$, we would have

$+.1000000 \times 2^{-1}$

Internally, this is

1 2 3 4 5 6 7 8   1 2 3 4
|0|1|0|0|0|0|0|0| |1|1|1|1|

Since 3_{10} is 11_2, we have the representation

$+.1100000 \times 2^{+2}$

or internally,

1 2 3 4 5 6 7 8   1 2 3 4
|0|1|1|0|0|0|0|0| |0|0|1|0|

Write the internal representation for

a. 5_{10} b. $.0625_{10}$ c. -5_{10} d. $-\frac{1}{2}_6$

e. 16_{10} f. 31_{10} g. 1   h. -1

6-21.   Refer to Exercise 6-18 if needed.   The maximum positive number that can be held in two's-complement (high-order-bit = sign) binary notation in five bit positions is

01111

or $+15$.

a.   Add in above 5-bit binary notation 11_{10} and 7_{10}.   Describe your result.   Is it correct or not?

b.   Perform part a using 6-bit binary notation.   Is your answer correct or not?

c.   Add in two's-complement 6-bit binary notation -17_{10} and -18_{10}.   Why is the result incorrect?

d.   Perform part c using 7-bit binary notation.   Why is the result correct?

6-22. Convert the following octal numbers to decimal and the decimal numbers to octal.

      a. 100_{10} b. 100_8 c. 77_{10} d. 99_{10}

      e. 88_{10} f. 10_{10} g. 10_8 h. 1759_{10}

      i. 2453_8

6-23. Write the following octal numbers in binary and the binary numbers in octal.

      a. 444_8 b. 011101110111_2 c. 111111111_2

6-24. a. Why must we interpret zero in two's-complement binary as positive zero?

      b. Is

$$100000000_2$$

interpreted as negative zero? If not, what is it?

      c. Write the octal representation of the binary number in part b.

6-25. Add

      a. 765_8 b. 0111111100 c. 462_8

         124_8 1000000000 477_8

6-26. a. Write the hexadecimal and octal equivalent of each binary number.

        01101101001   000110110011   001001

        01111011110110   011110110001010110

      b. Convert each octal and hex number obtained in part a to decimal. You should obtain the same base 10 number.

6-27. What binary numbers do the following hex numbers represent?

      a. 111   b. AAA   c. ABX   d. 162

      e. 1AE49   f. 97CB8   g. 77A

6-28. Write

$$001111111111111$$

as a sum of powers of 2. Now start on the right and enclose the first three terms in parentheses, then the next three, and so on.

      a. Factor 2^3 from the second right three-term group, 2^6 from the next three-term group, 2^9 from the next, 2^{12} from the next.

      b. Write the factored powers of 2 as powers of 8 and write the sums in parentheses as single numbers.

      c. From part b write the octal number it represents.

6-29. Name the hex digits that will be in high-order position of a negative number when hex representation is used to represent a negative number in two's-complement binary.

6-30. The following scheme could be used to convert a decimal fraction to its equivalent in binary. For a given decimal fraction, repeatedly multiply the fraction by 2. The integers that are formed during multiplication are the digits of the binary equivalent. The first integer is the *leftmost digit* of the equivalent binary fraction. During the multiplications, the integer parts (if any) are not considered. We continue to multiply by 2 until the product becomes zero, or enough binary digits have been generated. For example, convert .6725 to a six-digit binary fraction.

> *solution:* $.6725 \times 2 = 1.3450$ integer 1
> $.3450 \times 2 = 0.6900$ 0
> $.6900 \times 2 = 1.3800$ 1
> $.3800 \times 2 = 0.7600$ 0
> $.7600 \times 2 = 1.5200$ 1
> $.5200 \times 2 = 1.0400$ 1

Thus $(0.6725)_{10} = (0.101011)_2$.

Convert to binary:

   a. 0.828125 to 6 bits
   b. 0.3623 to 6 bits
   c. 0.7055
   d. 0.6055
   e. 0.5555
   f. 0.3333

PART TWO

chapter seven

ELEMENTARY LOGIC AND SET THEORY

INTRODUCTION

Logic occupies a unique position in the academic spectrum: it is studied by mathematicians and philosophers for its abstract structure, and it is used by scientists and engineers because it conveniently describes complex situations, particularly in electronics. The logic of propositions, or propositional calculus, as it is sometimes called, is fundamentally concerned with logical relations between propositions.

7-1 PROPOSITIONS

A proposition, in the present context, is a statement that is either true or false. The only restriction placed on a proposition is that its truth or falsehood is unambiguous; in other words, it should never be necessary for two intelligent people to debate whether or not a given proposition is true. The statements

>   *It is raining*
>   *No cats can bark*

are examples of propositions. Notice that each has the binary property of being either true or false, and there is no doubt as to which quality applies. Contrast the examples above with the statement

>   *Ghosts weigh two pounds*

This may or may not be true, but there is much room for discussion on this point; so it does not qualify as a proposition. The truth or falsehood of a proposition is its *truth value*, and will be denoted T or F.

New propositions can be constructed from other propositions using logical connectives. The most common logical connectives are AND, OR, and NOT.

These will be denoted by $\wedge$, $\vee$, and $\sim$, respectively. The object of the present study is to see how the truth value of a proposition compounded from simpler propositions using a logical connective is related to the truth values of the simpler propositions.

To define a logical connective, its effect on the truth value of a compound proposition must be made explicit. Since, in the case of AND and OR, the compound proposition is constructed from two simpler propositions, each of which is true or false, there are four cases to consider. Truth tables are a means of concisely showing the relation of a compound proposition to its component propositions. The letters p, q, and r will be used as proposition names. With this convention the logical connective AND is defined by the truth table

p	q	$p \wedge q$
T	T	T
T	F	F
F	T	F
F	F	F

The four rows of this truth table summarize all the possible combinations of truth and falsehood for the propositions p and q. The third column shows the truth value of the compound proposition corresponding to the truth values of the component propositions in each row.

The logical connective OR is defined by the truth table

p	q	$p \vee q$
T	T	T
T	F	T
F	T	T
F	F	F

The difference between the logical connectives is readily seen from their truth tables. A compound proposition formed using AND is true only when both components are true; in the case of OR, only one component must be true in order to make the compound proposition true.

The logical connective NOT differs from AND and OR in the sense that NOT acts on one proposition. The truth table for NOT, then, has only two rows.

p	$\sim p$
T	F
F	T

7-2 TRUTH TABLES

Once the meanings of AND, OR, and NOT have been mastered, these connectives can be used to form longer and more complicated compound propositions.   The truth table of the "final" proposition is constructed using the definitions of the logical connectives and the truth tables of the component propositions.   Suppose, for example, the truth table of

$$(\sim p \vee q) \wedge (p \vee \sim q)$$

is to be found.   There are two ways to find its truth value.   The first way is to break it up into components, and then break the components until the propositional names are reached.   When this is done, the truth table of the original proposition is "built up" from the components.

p	q	$\sim p$	$\sim q$	$(\sim p \vee q)$	$(p \vee \sim q)$	$(\sim p \vee q) \wedge (p \vee \sim q)$
T	T	F	F	T	T	T
T	F	F	T	F	T	F
F	T	T	F	T	F	F
F	F	T	T	T	T	T

The second way is to write the original proposition (with wide spacing) and to insert the initial truth values under each proposition name, as is usually done in the first two columns of the truth table.

$(\sim p \vee q) \wedge (p \vee \sim q)$

T	T	T	T
T	F	T	F
F	T	F	T
F	F	F	F

Then, working out from the innermost parentheses, the truth tables of the results of each connective are written.

$(\sim \quad p \vee q) \wedge (p \vee \sim \quad q)$

F	T	T	T	F	T
F	T	F	T	T	F
T	F	T	F	F	T
T	F	F	F	T	F

$(\sim \; p \; \lor \; q)\land(p \; \lor \sim \; q)$

F	T	T	T	T	T	F	T
F	T	F	F	T	T	T	F
T	F	T	T	F	F	F	T
T	F	T	F	F	T	T	F

$(\sim \; p \; \lor \; q) \; \land \; (p \; \lor \sim \; q)$

F	T	T	T	T	T	T	F	T
F	T	F	F	F	T	T	T	F
T	F	T	T	F	F	F	F	T
T	F	T	F	T	F	T	T	F

Each method of finding the truth table has its advantages: the first method shows more clearly the effect of the connectives within the final proposition, while the second method requires less space. The space consideration becomes important when propositions containing three or more propositional variables are needed. In the example below, the second method is used on a proposition containing three variables. Notice that parentheses are used in exactly the same way as in algebra to indicate in which order the connectives operate. The connective NOT is used in much the same way as a minus sign in algebra—it affects the proposition immediately to its right.

$[(p \; \lor \sim \; q) \; \land \; r] \; \land \; [\sim \; (p \; \land \; q) \; \lor \sim \; r]$

T	T	F	T	T	T	F	F	T	T	T	F	F	T
T	T	F	T	F	F	F	F	F	T	T	T	T	F
T	T	T	F	T	T	T	T	T	F	F	T	F	T
T	T	T	F	F	F	F	T	T	F	F	T	T	F
F	F	F	T	F	T	F	T	F	F	T	T	F	T
F	F	F	T	F	F	F	T	F	F	T	T	T	F
F	T	T	F	T	T	T	T	F	F	F	T	F	T
F	T	T	F	F	F	F	T	F	F	F	T	T	F
1	3	2	1	4	1	6	4	1	3	1	5	2	1

The numbers below each column correspond to the stages in reaching the truth table of the whole expression.

Two other connectives are used often enough to warrant consideration here. Material implication, $\rightarrow$, and EXCLUSIVE OR, $\oplus$, are defined by the truth table

p	q	$p \rightarrow q$	$p \oplus q$
T	T	T	F
T	F	F	T
F	T	T	T
F	F	T	F

The proposition $p \rightarrow q$ is read "if p, then q," and $p \oplus q$ is "p exclusive or q." These connective are related to each other in a very important way. Consider the proposition $(p \rightarrow q) \wedge (q \rightarrow p)$. Its truth table is

p	q	$(p \rightarrow q)$	$\wedge$	$(q \rightarrow p)$
T	T	T	T	T
T	F	F	F	T
F	T	T	F	F
F	F	T	T	T

which is exactly the truth table of $\sim(p \oplus q)$. When two propositions have the same truth table, they are *logically equivalent*. Another pair of logically equivalent propositions is $\sim(p \vee q)$ and $(\sim p \wedge \sim q)$.

p	q	$\sim(p \vee q)$	$(\sim p \wedge \sim q)$
T	T	F	F
T	F	F	F
F	T	F	F
F	F	T	T

An easy way to see if two propositions are logically equivalent is to form their EXCLUSIVE-OR sum. If they are equivalent, their EXCLUSIVE-OR- sum truth table will be all F's.

$\sim(p \vee q)$	$\oplus$	$(\sim p \wedge \sim q)$
F	F	F
F	F	F
F	F	F
T	F	T

This relation of logical equivalence is written with the symbol $\equiv$. In the last example, $\sim(p \vee q) \equiv (\sim p \wedge \sim q)$ is one of DeMorgan's laws, a topic considered in Chap. 8. As an exercise, show that DeMorgan's second law is valid:

$$\sim(p \wedge q) \equiv (\sim p \vee \sim q)$$

In Chap. 8 this notion of equivalence will be discussed more thoroughly in terms of Boolean algebra.

DeMorgan's laws make it possible to express AND and OR in terms of each other and the connective NOT. In this sense, AND and OR are redundant; that is, any proposition that can be formed using AND, OR, and NOT has a logically equivalent proposition either in terms of AND and NOT or in terms of OR and NOT. For example, $(p \wedge q) \vee r$ can be expressed as

$$(p \wedge q) \vee r \equiv \sim(\sim(p \wedge q) \wedge \sim r)$$
$$(p \wedge q) \vee r \equiv [\sim(\sim p \vee \sim q) \vee r]$$

The equivalent expressions are so much more cumbersome that it is easier to use all three connectives. The importance of this is that all logical connectives can be expressed in terms of AND and NOT or OR and NOT.

7-3 AN APPLICATION OF TRUTH TABLES

Truth tables can be used to check the validity of syllogistic inferences, a very exact form of inference in logic. Our purpose here is not to develop all the characteristics of valid syllogisms. We will show a way to check a variety of syllogisms to see if they are valid.

A syllogism consists of three statements: a major premise, a minor premise, and a conclusion. The two premises are assumptions, and in a valid syllogism, true premises force the truth of the conclusion. One useful type of syllogism is the hypothetical syllogism. The syllogism below is an example of this type:

Major premise: *If I step on the brake, my car will stop.*
Minor premise: *I step on the brake.*
Conclusion: *Therefore the car will stop.*

This example is a valid hypothetical syllogism. If we accept the premises as true statements, then we are forced to accept the conclusion as a true statement. The conclusion is inferred from the premises, and the whole syllogism can be considered as a rule of inference.

The validity of any syllogistic inference depends only on the form of the premises and conclusion, and is independent of their meanings. The form of the hypothetical syllogism above is

$$P \rightarrow Q$$
$$\underline{P}$$
$$\therefore Q$$

(The $\therefore$ notation is an abbreviation for "therefore.")

We will give an example of an invalid hypothetical syllogism, and then present the truth-table method of determining validity. The syllogism

If I study diligently, I will pass my course
I passed my course
Therefore I studied diligently

is invalid. The general form of this syllogism is

$$P \rightarrow Q$$
$$\underline{Q}$$
$$\therefore P$$

To test for validity of a syllogism, we construct the truth table of the premises and conclusion.

P	Q	$P \rightarrow Q$	
T	T	T	$\leftarrow 1$
T	F	F	
F	T	T	
F	F	T	

Since we assume that the premises are true, we examine only those rows of the truth table in which both premises are true. For the syllogism

$$1 \quad P \rightarrow Q$$
$$\underline{P}$$
$$\therefore Q$$

we are concerned only with the first row of the truth table, because this is the only row in which both premises are true. The conclusion Q is also true in this row. If a syllogism is valid, the conclusion must be true in every row in which both premises are true. This is the case for our first example; so the truth-table method guarantees that the syllogism is valid.

If we apply this test to the second example,

$$P \rightarrow Q$$
$$\underline{Q}$$
$$\therefore P$$

we examine the first and third rows of the truth table, because these are the rows in which both premises are true. When we look at the truth value of P in these rows, we see that P is true in the first row and false in the third row. *Since P is not true in every case that both premises are true, the interference is invalid.* We conclude this section with a table that shows the validity or invalidity of several common syllogism forms.

Hypothetical Syllogism

					P	Q	$\sim P$	$\sim Q$	$P \to Q$	
2	$P \to Q$									
	$\sim Q$				T	T	F	F	T	
	$\therefore \sim P$	(valid)			T	F	F	T	F	
3	$P \to Q$				F	T	T	F	T	←3
	$\sim P$				F	F	T	T	T	←2,3
	$\therefore \sim Q$	(invalid)								

Alternative Syllogism

					P	Q	$\sim P$	$\sim Q$	$P \vee Q$	
4	$P \vee Q$									
	$\sim P$				T	T	F	F	T	←5
	$\therefore Q$	(valid)			T	F	F	T	T	←5
5	$P \vee Q$				F	T	T	F	T	←4
	P				F	F	T	T	F	
	$\therefore \sim Q$	(invalid)								

Exclusive-or Syllogism

					P	Q	$\sim P$	$\sim Q$	$P \oplus Q$	
6	$P \oplus Q$									
	$\sim P$				T	T	F	F	F	
	$\therefore Q$	(valid)			T	F	F	T	T	←7
7	$P \oplus Q$				F	T	T	F	T	←6
	P				F	F	T	T	F	
	$\therefore \sim Q$	(valid)								

7-4 SETS

Set theory, like the logic of propositions, is a useful device for describing abstract situations. Because of this flexibility, care must be taken in defining a set, or else the definition could impede the application of set theory. Rather than give an explicit definition which may prove too limited in an unforeseen application, we will just reach an agreement on the notion of what a set is. A set is a collection of objects, or in different terms, a bunch of things. The objects of which the set is a collection are called *members*, or *elements*, of the set.   Many collective nouns tacitly describe sets, for example, team, herd, band, and class.   The only restriction placed on the notion of a set is that, once a set is specified, it must be possible to positively identify the members of that set.

The Membership Relation

A set may be specified in two ways: All elements of the set can be listed, or a rule may be given such that membership in the set is completely determined by the rule.   When a set is specified in the second way, the notation

$$A = \{x : p(x)\}$$

is used.   This is read "A is the set of all x such that $p(x)$," where $p(x)$ is a rule or proposition involving x.   As an example, consider the set

$$A = \{x : x \text{ is a whole number between } \tfrac{1}{2} \text{ and } 9\tfrac{1}{2}\}$$

This set could be specified by listing its elements.

$$A = \{1,2,3,4,5,6,7,8,9\}$$

Capital letters are commonly used as names for sets.   When a set is specified with a rule, the rule must be phrased in an unambiguous way.

Using the set $A = \{1,2,3,4,5,6,7,8,9\}$, what is the relationship between any of the numbers 1 to 9 and the set A?   Each of these numbers is said to be in the *membership relation* with the set A.   The membership relation is denoted by the lowercase Greek letter ϵ.   To express the fact that the number 4 is in the membership relation with the set A, we write

$$4 \epsilon A$$

$4 \epsilon A$ is read "Four is an element (a member) of A."   Now consider a set consisting of exactly one element.

$$B = \{5\}$$

Notice the difference between B and 5. B is a set, while 5 is a number, and further, $5 \epsilon B$.

The Empty Set

The rule that specifies the members of a set can be in the form of a logical proposition involving the variable x.   In this situation, the set consists of those values of x that give the proposition the truth value T.   The set determined by the rule (which is also a proposition)

$$x = 3$$

is the set

$$A = \{x : x = 3\} = \{3\}$$

Now suppose a set is defined by a rule that is never true, such as $(x < 1) \wedge (x > 3)$.

$$B = \{x : (x < 1) \wedge (x > 3)\}$$

Since there is no value of x that will make the proposition true, there can be no elements in the set B. This situation is unavoidable and, in some cases, useful; so it must be considered. The set defined by a (universally) false rule is called the *empty set*, and is denoted $\emptyset$.

The Subset Relation

There are many times when two sets are under consideration where all the members of one set are also members of the other set. The set A is said to be a *subset* of the set B if every element of A is an element of B. This subset relationship is written $A \subset B$. The starting five basketball players are a subset of the set consisting of all the members of their basketball team. A statement about subsets that is always true is, for any set A,

$$\emptyset \subset A$$

A moment's reflection on the empty set and the definition of the subset relation shows this to be the case. Since there are no elements in the empty set, all of them are members of A.

7-5 OPERATIONS ON SETS

There are three basic set operations that correspond in a unique way to the logical connectives AND, OR, and NOT. This correspondence is the closing topic of the chapter. The three set-theory operations and their notations are union, $\cup$; intersection, $\cap$; and complementation, $'$. Given two sets A and B, their *union* is the set consisting of all the elements either in A or in B.

$$A \cup B = \{x : x \in A \text{ or } x \in B\}$$

The *intersection* of A and B is the set that consists of all elements of A that are also elements of B.

$$A \cap B = \{x : x \in A \text{ and } x \in B\}$$

Let A and B be the sets

$$A = \{1,2,3,4,5,6\}$$
$$B = \{4,5,6,7,8,9\}$$

The union and intersection of A and B are

$$A \cup B = \{1,2,3,4,5,6,7,8,9\}$$
$$A \cap B = \{4,5,6\}$$

The complement of a set A is the set of all objects that are not elements of A. To indicate this nonmembership relation, we write

$$x \notin A$$

This is read "x is not a member (an element) of A." Given a set A, its complement A' is

$$A' = \{x : x \notin A\}$$

The negative aspect of the complement introduces a fairly serious problem, namely, what are the elements in the complement of a set? The easiest answer is negative itself: the elements of A' are all those objects (or entities) that are not members of the set A. The problem is that A' now has a magnitude difficult to comprehend. It is clearly impossible to list all the elements of the complement of a set. If A is the set,

$$A = \{1,2,3\}$$

then A' includes, among many other things, 0,4,5, cabbages, and kings. The only way to describe A' is to negate the rule that describes A. In other words, if A is defined by the proposition $p(x)$,

$$A = \{x : p(x)\}$$

then A' is described by the negation of p:

$$A' = \{x : \sim p(x)\}$$

Another way to resolve this problem is to work within a specific universe. If the sets under consideration are all sets whose elements are numbers, cabbages and kings are entirely irrelevant to the discussion, and hence would not even be in the universe of objects under consideration. This universe is sometimes called the *universe of discourse*. If the sets are all sets of numbers, a wise choice of universe of discourse is the set of all numbers. If this choice is made, then the complement of the set

$$A = \{1,2,3\}$$

(with respect to the universe of all numbers) is the set

$$A' = \{x : x \text{ is a number and } x \neq 1,\ x \neq 2,\ x \neq 3\}$$

7-6 VENN DIAGRAMS

Venn diagrams are a useful device by which set operations can be graphically represented. Their use in set theory is, roughly, the same as the use of truth tables in the logic of propositions. In a Venn diagram, a set is represented by a circle, and the elements of the set correspond to points inside the circle.

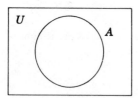

The universe of discourse is usually represented by a rectangle. The subset relation is portrayed by one set being entirely within (or contained in) another set.

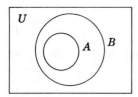

To indicate unions, intersections, and complements, shading is used. In the Venn diagrams below, the union and intersection of the sets A and B and the complement of A are shaded.

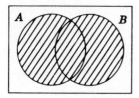 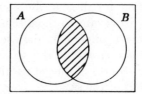 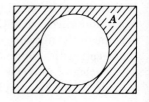

When a Venn diagram of two or more sets is made, the circles corresponding to the sets should overlap. This allows intersections to be represented.

As an example of the use of Venn diagrams, we shall give the representations of one of DeMorgan's laws for set theory:

$$(A \cup B)' = (A' \cap B')$$

Notice that the area corresponding to $(A \cup B)'$ is the same as the area corresponding to $(A' \cap B')$.

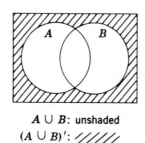

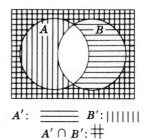

$A \cup B$: unshaded

$(A \cup B)'$: //////

A': ═══ B': ||||||

$A' \cap B'$: #

Since Venn diagrams can be used to show equality of sets, the meaning of set equality should be made clear. Two sets A and B are said to be equal if they contain exactly the same elements. Every element of A must be an element of B, and conversely, every element of B must be an element of A. If every element of A is also an element of B, then A is a subset of B. This leads to a more useful definition of set equality:

Given two sets A and B, $A = B$ if and only if $A \subset B$ and $B \subset A$.

Using this definition, if two sets are to be shown equal, it is sufficient to show that each is a subset of the other. This is done in the example below for the sets in DeMorgan's law $(A \cup B)' = (A' \cap B')$.

Example

Show that $(A \cup B)' = (A' \cap B')$.

Let $C = (A \cup B)'$ and $D = (A' \cap B')$. Using the second definition of set equality, we must show that $C \subset D$ and $D \subset C$. Suppose that x is any element of C. Since C is the complement of $A \cup B$, $x \notin A$ and $x \notin B$. If $x \notin A$, then $x \in A'$ and similarly, $x \in B'$. By definition of set intersection, $x \in (A' \cap B')$. Since x is an arbitrary element of C, the above argument could be repeated for every element of C; so we have proved $C \subset D$.

Now let y be any element in $D = (A' \cap B')$. Since D is the intersection of the complements of A and B, $y \in A'$ and $y \in B'$. This means that y is neither an element of A nor an element of B, or in other words, $y \notin (A \cup B)$. But this is precisely the same as $y \in (A \cup B)'$; so we have shown $D \subset C$.

Now, since $C \subset D$ and $D \subset C$, we can say

$$C = D$$

or

$$(A \cup B)' = (A' \cap B')$$

This argument is much more detailed than the Venn-diagram argument. The reason for this is that the above argument is a mathematical proof of set equality, where the Venn diagram is merely a graphic illustration. Often a Venn diagram will indicate what must be done in a mathematical proof, but the diagram itself is not a proof.

7-7 AN APPLICATION OF SET THEORY

One extremely useful application of set theory depends on the notion of a partition. Two sets A and B are disjoint if $A \cap B = \emptyset$. Given a universe U, the sets $A_1, A_2, \ldots , A_n$ form a partition of U if

$$U = (A_1 \cup A_2) \cup A_3 \cdots \cup A_n$$

and $A_1, A_2, \ldots , A_n$ are all disjoint. A Venn diagram of a partition might look like the map of a country. In fact, the 48 states and the District of Columbia form a partition of the continental United States (see Fig. 7-1).

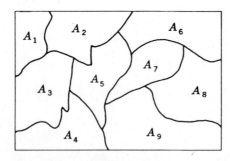

Fig. 7-1   A partition.

We will be more concerned with partitions of a given universe that consist of exactly two disjoint sets. In particular, consider the situation in which there are several two-set partitions of a given universe.

$$U = A_1 \cup A_2 \qquad A_1 \cap A_2 = \emptyset$$
$$U = B_1 \cup B_2 \qquad B_1 \cap B_2 = \emptyset$$
$$U = C_1 \cup C_2 \qquad C_1 \cap C_2 = \emptyset$$
$$U = D_1 \cup D_2 \qquad D_1 \cap D_2 = \emptyset$$

Sets belonging to different partitions are not necessarily disjoint. A Venn diagram for the four above partitions is shown in Fig. 7-2.

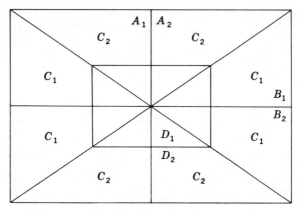

Fig. 7-2

This is a composite of the four partitions shown in Fig. 7-3.

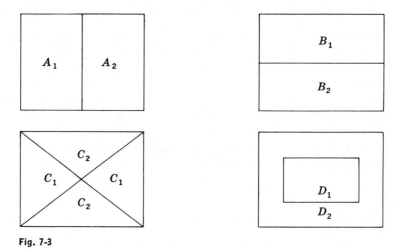

Fig. 7-3

In real-life situations that can be described by several partitions of the same universe, the disjointness of the sets in the partitions can be used for classification and identification purposes. An example of this can be seen in the problem confronting a microbiologist. Given a culture containing an unknown organism, a microbiologist applies a sequence of tests to the sample in order to identify it. These tests can be considered to be the defining rules for sets in various partitions. The universe, in this example, is the set of all bacteria and viruses.   The outcome of each test places the unknown organism into one (the outcome set) of the two disjoint sets corresponding to the test. When several tests are made, the organism must be a member of each outcome set; hence it is in the intersection of these sets.

Perhaps a better example of this can be seen in the categories an insurance company might apply to its policyholders.   If the universe of discourse is taken to be the set of all policyholders of the company, the following categories might be defined:

A = males	A' = females
B = single policyholders	B' = married policyholders
C = under 25	C' = over 25
D = teetotalers	D' = drinkers

Suppose John X is a policyholder, and he is twenty-six, single, and a teetotaler. Then he is in the set $A \cap B \cap C' \cap D$.   This set describes John's insurance category, and would be useful in various computer-oriented information studies. This example will be referred to again as an example of Boolean algebra.

7-8 TRUTH SETS—THE CONNECTION BETWEEN SET THEORY AND LOGIC

If p and q are propositions containing a variable term x, the universe of logical possibilities of p and q will be a set that contains all the values of x for which p is true, all for which p is false, all the values of x that make q true, and all for which q is false.   By choosing the universe of discourse to be the set of logical possibilities of logical propositions, a vehicle to show the connection between set theory and logic is established.   To this end, let U be the set of logical possibilities of the propositions p and q.

The truth set of a proposition is the set of logical possibilities for which the proposition is true.   The truth set of p is easily defined.

$$P = \{x : p(x) \text{ is true}\}$$

Similarly, the truth set of q is

$$Q = \{x : q(x) \text{ is true}\}$$

Early in the discussions of set theory and logic, it was pointed out that each has a binary property: propositions are either true or false, and a given object either is or is not an element of a given set.   Notice that, in truth sets, these binary roles are superimposed on each other.   For a given value of x, p is either true or false.   If $p(x)$ is true, then $x \in P$; if $p(x)$ is false, $x \notin P$.   Since $p(x)$ is either true or false, either $x \in P$ or $x \notin P$—the nonambiguity of logic and set theory connect here.   In Venn diagram form, the truth sets P and Q of the

propositions p and q are

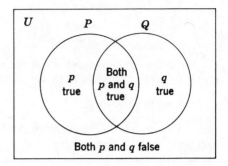

The logical connectives AND, OR, and NOT have the set-theory operations of intersection, union, and complement as exact analogs. Rather than write "$p(x)$ is true," we shall consider p to have the same meaning, with the understanding that p is a proposition having x as a variable term.

With this convention,

$$P = \{x:p\}$$
$$Q = \{x:q\}$$

Now consider the sets defined by the propositions $p \wedge q$, $p \vee q$, and $\sim p$:

$$A = \{x:p \wedge q\}$$
$$B = \{x:p \vee q\}$$
$$C = \{x:\sim p\}$$

If $x \in A$, then, by definition of the connective AND, p is true and q is true. If $p(x)$ is true, then $x \in P$; similarly, $x \in Q$; hence $x \in P \cap Q$. The set A, then, is exactly $P \cap Q$. If $x \in B$, then the proposition $p \vee q$ is true. Since it is necessary for only one of p,q to be true to make $p \vee q$ true, all we can say is that either p is true or q is true; hence either $x \in P$ or $x \in Q$. This is precisely $x \in P \cup Q$. Thus $B = P \cup Q$. Finally, if $x \in C$, then $\sim p$ is true; so p is false, and $x \notin P$. But $x \notin P$ implies that $x \in P'$; so $C = P'$. The relation between set-theory operations and logical connectives, using P and Q as truth sets of the propositions p,q, is summarized:

$$P \cap Q = \{x:p \wedge q\}$$
$$P \cup Q = \{x:p \vee q\}$$
$$P' = \{x:\sim p\}$$

A natural question to ask is whether or not logically equivalent propositions have the same truth set. The answer is yes, they do; and this has been shown for the examples referring to DeMorgan's law.

$$\sim(p \lor q) \equiv (\sim p \land \sim q)$$
$$(P \cup Q)' = (P' \cap Q')$$
$$(P \cup Q)' = \{x : \sim(p \lor q)\}$$
$$P' \cap Q' = \{x : \sim p \land \sim q\}$$

Finally, one may ask what the significance of the empty set is in relation to truth sets. To answer this, consider the truth set

$$A = \{x : p \land \sim p\}$$

By definition of the connective AND, there is no value of x that will make $p \land \sim p$ true. A proposition that is never true has as its truth set the empty set ϕ. By the same token, a proposition that is always true, such as $p \lor \sim p$, has the whole universe as its truth set.

$$A = \{x : p \land \sim p\} = P \cap P' = \phi$$
$$B = \{x : p \lor \sim p\} = P \cup P' = U$$

7-9 AN EXAMPLE OF TRUTH SETS

Let p and q be the propositions about integers

$$p : x \leq 3$$
$$q : x < 6$$

and take as a universe of discourse the set

$$U = \{0,1,2,3,4,5,6,7,8,9\}$$

The truth set of the proposition p is the set P that consists of all those elements in the universe for which the proposition p is true. Here the truth set of p is

$$P = \{x : x \leq 3\} = \{0,1,2,3\}$$

Similarly, the truth set of q is the set

$$Q = \{x : x < 6\} = \{0,1,2,3,4,5\}$$

We can use this example to illustrate truth sets of compound statements. For example, the truth set of the proposition $p \land q$ is the set

$$P \cap Q = \{x : x \leq 3 \land x < 6\} = \{0,1,2,3\}$$

The truth set of $\sim p$ is the set

$$P' = \{x : x > 3\} = \{4,5,6,7,8,9\}$$

where $x > 3$ is the negation of $x \leq 3$.

We shall conclude our discussion of set theory and the logic of propositions with an interesting relationship between the two systems. The reader may have noticed that, for the propositions p and q in this example, their truth sets satisfy

$$P \subset Q$$

Looking closely at the propositions, we see that every value of x that makes p true also makes q true. In other words, the truth of p implies the truth of q. We shall see how this relates to the material implication connective $\rightarrow$. The truth table of the proposition $p \rightarrow q$ is

p	q	$p \rightarrow q$
T	T	T
T	F	F
F	T	T
F	F	T

We now wish to find the truth set of $p \rightarrow q$. Since logically equivalent propositions have identical truth sets, we will find the truth set of $\sim p \vee q$.

p	q	$p \rightarrow q$	$\sim p \vee q$
T	T	T	T
T	F	F	F
F	T	T	T
F	F	T	T

The truth set of $\sim p$ is P', and the truth set of q is Q; so the truth set of $\sim p \vee q$ (and $p \rightarrow q$!) is $P' \cup Q$. For the propositions p and q in this example, this truth set is

$$P' \cup Q = \{0,1,2,3,4,5,6,7,8,9\} = U$$

We said before that the truth set of a statement that is always true is the whole universe; so we can see that, for the p and q in this example, $p \rightarrow q$ is always true.

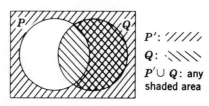

P': /////
Q: \\\\\
$P' \cup Q$: any shaded area

By looking at the Venn diagram for $P' \cup Q$, we can arrive at a very simple criterion for determining whether an implication is *logically true* (truth set $= U$). The unshaded region is the set $P - Q$ that is defined in Exercise 7-8. Since $P' \cup Q = U$ in this example, we know that $P - Q = \emptyset$. Here, at last, is a definite use for the empty set. Given two propositions p and q, if the set $P - Q = \emptyset$, then $p \rightarrow q$ is logically true. If $P - Q = \emptyset$, then $P \subset Q$. An easy way to determine whether or not a proposition p implies a proposition q is to find the truth sets P and Q. If $P \subset Q$, then $p \rightarrow q$ is logically true, and p implies q.

EXERCISES

7-1.   Let p, q, and r be the propositions

    p: professors are absent-minded.
    q: students are lazy.
    r: librarians dislike noise.

State in sentences the following compound propositions:

a.	$p \wedge q$	d.	$(\sim q \vee \sim p) \wedge \sim r$
b.	$(p \vee q) \wedge r$	e.	$r \wedge \sim q$
c.	$(\sim p \vee r) \vee \sim q$	f.	$\sim p \wedge (\sim q \wedge r)$

7-2.   Define your own propositions, and then write the compound proposition that corresponds to each sentence.

   a.   Either boating is a safe sport or many people are foolish.
   b.   It is not true that either boating is a safe sport or many people are foolish.
   c.   October is neither too hot nor too cold.
   d.   Either October is neither too hot nor too cold or Indian summer is late.

7-3.   Make truth tables for the propositions

a.	$p \wedge (q \wedge r)$	d.	$\sim p \vee (\sim q \wedge r)$
b.	$p \wedge (q \vee r)$	e.	$\sim q \vee (\sim p \wedge r)$
c.	$p \wedge \sim (q \vee r)$	f.	$(p \vee \sim p) \wedge (q \wedge \sim q)$

7-4.   Let p, q, and r be the propositions

    p: I study the material for my course.
    q: I understand the material for my course.
    r: I (will) pass my course.

State in words the following propositions:

a. $p \rightarrow q$ d. $\sim q \rightarrow \sim r$
b. $\sim q \rightarrow \sim p$ e. $q \oplus \sim r$
c. $q \rightarrow r$ f. $(q \rightarrow r) \oplus (\sim q \rightarrow \sim r)$

7-5.   Define p, q, and r to be propositions referring to stepping on the accelerator of a car, stepping on the brakes of a car, and stopping a car; then
write the sentences below as compound propositions.

   a.   If I step on the accelerator, then I do not stop the car.
   b.   If I step on the brake, I stop the car.
   c.   I stop the car only if I step on the brake.
   d.   Either I step on the accelerator or on the brake, but not both
        simultaneously.
   e.   If I step on the brake, then I do not step on the accelerator.
   f.   If I step on the accelerator, then I do not step on the brake.
   g.   It is not true that if I do not step on the brake, then I do
        step on the accelerator.   Similarly, (and) it is false to assume
        that if I do not step on the accelerator, then I do step on the
        brake.

7-6.   List the elements of the sets defined below:

   $N = \{x : x$ is a natural number$\}$

   a. $A = \{x : (x \in N) \wedge (1 < x < 9)\}$
   b. $B = \{x : (x \in N) \wedge x$ is even$\}$
   c. $C = \{x : (x \in A) \vee (x \epsilon B)\}$
   d. $D = \{x : (x \in A) \wedge (x \epsilon B)\}$

7-7.   Find simple rules to define the sets listed below.

   a. $A = \{1,4,9,16,25\}$
   b. $B = \{1,3,5,7,9\}$
   c. $C = \{1,2,3,5,7,11,13,17,19\}$
   d. $D = \{1,8,27,64,125\}$
   e. $E = \emptyset$

7-8.   The complement A' of a set A is defined by $A' = \{x : x \notin A\}$.   We saw
that this definition makes comprehension of the members of A' quite
difficult.   One way to avoid this difficulty is by means of *relative complements*.   Given two sets A and B, where $A \subset B$, the relative complement
of A in B is $B - A = \{x : (x \notin A) \wedge (x \in B)\}$.

   a.   For $B = \{1,2,3,4,5,6,7,8,9\}$ and $A = \{2,4,6,8\}$, list the ele-
        ments of $B - A$.

     b.   Make a Venn diagram of $B - A$.

     c.   Show that $B - A = B \cap A'$ either with a proof (see p. 241) or with a Venn diagram.

     d.   Is it true that $B - A = A - B$?

7-9.   We can define another set operation in terms of relative complement. Given two sets A and B, the *symmetric difference* of A and B is defined

$$A + B = (A - B) \cup (B - A)$$

     a.   Make a Venn diagram of $A + B$.

     b.   Suppose $A = B$. Describe the sets $B - A$, $A + B$.

     c.   Show that $A + B = B + A$.

7-10.   By defining $A + B$ in terms of the membership relation ϵ, rather than in terms of set operations $-, \cup$, you will get more insight into the meaning of symmetric difference. Once you have done this, what logical connective relating propositions p and q has $P + Q$ as its truth set?

7-11.   There is a set operation that has a very important geometric meaning. The *cartesian product of sets A and B* is the set

$$A \times B = \{\langle a,b \rangle : (a \,\epsilon\, A) \wedge (b \,\epsilon\, B)\}$$

where $\langle a,b \rangle$ is an ordered pair of numbers. If $A = \{1,2\}$ and $B = \{0,1,2\}$, then

$$A \times B = \{\langle 1,0 \rangle, \langle 1,1 \rangle, \langle 1,2 \rangle, \langle 2,0 \rangle, \langle 2,1 \rangle, \langle 2,2 \rangle\}$$

By taking A and B to be sets of points on the x and y axes of the cartesian coordinate plane, $A \times B$ is then a grid of points in the plane.

     a.   Find and draw the grid $A \times B$ for

$$A = \{0,1,2,3\} \quad \text{and} \quad B = \{1,2,3,4\}$$

         Let A correspond to points on the x axis and B correspond to points on the y axis.

     b.   Let A and B be sets, each consisting of all the real numbers, and let A correspond to the x axis, B to the y axis. Describe $A \times B$.

     c.   Let R be the set of real numbers, and

$$A = \{x : (x \,\epsilon\, R) \wedge (0 \leq x \leq 1)\}$$
$$B = \{y : (y \,\epsilon\, R) \wedge (-1 \leq y \leq 1)\}$$

         Describe and sketch $A \times B$.

7-12. In Chap. 3 we considered the graphs of various equations. By using sets consisting of ordered pairs of real numbers, we can define sets (of points) that correspond to the graphs of equations.

    a. Describe the sets

$$A = \{\langle x,y\rangle : 2y - x = 3\}$$
$$B = \{\langle x,y\rangle : y + 2x = 9\}$$

    b. What is the significance of $A \cap B$, where A and B are the sets described above?

7-13. List as many parallel features of set theory and logic as you can. One such pair is the logical connective $\wedge$ and the set operation $\cap$; another is that, in logic, each connective can be defined in terms of $\wedge$, $\vee$, and $\sim$, and in set theory each set operation can be defined in terms of $\cap$, $\cup$, and $'$.

7-14. Find truth tables for the propositions

$$p \vee \sim q, \ q \to p, \ (p \to q) \wedge (\sim q \to \sim p), \ (p \wedge \sim q) \vee (\sim p \wedge q)$$

Are there any pairs of logical equivalents?

7-15. For $A = \{1,2,3,4,5,7,9,11\}$, $B = \{1,3,5,6,7,8,9,10\}$, list the elements of the sets

$$A \cup B, \ A \cap B, \ A - B, \ B - A, \ A + B$$

7-16. Make Venn diagrams of the sets $B - A$ and $B \cap A'$. Are they the same set?

7-17. If $A \subset B$, describe the sets $A \cap B$, $A \cup B$, $A' \cap B'$, $A - B$. Use Venn diagrams.

7-18. Let p and q be the propositions

$$p : x > 6$$
$$q : x > 4$$

and let $U = \{0,1,2,3,4,5,6,7,8,9\}$ be the universe of discourse. List the elements in the truth sets of the propositions below.

    a. p b. $p \wedge q$ c. q
    d. $\sim p \vee q$ e. $p \to q$

7-19. Let P and Q be the truth sets of the propositions p and q from Exercise 7-18. Describe the set $P - Q$. From the nature of $P - Q$, what can you say about the proposition $p \to q$?

chapter eight

BOOLEAN ALGEBRA

INTRODUCTION

In the late 1800s, George Boole, an English mathematician, became fascinated by the algebraic nature of logic. In an effort to express logic mathematically, he wrote "An Investigation of the Laws of Thought." In his book, Boole treated logical propositions as algebraic variables, and developed an algebra of logic. This algebra is now known as Boolean algebra, and has applications not only in logic, but also in computer programming and in computer design, particularly switching circuits. It is also possible to express binary arithmetic in terms of Boolean algebra. These applications will be considered after a fairly thorough discussion of the rich structure of Boolean algebra.

8-1 BOOLEAN VARIABLES

In ordinary algebra, variables are abstract entities that have numerical values. Boolean variables are quite similar to algebraic variables, except that Boolean variables are two-valued. It is this binary property of Boolean variables that allows Boolean algebra to be easily applied to logic, switching circuits, and computer instructions. Each of these fields has a binary nature: logic propositions are either true or false; switches are either open or closed; signals are either present or absent; bits are either on or off. If an area of study has such a binary property—two mutually exclusive alternatives—it can probably be represented by Boolean algebra.

The two values a Boolean variable can have will be called 0 and 1. At this time it is important to distinguish between the Boolean constants 0 and 1 and the numbers 0 and 1. No numeric connotations are intended in the Boolean constants 0 and 1; they merely represent two distinct states. When the value of a Boolean variable is unknown, the variable will be represented by

one of the capital letters A, B, C, D.   In cases where more than four variables
are needed, subscripts will be used.

One final convention must be established.   It will be necessary to consider Boolean variables that always have the same value.   In this case, since
it is no longer "variable," it will be denoted either by a 0 or a 1.   This seems
confusing, because 0 and 1 are the two values that a Boolean variable can
have, but this confusion is rectified by saying that if a Boolean variable always
has the value 1, this is shown by naming it 1.   Similarly, if a Boolean variable
always has the value 0, it may as well be called 0.   The multiple meanings of
0 and 1 will be less confusing later, because it will always be easy to see which
meaning is intended.

8-2 BOOLEAN OPERATIONS

Ordinary algebra has two primary operations, addition and multiplication.
Subtraction and division are, essentially, the inverse operations of addition and
multiplication.   In ordinary algebra, the meaning of addition and multiplication is made clear by showing their effect on numbers.   This is usually done in
grade school with the rote-memory addition and multiplication tables.

Boolean algebra has additive and multiplicative operations and, also, a
third operation, which might be called opposition.   As with the Boolean constants 0 and 1, great care must be taken so that the addition and multiplication
of Boolean algebra are not confused with ordinary addition and multiplication.
Boolean addition will be symbolized by $+$, and Boolean multiplication by $\cdot$;
the third Boolean operation, complementation, will be symbolized by $'$.   Since
there are only two values in Boolean algebra, these operations are easy to
define.   The operation tables for the Boolean operations $+$, $\cdot$, and $'$ are

$+$	0	1		$\cdot$	0	1		$'$	0	1
0	0	1		0	0	0			1	0
1	1	1		1	0	1				

$$0 + 0 = 0 \qquad 0 \cdot 0 = 0 \qquad 0' = 1$$
$$0 + 1 = 1 \qquad 0 \cdot 1 = 0 \qquad 1' = 0$$
$$1 + 0 = 1 \qquad 1 \cdot 0 = 0$$
$$1 + 1 = 1 \qquad 1 \cdot 1 = 1$$

These operations look very much like binary arithmetic, and indeed there
is a very important connection, which will be discussed later in this chapter.
At the present time, however, these tables should be understood as definitions,
and entirely devoid of any external meaning.   This is particularly true of the
Boolean sum of 1 and 1.   In the addition table, the sum is defined

$$1 + 1 = 1$$

This certainly does not correspond to ordinary addition, but there is no need for a correspondence. The Boolean equation

$$1 + 1 = 1$$

is merely the definition of the result of combining the Boolean variable 1 with itself using Boolean addition.

From now on, it will be more convenient to write Boolean operation tables in a slightly different form. Thus the Boolean operations of $+$, $\cdot$, and $'$, along with Boolean variables, are

A	B	$A + B$	A	B	$A \cdot B$	A	A'
0	0	0	0	0	0	0	1
0	1	1	0	1	0	1	0
1	0	1	1	0	0		
1	1	1	1	1	1		

8-3 ALGEBRAIC PROPERTIES OF BOOLEAN OPERATIONS

The Boolean operations of addition, multiplication, and complementation allow the development of Boolean expressions. Just as in ordinary algebra, it is possible for two different Boolean expressions to have the same meaning. For example, in algebra, the equation

$$(x + y)^2 = x^2 + 2xy + y^2$$

is true for all values of x and y. When an equation is true for all values of the variables in the equation, it is called an identity. In Boolean algebra this identity relation is called equivalence, a topic which will be discussed shortly.

The Boolean operations, when considered as operating on Boolean variables, exhibit certain algebraic properties. These properties are listed below as (Boolean) algebraic laws. In these laws, A, B, and C are Boolean variables whose values are not known, and 0 and 1 are Boolean constants.

1. Laws of commutativity: $A + B \equiv B + A$
    $$A \cdot B \equiv B \cdot A$$
2. Laws of associativity: $A + (B + C) \equiv (A + B) + C$
    $$A \cdot (B \cdot C) \equiv (A \cdot B) \cdot C$$
3. Laws of distribution: $A \cdot (B + C) \equiv (A \cdot B) + (A \cdot C)$
    $$A + (B \cdot C) \equiv (A + B) \cdot (A + C)$$
4. Laws of identity: $A + 0 \equiv A \qquad A + 1 \equiv 1$
    $$A \cdot 1 \equiv A \qquad A \cdot 0 \equiv 0$$
5. Laws of idempotency: $A + A \equiv A$
    $$A \cdot A \equiv A$$

6. Laws of complementation: $A + A' \equiv 1$
$$A \cdot A' \equiv 0$$
7. DeMorgan's laws: $(A + B)' \equiv A' \cdot B'$
$$(A \cdot B)' \equiv A' + B'$$
8. Laws of absorption: $A + (A \cdot B) \equiv A \qquad A + (A' \cdot B) \equiv A + B$
$$A \cdot (A + B) \equiv A \qquad A \cdot (A' + B) \equiv A \cdot B$$
9. Law of involution: $(A')' \equiv A$

The careful reader will have noticed a symmetry in the pairing of these laws. This symmetry is the *principle of Boolean duality*. In any Boolean identity, if the replacements are made:

$+$ replaces $\cdot$
$\cdot$ replaces $+$
0 replaces 1
1 replaces 0

the dual of the original identity is formed. The pairs of equations in each law are duals. Given any Boolean identity, then its dual is also an identity. Here is one place where Boolean algebra has a richer structure than ordinary algebra: Boolean algebra has two distributive laws, and Boolean algebra has a duality principle. These features will allow the manipulation of Boolean expressions to be much more flexible.

8-4 ALGEBRAIC SIMPLIFICATION OF BOOLEAN EXPRESSIONS

Boolean expressions are constructed from Boolean variables and operations in much the same way that algebraic expressions are made up from algebraic variables and operations. This is particularly true with respect to the use of parentheses as grouping symbols. As an example, one Boolean expression is

$$(A + (B \cdot C)')$$

A verbal description of this expression is: *the (Boolean) sum of A and the complement of the (Boolean) product of B and C.* The grouping symbols show that first the product

$$B \cdot C$$

is formed; next it is complemented:

$$(B \cdot C)'$$

and then the sum of that result and A is taken:

$$(A + (B \cdot C)')$$

In algebra, the product is often indicated by writing the two multiplicands adjacent to each other and omitting the multiplication sign. This can be, and often is, done in Boolean algebra. When this is done, a convention is adopted to the effect that all products are formed before sums. Similarly, complementation takes precedence over multiplication. Thus the Boolean expression

$$A + BC'$$

is an abbreviation of

$$A + (B \cdot (C'))$$

We shall need this abbreviation convention only when there is an occasion to consider extremely long Boolean expressions.

The laws of Boolean algebra are used in the simplification of Boolean expressions and in deriving Boolean equivalences. To illustrate this, we shall derive one of the absorption laws, and also simplify an expression. We derive

$$A + (A \cdot B) \equiv A$$

Using the law of identity,

$$A + (A \cdot B) \equiv A \cdot 1 + A \cdot B$$

Now, applying a distributive law,

$$A \cdot 1 + A \cdot B \equiv A \cdot (1 + B)$$

By commutativity,

$$A \cdot (1 + B) \equiv A \cdot (B + 1)$$

and then by identity,

$$A \cdot (B + 1) \equiv A \cdot 1$$
$$\equiv A$$

This derivation is actually a proof of the particular absorption law, because we started with one member of the identity, $(A + (A \cdot B))$, applied various identities to it, and reached the other member of the identity. This process, while it is a proof of a particular equivalence, is also an example of the simplification of Boolean expressions. As a second example, we simplify

$$(A \cdot B + A \cdot B') + (A \cdot (B + B'))$$

$$
\begin{aligned}
(A \cdot B + A \cdot B') + (A \cdot (B + B')) &\equiv (A \cdot (B + B')) + (A \cdot (B + B')) \\
&\equiv (A \cdot (B + B')) \\
&\equiv (A \cdot 1) \\
&\equiv A
\end{aligned}
$$

Just as an algebraic expression has a numeric value when the values of its variables are known, Boolean expressions have a value when the values of the Boolean variables are known. Since the only values in Boolean algebra are 0 and 1, evaluating a Boolean expression is usually easier than evaluating an algebraic expression of the same length. To find the value of a Boolean expression, the values of the variables in the expression must all be known. Then, beginning at the innermost pair of parentheses, the indicated operation is performed, and then the next operation, and so on, always applying the operations as they were originally defined. As an example, take $A = 1$, $B = 0$, $C = 1$, and $D = 0$ in the Boolean expression

$$(A + (B \cdot C)') \cdot (D' \cdot (A + B))$$

a. $B \cdot C = 0$
b. $(B \cdot C)' = 1$
c. $(A + B) = 1$
d. $D' = 1$
e. $D' \cdot (A + B) = 1$
f. $A + (B \cdot C)' = 1$
g. $(A + (B \cdot C)') \cdot (D' \cdot (A + B)) = 1$

Fig. 8-1

A somewhat simpler method for evaluating a long Boolean expression is to write the expression with wide spacing and write the value of each variable immediately below each occurrence. The result of an operation is then written below the operation sign. The preceding example, when evaluated in this way, appears as

$$(A + (B \cdot C)') \cdot (D' \cdot (A + B))$$
$$1 \quad\quad 0 \;\; 1 \quad\quad 0 \quad 1 \quad 0$$

Evaluating each operation in the indicated order:

$$(A + (B \cdot C)') \cdot (D' \cdot (A + B))$$
$$1 \; 1 \quad 0\,0\,1\,1\,1 \quad 0\,1\,1 \; 1\; 1\; 0$$
$$f \quad\; a \;\; b\,g \quad d\,e \quad\; c$$

The letters a, b, . . . , g correspond to the same letters in Fig. 8-1 to show the order in which the operations were performed. This process of constructing larger Boolean expressions from shorter ones is called *concatenation*.

Now suppose, for some reason, we want to know the values of a Boolean expression for all the possible combinations of values of its variables. If there are only two variables, each can be 0 or 1; so there are four combinations. If there are three variables, there are eight possibilities. In general, if a Boolean expression contains n variables, then there are 2^n combinations. All these combinations can be summarized in tabular form:

A	B		A	B	C
0	0		0	0	0
0	1		0	0	1
1	0		0	1	0
1	1		0	1	1
			1	0	0
			1	0	1
			1	1	0
			1	1	1

Notice that if the entries of each row are interpreted as a binary number, the binary numbers go from 0 to $2^n - 1$. If the expression in question is written to the right of the n variables, its value can be found for each of the 2^n combinations, as in Fig. 8-2. Doing this for a three-variable example, we have the result

A	B	C	$A + (B \cdot C)'$		
0	0	0	1	0	1
0	0	1	1	0	1
0	1	0	1	0	1
0	1	1	0	1	0
1	0	0	1	0	1
1	0	1	1	0	1
1	1	0	1	0	1
1	1	1	1	1	0

Fig. 8-2

A *Boolean equation* is simply a statement that two Boolean expressions have the same value. For $A = 1$ and $B = 1$, the equation

$$A + B = A \cdot B \tag{8-1}$$

is true. It is true because the value of each expression is 1. Equation (8-1) is not always true. If $A = 1$ and $B = 0$, then $A + B = 1$, while $A \cdot B = 0$. Thus, as in ordinary algebra, an equation is true for certain values of its variables. If an equation is true for all the possible combinations of values of the variables in the expressions, then a very special condition is present. If two Boolean expressions have the same value for any combination of values of their variables, they are said to be equivalent. Boolean equivalence is denoted by the symbol $\equiv$. Notice that all the laws of Boolean algebra are Boolean equivalences. It is good practice for the student to verify these equivalences by tables like the one below.

Boolean Table for DeMorgan's Law

A	B	$(A + B)'$		$(A' \cdot B')$		
0	0	0	1	1 1		1
0	1	1	0	1 0		0
1	0	1	0	0 0		1
1	1	1	0	0 0		0

The table shows that

$$(A + B)' \equiv (A' \cdot B')$$

Since Boolean expressions that are equivalent have the same value for each possible assignment of values to their variables, equivalent Boolean expressions have the same meaning (or behavior). Boolean equivalence has an extremely important role in the application of Boolean algebra to electronic switching circuits. This will be discussed more thoroughly in Sec. 8-6.

8-5 BOOLEAN OPERATIONS WITH COMPUTERS

Most computers have machine instructions that act like Boolean operations. The main difference is that the operands are memory locations and registers, rather than Boolean variables. In this section we shall see how Boolean instructions can be very useful, but first the representation of numbers in registers and memory locations must be clarified.

A computer memory location consists of a fixed number of positions that are called *bits*. A bit can either be a 1 or a 0, and its value can be changed by machine instructions. There are several bits in a memory location; the actual number varies from one computer to the next, but this number is usually in the range from 8 to 64. A memory location is often referred to as a *word*, and the number of bits in a word is the *word size*. For the present, we shall work with a word size of eight. We can conveniently represent one of these words as a row of eight numbered boxes.

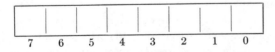

The bit-position numbers provide a handy reference to a particular bit position. They are also useful in determining the value of a number stored in a memory word.

The 8-bit memory word can be considered to be an eight-digit binary number, since each bit (or digit) can be either 0 or 1.   When the bit values are interpreted in this way, the bit-position number corresponds to a power of 2. Thus, if we have a memory word with bits 1 and 3 having the value 1 and all others having 0 as their value,

0	0	0	0	1	0	1	0
7	6	5	4	3	2	1	0

we represent the binary number

1010

which has the decimal value

$$0 \cdot 2^0 + 1 \cdot 2^1 + 0 \cdot 2^2 + 1 \cdot 2^3 = 10$$

To compute the value of a number represented in a memory word, we can consider the bits to be binary coefficients a_i of a polynomial

$$a_0 2^0 + a_1 2^1 + a_2 2^2 + a_3 2^3 + \cdots + a_7 2^7$$

The bit-position number in the memory word is the subscript on the coefficient and the exponent of 2 in the polynomial that corresponds to the memory location.

A computer register is much the same as a computer word. It has the same number of bits, and the bits have the same meaning in a register as they do in a memory word. The only real difference between a register and a memory word is that a register is used as a work area, or scratch pad, by the computer.

Boolean computer instructions are defined by their effect on the bits in their operands (registers, or memory words).   Three common Boolean instructions, AND, OR, and EXCLUSIVE-OR, are defined in Fig. 8-3.

Register bit	Memory bit	AND	OR	EOR
0	0	0	0	0
0	1	0	1	1
1	0	0	1	1
1	1	1	1	0

Fig. 8-3

When these Boolean computer instructions are applied to 1-bit words, they are the same as ordinary Boolean operations. In practice, however, they are applied to multibit words on a bitwise basis. As an example, suppose the memory word and the register in Fig. 8-4 are operands of a Boolean OR instruction.

Register | 0 | 0 | 0 | 0 | 1 | 0 | 1 | 0 | Memory | 0 | 0 | 1 | 0 | 1 | 1 | 0 | 1 |
           7   6   5   4   3   2   1   0   word   7   6   5   4   3   2   1   0

Fig. 8-4

The result would be

OR: | 0 | 0 | 1 | 0 | 1 | 1 | 1 | 1 |
      7   6   5   4   3   2   1   0

Notice that in each bit position, the result is obtained by applying the definition in Fig. 8-3.

A fourth computer instruction having Boolean algebraic properties is the NOT instruction, which corresponds to complementation.

Register bit	NOT
0	1
1	0

We now introduce notation to make the description of sequences of Boolean instructions easier. Denote a register by R and a memory word by M. If we store the result of combining R and M with an OR instruction in a register $R1$, we write R1 = OR (R,M). The arguments of an instruction appear between parentheses to the right of the instruction name. We can indicate sequences of instructions in two ways. One way is to introduce intermediate terms, which actually correspond to the use of various registers. We will apply a sequence of instructions to the register (R) and memory word (M) of Fig. 8-4. The result of OR (R,M) is shown below Fig. 8-4. The complement of this could be expressed by the sequence below. The actual bit configurations are also shown.

$$R1 = OR\ (R,M) \qquad 00101111$$
$$R2 = NOT\ (R1) \qquad 11010000$$

The second way to describe this sequence would be to write

$$R2 = NOT\ (OR(R,M))$$

which is closer to the Boolean algebra equation

$$R2 = (R + M)'$$

The second method of describing sequences of instructions clearly shows the order in which the operations are concatenated, but this way becomes cumbersome for long sequences. Longer sequences can best be handled by the use of both methods, concatenation and introduction of intermediate variables.

The laws of Boolean algebra have instruction-sequence interpretations. One of DeMorgan's laws is interpreted via the following instruction sequences.

$(R + M)' \equiv (R' \cdot M')$
$(R + M)' : NOT\ (OR(R,M))$ or $R1 = OR(R,M)$
                                              $R2 = NOT\ (R1)$

$(R' \cdot M') : AND\ (NOT(R),\ NOT(M))$ or $R3 = NOT(R)$
                                              $R4 = NOT(M)$
                                              $R5 = AND\ (R3,R4)$

We would expect that the results of $NOT(OR(R,M))$ and $AND(NOT(R),NOT(M))$ are identical, and also that $R2 = R5$; this is indeed the case.

Example

Boolean computer instructions are commonly used to make comparisons. Suppose, for example, that we have delinquent credit-card account numbers stored in 200 memory locations, with one account number per location. A credit manager wishes to know whether or not a certain account is delinquent. In the computer solution to this question we shall show two ways to use Boolean computer instructions. The flowchart in Fig. 8-5 shows the method of solution. The two diamond-shaped boxes indicate decisions to be made. These decisions will be made using Boolean instructions. Let N be the account number in question, and (I) denote the account number in memory location I. The notation (I) is read "the contents of memory location I."

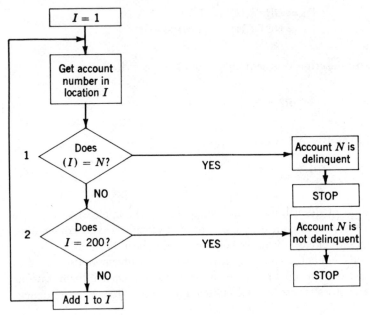

Fig. 8-5

In decision box 1, the account number (I), in memory location I, is to be compared with the number N of the account in question. If they are the same, then account N is delinquent. If they are different, the next account is to be checked. In the second decision box, we want to know whether or not all 200 delinquent accounts have been checked. If they have, then account N was not in any of the 200 memory locations; so it is not delinquent. If (I) is less than 200, it is incremented so that the next location is checked.

Suppose the account in question is credit card number 37. The binary representation of this account number is

0	0	1	0	0	1	0	1

If two locations contain the same number, the result of operating on them with a Boolean EXCLUSIVE-OR instruction is a word with all bits having the value 0. This enables us to test whether or not two numbers are equal.

We form their EXCLUSIVE-OR and then check to see if the result is all 0's. If it is, then the two numbers have identical binary representations; hence they are equal. If the result has at least one bit set to 1, that means the binary representations differ in that bit position; hence the numbers are not equal. As an example, suppose account number 36 is stored in memory location I.   Then the result of combining the contents of location I with the location containing 37 is shown below.

Memory location I	0	0	1	0	0	1	0	0
	7	6	5	4	3	2	1	0

MASK	0	0	1	0	0	1	0	1

EXCLUSIVE-OR result	0	0	0	0	0	0	0	1

Using the notation introduced earlier, this would be written as

$$EOR(MASK,(I)) = 00000001,$$

where MASK is a name for a memory location containing 37.   Use of a mask makes a computer program more flexible, because then, if another account number is to be checked, that number is stored in the mask location, and the program proceeds as before.

Another way to check for a given number is to store that number in a location and then complement it, using a NOT instruction.   If we store the account number (37) in MASK, complement MASK, and then form EXCLU-SIVE-OR sums with the account-number locations, equality will be indicated by an EXCLUSIVE-OR result, each bit having 1 as its value.   Thus, suppose account number 37 is actually delinquent and is stored in location 183.

EOR (NOT (MASK), (183))

MASK	0	0	1	0	0	1	0	1

NOT (MASK)	1	1	0	1	1	0	1	0

Memory location 183	0	0	1	0	0	1	0	1	$(= 37_{10})$

EXCLUSIVE-OR result	1	1	1	1	1	1	1	1

8-6   APPLICATION OF BOOLEAN ALGEBRA TO SWITCHING CIRCUITS

The notions of Boolean algebra have concrete interpretations in electronic switching circuits.   Boolean equivalence is particularly valuable, and will be discussed at the end of this section.   In order to appreciate this important application of Boolean algebra, we begin with some elementary notions of electric circuits.

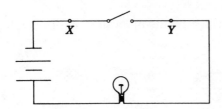

Fig. 8-6

In Fig. 8-6, the switch controls the light bulb. If the switch is closed, the bulb is lit; if the switch is open, the bulb is not lit. The bulb being lit depends entirely on whether or not current flows between points X and Y of the circuit. Since current flow will be our primary concern, we shall omit the battery and bulb from our circuits, and consider only whether or not current flows from point X to point Y. Suppose we have two switches positioned as in Fig. 8-7, and for easy reference we call these switches A and B. In order for current to flow from X to Y, at least one switch must be closed. If both switches are closed, then current will also flow from X to Y.

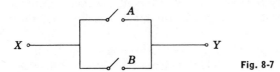

Fig. 8-7

When two switches are arranged in this manner, they are said to be *connected in parallel.* Two switches are *connected in series* if they are arranged as in Fig. 8-8. When switches A and B are in series, the only way current can flow from X to Y is for both A and B to be closed. If either switch is open, current will not flow.

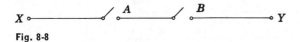

Fig. 8-8

A circuit is *closed* if current will flow from X to Y, and *open* if current will not flow from X to Y. With this in mind, the results of switches connected in parallel and series can be tabulated.

Switch A	Switch B	Parallel	Series
Open	Open	Open	Open
Open	Closed	Closed	Open
Closed	Open	Closed	Open
Closed	Closed	Closed	Closed

The relation between switching circuits and Boolean algebra now is apparent. If we let switches be denoted by Boolean variables, and let the two states open and closed correspond, respectively, to the Boolean values 0 and 1, then we see that parallel connection corresponds to the Boolean OR, and series connection corresponds to the Boolean AND.

Switch A	Switch B	Parallel (OR)	Series (AND)
0	0	0	0
0	1	1	0
1	0	1	0
1	1	1	1

There is a special electronic device called an inverter that allows a Boolean complement to be implemented in switching circuits. This device couples two switches so that they are always in opposite states; that is, if one is open, then the other is closed, and vice versa. Since these switches are paired, they are symbolically denoted by the same capital letter, and one of them is followed by a prime ('), to indicate that it is the complement of the first switch.

Fig. 8-9 Switches paired by an inverter: A, parallel; B, series.

By looking at Fig. 8-9, it is easy to see that an inverter guarantees current flow in parallel and that no current will flow when used in series. This, and the effect of the inverter itself, are shown below.

A	A'	$A + A'$	$A \cdot A'$
0	1	1	0
1	0	1	0

The basis for the application of Boolean algebra to switching circuits is now complete. We have switching-circuit meanings for the Boolean connectives AND, OR, and NOT. Boolean variables correspond to switches, and the Boolean constants 0 and 1 correspond to the two possible states of a circuit, open and closed. Boolean expressions can be used to describe a complicated circuit in a more compact form than a diagram. The order in which switches are connected corresponds to the order of operations determined by parentheses in the Boolean expression corresponding to the circuit. Thus the circuit in Fig. 8-10 corresponds to the Boolean expression

$A \cdot ((B \cdot C) + (B \cdot D))$

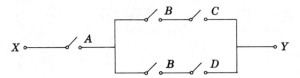

Fig. 8-10

Notice that the variable B occurs twice, both in the circuit and in the corresponding Boolean expression. To allow for this possibility, we make the convention that if a switch variable appears in more than one point in a circuit, it is in the same state (open or closed) at each point in the circuit. In Fig. 8-10, for example, switch B cannot be open in the upper branch and closed in the lower branch. If this were the case, it would be denoted by a prime to show the presence of an inverter, as in Fig. 8-11.

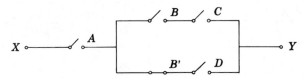

Fig. 8-11

One advantage of the close correspondence between Boolean algebra and switching circuits is that the Boolean expression of a circuit is a more concise way of describing the circuit than a circuit diagram. Each correspondent can be obtained from the other: given a Boolean expression, we can draw the circuit, and given a circuit diagram, we can form its Boolean expression.

A second advantage to the connection between Boolean algebra and switching circuits comes from the notion of Boolean equivalence. Consider the expression for the circuit in Fig. 8-10.

$A \cdot ((B \cdot C) + (B \cdot D))$

Applying the distributive law, we can factor this to get

$A \cdot (B \cdot (C + D))$

The circuit diagram of $A \cdot (B \cdot (C + D))$ is shown in Fig. 8-12. Notice that switch B occurs only once in Fig. 8-12, while it occurred twice in Fig. 8-10.

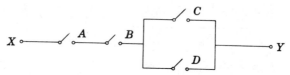

Fig. 8-12

The expressions $A \cdot ((B \cdot C) + (B \cdot D))$ and $A \cdot (B \cdot (C + D))$ are equivalent (show this); so the two circuits must have the same current-flow behavior. The fact that the circuit in Fig. 8-12 behaves exactly the same as the circuit in Fig. 8-10 is important, because the circuit in Fig. 8-10 contains one more switch. Boolean equivalence can thus be used to produce equivalent circuits. If the equivalent expression contains fewer variables, the corresponding circuit contains fewer switches, and is then cheaper to build. This is an example of *Boolean minimization.* If a manufacturer of electronic devices can substitute shorter equivalent circuits in his product, the function of the circuit remains unchanged, while the cost of the device is reduced. An additional advantage is that the product is more reliable, since there are fewer parts that can fail.

Example

We conclude this chapter with a sample problem that can be solved easily with Boolean algebra.

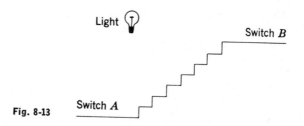

Fig. 8-13

In many two-story homes there is a light for the stairs controlled by two switches, one at the top of the stairs, and the other at the bottom. Since the light is a binary device (on or off), we can consider the light to be a Boolean function of the two switches. We will refer to the situation in Fig. 8-13. Our objective is to find a Boolean expression that describes the relation between the light and the two switches.

Suppose, initially, that when both switches are in the off position, the light is off. When either switch is reversed, the light goes on. Once the light is on, reversing either switch turns it off. These conditions are summarized in Fig. 8-14. In this case, on and off are only names for the two

Switch A	Switch B	Light
On	On	Off
On	Off	On
Off	On	On
Off	Off	Off

Fig. 8-14

positions of the light switch; they do not describe the condition of the light. If we agree to denote the on state of each switch in Fig. 8-13 by the Boolean constant 1, and the off state by the constant 0, then the table in Fig. 8-14 becomes

A	B	Light
1	1	0
1	0	1
0	1	1
0	0	0

Fig. 8-15

Exercise 8-15 describes a way to find a Boolean expression for a given Boolean function, such as the light function in Fig. 8-15. The expression for the light function is $(A \cdot B') + (A' \cdot B)$.

A	B	$(A \cdot B') + (A' \cdot B)$
1	1	0
1	0	1
0	1	1
0	0	0

Fig. 8-16

Since the expression $(A \cdot B') + (A' \cdot B)$ is equivalent to the light function, the switching circuit that corresponds to $(A \cdot B') + (A' \cdot B)$ is the desired switch arrangement. This network is shown in Fig. 8-17.

$(A \cdot B') + (A' \cdot B)$ **Fig. 8-17**

In this network, it would seem that there are four switches present, while the original problem had only two switches. This is true; but notice that the four switches are actually two pairs of complementary switches. One simple implementation of a pair of complementary switches is shown in Fig. 8-18.

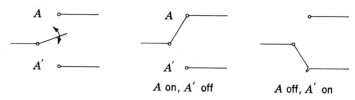

Fig. 8-18 A complementary pair of switches.

We can see that, in this arrangement, when one switch is on, the other is off.

The switching network for the stair light is now easily described (see Fig. 8-19). In practice, the switches used in these applications actually have three terminals, and behave like the switches shown in Fig. 8-18.

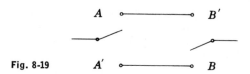

Fig. 8-19

EXERCISES

8-1. Construct a Boolean table to check the equivalence $(A \cdot B)' \equiv A' + B'$.

8-2. Use the principle of duality to convert the proof of $A + (A \cdot B) \equiv A$ to a proof of its dual, $A \cdot (A + B) \equiv A$.

8-3. Using any of the first seven laws of Boolean algebra, try to prove $A + (A' \cdot B) \equiv A + B$. (*Hint:* Apply one of the distributive laws.)

8-4. Using any of the first seven laws of Boolean algebra, simplify the following expressions:

   a. $A + B' + (A' \cdot B) + (A + B') \cdot A' \cdot B$
   b. $(A + B' + (A' \cdot B)) \cdot (A + B') \cdot A' \cdot B$

8-5. Determine the Boolean laws used at each step in the simplification of $(A \cdot B + A \cdot B') + (A \cdot (B + B'))$ in the text.

8-6. In the credit-card example given in the text, suppose that the delinquent-account information were stored in a 32-bit memory location in this format:

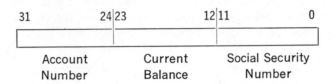

| | Account Number | Current Balance | Social Security Number |

Find a mask that can be used in conjunction with an AND instruction to extract just the account number from the word. Do the same for the current balance.

8-7. Suppose that a delinquent-account holder sends in a payment for his account. We would want to find the location containing his account information, extract the balance, and then compute the new balance and insert it into the memory location. What happens if the new balance is added to the string of bits in the memory location?

8-8. Because of the situation in Exercise 8-7, it is necessary to insert the new current balance into the memory location using Boolean instructions. Using the appropriate mask (what is it?), we could alter the memory location to

| | 31   24 | 23   12 | 11   0 |
| Memory | Acct. No. | 000000000000 | Soc. Security No. |

We could also put the new current balance into a register in the position

| | 31   24 | 23   12 | 11   0 |
| Register | 00000000 | New Current Balance | 000000000000 |

What instruction could we use to insert the contents of the register into the memory location? Why is it necessary to first insert zeros into the current-balance field?

8-9. Find the Boolean expressions that correspond to the circuits

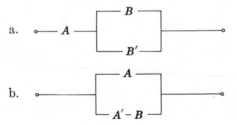

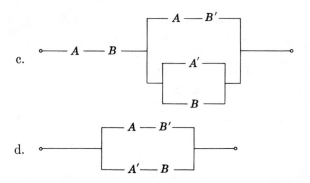

c.

d.

8-10. Sketch the circuits that correspond to the following Boolean expressions:

    a. $(A \cdot B) + (A \cdot B') + (A' \cdot B)$
    b. $(A + B) \cdot (A + B') \cdot (A' + B)$
    c. $A \cdot (B + C) + B \cdot (C + D)$

8-11. In Chap. 7 we saw that any logical function can be expressed in terms of the connectives $\wedge$, $\vee$, and $\sim$. The analog of this is true for Boolean algebra: Any Boolean function can be expressed in terms of $\cdot$, $+$, and $'$. Express the Boolean EXCLUSIVE-OR in these terms, and then sketch the corresponding switching circuit.

8-12. We can use Boolean operations to perform binary arithmetic. Note first the similarity between binary addition and the Boolean EXCLU-SIVE-OR:

x	y	$x + y$		A	B	$A \oplus B$
0	0	0		0	0	0
0	1	1		0	1	1
1	0	1		1	0	1
1	1	10		1	1	0

The only difference is that the carry bit is lost for $1 \oplus 1$. If we define S and C to be Boolean variables corresponding to the sum and carry of A and B, we can then get a *Boolean half-adder.*

A	B	S	C	
0	0	0	0	
0	1	1	0	$S = A \oplus B$
1	0	1	0	$C = A \cdot B$
1	1	0	1	

A Boolean half-adder is a circuit having A and B as inputs (positions of switches) and S and C as outputs. A half-adder circuit is then

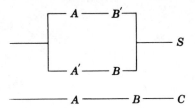

Using this technique, develop a full Boolean adder circuit. As a start, complete the table below:

A	B	C_{in}	S	C_{out}
0	0	0	0	0
0	0	1	1	0
0	1	0		
0	1	1		
1	0	0		
1	0	1		
1	1	0		
1	1	1		

You will find that $S = A \oplus B \oplus C_{\text{in}}$ and $C_{\text{out}} = A'BC + AB'C + ABC' + ABC$.

8-13. The laws of Boolean algebra (p. 255) can be applied to set theory and the logic of propositions when suitable interpretations of the Boolean algebra, $+, \cdot, ', 0,$ and 1, are made. Use the interpretations (meanings) from the table below to produce analogs of the laws of Boolean algebra for set theory and for logic of propositions.

Boolean algebra	*Set theory*	*Logic of propositions*
A, B, C (variables)	P, Q, R (sets)	p, q, r (propositions)
0	$\emptyset$	F (a false proposition)
1	U	T (a true proposition)
$+$	$\cup$	$\vee$
$\cdot$	$\cap$	$\wedge$
$'$	$'$	$\sim$

8-14. Decide upon suitable interpretations for Boolean algebraic notions to apply to switching circuits. Interpret the laws of Boolean algebra as principles of switching circuits.

8-15. A problem that occurs in the design of switching circuits is that the function of the switches is specified but the Boolean expression is not given. The problem then is, given a Boolean function, find a Boolean expression of it. One way to accomplish this is to use the "atomic" functions in the table below.

A	B	$A' \cdot B'$	$A' \cdot B$	$A \cdot B'$	$A \cdot B$
0	0	1	0	0	0
0	1	0	1	0	0
1	0	0	0	1	0
1	1	0	0	0	1

Notice that each function has a 1 in exactly one row. Now, if the expression of the function F in the table below is to be found, we can use the "atomic" functions above for each 1 in the table of F, combine these with the Boolean $+$, and obtain an expression for F.

A	B	F
0	0	1
0	1	1
1	0	0
1	1	1

In this case,

$$F \equiv A' \cdot B' + A' \cdot B + A \cdot B$$

This process is known as finding the *disjunctive normal form* of a Boolean function. Once a function is expressed in its disjunctive normal form, it can usually be simplified by algebraic manipulation. Simplify F above, and then find and simplify expressions for F_1 and F_2 given below.

A	B	F_1		A	B	C	F_2
0	0	1		0	0	0	0
0	1	0		0	0	1	1
1	0	1		0	1	0	1
1	1	1		0	1	1	0
				1	0	0	1
				1	0	1	0
				1	1	0	1
				1	1	1	0

8-16.   Using duality, develop the notion of the conjunctive normal form of a Boolean function.

8-17.   Use Boolean operation tables to prove

a. $(A \oplus B) \oplus 1 \equiv (A \oplus B)'$
b. $(A \oplus B) \oplus 0 \equiv A \oplus B$

8-18.   One of the laws of absorption is

$$A + (A \cdot B) \equiv A$$

We might expect that this is true for Boolean computer instructions OR and AND, where the Boolean variables A and B are either memory locations or registers.   Is the law of absorption true for A and B as shown below?

A: | 1 | 1 | 0 | 0 |

B: | 1 | 0 | 1 | 0 |

8-19.   The Boolean expression for carry-out in a full adder, $A'BC + AB'C + ABC' + ABC$, can be simplified to $AB + BC + CA$.   Use idempotent laws to introduce terms to make factoring with the distributive laws convenient.

8-20.   Indicate the results of combining the operands OP1 and OP2 below with the Boolean computer instructions OR, AND, and EOR.

OP1: | 1 | 1 | 1 | 0 | 1 | 1 | 0 | 0 |

OP2: | 1 | 1 | 0 | 0 | 1 | 0 | 0 | 1 |

8-21.   Referring to the example in Chap. 7, suppose the insurance company declares that a policy change applies to:
   "All persons under 25 who are either

   1. *Males, or*
   2. *Single females;*

   or to persons over 25 who are

   3. *males, or*
   4. *teetotalers."*

Find the Boolean expression for this category, and then simplify it. Translate the simplified version back into a verbal description.

chapter nine

ALGORITHMS AND ITERATIVE TECHNIQUES

In the Introduction we discussed the characteristics that make digital computers extremely useful for problem solving. In this chapter we consider two of these characteristics more thoroughly: the capacity for repetition and the exact execution of explicit instructions. Recall that the explicit instructions are actually machine instructions that are not too meaningful to computer users. For this reason programming languages were developed. A programming language allows the computer user to express, in more comprehensible terms, the method of solving a problem. This method of solving a problem is called an algorithm. Perhaps the most common example of an algorithm is a housewife's recipe for a cake.

An *algorithm* is an effective procedure by which the solution to a problem can be found. The word "effective" is of great importance when algorithms are developed for computer use. A procedure is effective if it contains all necessary information and requires no intuition. The need for effective procedures has caused computers to be termed "dull, uninspired clerks."

Some of the algorithms that we will study will exploit the repetitive capacity of computers. These algorithms, usually referred to as *iterative*, generate a sequence of numbers

$$x_1, x_2, x_3, \ldots, x_n, \ldots$$

where (hopefully) the terms in the sequence get closer to the solution being sought. Very often successive terms depend on information gained in computing earlier terms. The common notation for sequences is

$$\{x_i\} = x_1, x_2, \ldots, x_n$$

The most important property of a sequence is whether or not the terms get closer to some particular value, or limit. More specifically, the sequence

$\{x_i\}$ is said to *converge to a limit* x if, for any $\epsilon > 0$, there is a natural number N such that

$$|x_n - x| < \epsilon \qquad \text{for all } n \geq N$$

Looking closely at this definition, we see that the small number ϵ forces the terms to get arithmetically close to the limit. If the sequence $\{x_i\}$ does converge to the limit x, this is written in either of two ways:

$$\lim_{n \to \infty} x_n = x$$

or

$$\{x_n\} \to x$$

The first is read "the limit, as n increases without bound, of the sequence $\{x_n\}$ is x." The second reads "the sequence $\{x_n\}$ converges to the limit x." Iterative algorithms often generate sequences that converge to a limit which is the solution of the problem under consideration. This is not to say that all sequences converge to a limit, or that even if they do converge, the limit is actually the desired solution. Sequences that do not converge to a limit are called *divergent*. Many tests can be used to determine whether a sequence is convergent or divergent, but these methods are more properly discussed in a text on real variables. One notion that we will find useful is the Cauchy convergence criterion

$$|x_n - x_{n+1}| < \epsilon$$

for n sufficiently large.

Often, because of inherent error in data and error in computation, we may need a number that only approximates the true solution. In such situations, we specify ϵ as a stopping criterion, so that, when x_n is within ϵ (distance) of the true solution, we will have an acceptable approximation. In the remainder of this chapter we consider a variety of useful and instructive algorithms that will clarify the general properties discussed here.

These algorithms will be stated using flowcharts, a very useful device for specifying a dynamic process. A flowchart is an arrangement of boxes connected by arrows that describes some process. By convention, the box at the top of the flowchart is the starting point. Statements within a box indicate the function to be executed by that part of the process. Rectangular boxes are used for an almost endless variety of descriptive statements. Some examples of these are shown below. Notice that these statements can be quite general or very specific.

> Find inverse of matrix A

> Increase value of J by 3

> Compute $\sqrt{b^2 - 4ac}$

The second kind of box that commonly occurs in flowcharts is the diamond-shaped decision box.   A decision box is used to indicate an arithmetic comparison between two quantities.   The decision box shown below compares the value of the variable A with 4.5.   (A colon separates the quantities being compared.)   If the value of A is less than 4.5, the box at (1) is the next box to be executed.   Similarly, if A is equal to or greater than 4.5, the control flows, respectively, to the boxes at (2) or (3).

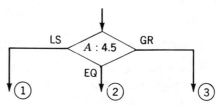

Flowcharts have one other characteristic that should be mentioned. Since flowcharts can be used to describe dynamic situations, the values of variables appearing in the flowchart can be changed.   When a variable receives a new value, this is indicated by a *replacement arrow* ($\leftarrow$).   Some common replacements are shown below:

$$DISC \leftarrow (b^2 - 4ac)$$
$$i \leftarrow i + 1$$
$$XSQ \leftarrow X \cdot X$$

The second example above shows how replacements can be used to reflect dynamic changes in values of variables.

As an example of flowcharts, suppose we wish to add successive integers 1, 2, 3, . . . , until the sum is greater than some specific number, say, 307. The flowchart to describe this process is shown below.   Notice that the successive integers are constructed by a replacement that increments the value of I by 1 each time that box is entered.   The second and third boxes are used for initialization, or giving initial values to variables.   The region between the dotted lines is known as a *loop*.   In this loop the integers 1, 2, 3, . . . are constructed and then added to the variable SUM.   The loop contains a decision box that provides an exit (the "greater than" branch) from the loop.

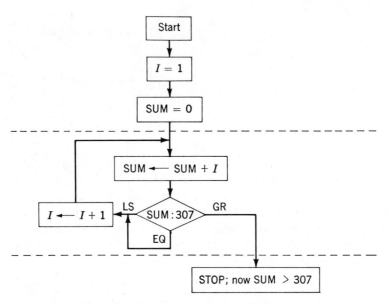

9-1 SQUARE ROOT BY BINARY CHOPPING

Given a number $a \geq 0$, we want to find $\sqrt{a}$. In Chap. 10 we will see that it is often impossible to ever represent $\sqrt{a}$, due to the nature of computer memories; so we will have to be content with an approximate square root in many cases. Although it is intellectually dismaying to be unable to compute $\sqrt{3}$ exactly, we gain the opportunity to specify how accurate the approximation should be. Our problem, restated to conform to the limitations of digital computers, is:

Given $a \geq 0$ and $\epsilon > 0$, find x such that $|a - x^2| \leq \epsilon$.

The Greek letter ϵ is used to denote a small number, in this case the maximum error we will tolerate in the approximation of $\sqrt{a}$. One way to find x is to start with $x = \epsilon$. We could then compute x^2 and compare it with a. If the difference is greater than ϵ, we increment x by ϵ and repeat the process. In this way we will find the desired approximate solution; however, the greater a is, the longer it will take, even on a computer.

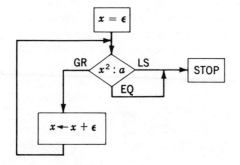

Fig. 9-1

A better way to approximate $\sqrt{a}$ is to use a technique called *binary chopping*. The algorithm gets its name because it uses nested intervals on the real-number line, each containing $\sqrt{a}$. At each iteration, half the interval is "chopped," so the intervals converge more quickly to the approximation. We shall denote closed intervals $a \leq x \leq b$ on the real-number line by $[a,b]$. In our statement of the algorithm, x_L and x_R denote the left and right endpoints of the current interval.

Binary-chopping Algorithm

Specify ϵ, a. Take $[0,a]$ as the initial interval. The midpoint of the current interval, x_i, is the trial approximation. Compare x_i^2 with a: if $|x_i^2 - a| \leq \epsilon$, the process is complete; if $x_i^2 < a$, take x_i as the new left endpoint of the interval, and repeat the process, beginning at the determination of the midpoint of the current interval; if $x_i^2 > a$, take x_i as the new right endpoint of the current interval, and repeat the process, beginning at the determination of the midpoint of the current interval. This algorithm is easier to comprehend in flowchart form.

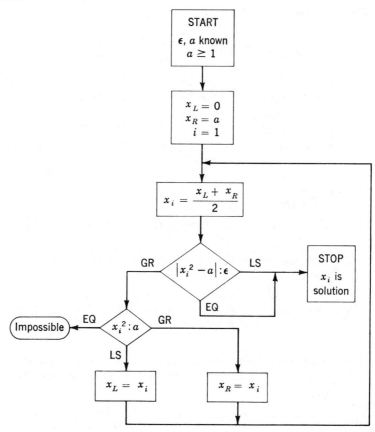

Notice that all necessary information is present in the algorithm: the values of ϵ and a, the initial interval, how to compute the midpoint, what comparisons are needed, and how to choose a new interval, and finally, when to stop. The results of the first five iterations for $a = 36$, $\epsilon = 0.005$, are given below, and then the intervals are sketched in Fig. 9-2.

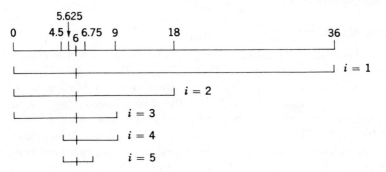

Fig. 9-2

$a = 36 \qquad \epsilon = 0.005$

$i = 1$	$[0,36]$	$x_1 = 18$	$18^2 > 36$	$\therefore x_R = 18$
$i = 2$	$[0,18]$	$x_2 = 9$	$9^2 > 36$	$\therefore x_R = 9$
$i = 3$	$[0,9]$	$x_3 = 4.5$	$4.5^2 < 36$	$\therefore x_L = 4.5$
$i = 4$	$[4.5,9]$	$x_4 = 6.75$	$6.75^2 > 36$	$\therefore x_R = 6.75$
$i = 5$	$[4.5,6.75]$	$x_5 = 5.625$	$5.625^2 < 36$	$\therefore x_L = 5.625$

EXERCISES

9-1. Use this algorithm to compute $\sqrt{9}$, taking $\epsilon = 0.05$.

9-2. Find the intervals for the first five iterations with $a = 5$, $a = 8$, $a = \frac{1}{2}$, $\epsilon = 0.05$.

9-3. Describe in detail what happens when this algorithm is applied to the case $a = 1$, $\epsilon = 0.005$.

9-4. Most computers could check to see if $a = 1$ in less than 3 microseconds. Revise the algorithm to avoid the situation demonstrated in Exercise 9-3.

9-5.   Would it be advisable to make an additional test for $a = 0$?

9-6.   What happens when $a = -4$?   Make an additional modification to cover the possibility of negative values of a.   Do the same for $0 \leq a < 1$.

9-2 GENERATION OF BINOMIAL COEFFICIENTS

The binomial theorem is frequently used in probability-theory applications.   Recall that the theorem states

$$(x + y)^n = x^n + \binom{n}{n-1} x^{n-1}y + \binom{n}{n-2} x^{n-2}y^2$$
$$+ \cdots + \binom{n}{1} xy^{n-1} + y^n$$

where $\binom{n}{r}$ is the abbreviation for $\dfrac{n!}{r!(n-r)!}$.   The binomial coefficients $\binom{n}{r}$ have several interesting properties, some of which appear in the exercises. One of these is a symmetry:

$$\binom{n}{r} = \binom{n}{n-r}$$

This is fairly obvious:

$$\binom{n}{r} = \frac{n!}{r!(n-r)!}$$

$$\binom{n}{n-r} = \frac{n!}{(n-r)!(n-(n-r))!}$$

$$= \frac{n!}{(n-r)!(n-n+r)!}$$

$$= \frac{n!}{(n-r)!r!}$$

The most common use of these coefficients is in expanding binomials such as $(1 + x)^3$, $(x - \epsilon)^{10}$.   When n is small, say, $n \leq 6$, the easiest way to compute the coefficients is either to use their factorial definition or else Pascal's triangle (see Fig. 9-3).   An element in the nth row is found by summing the

$$n = 0 \qquad\qquad\qquad 1 \overset{\displaystyle r = 0}{\swarrow}$$

$$n = 1 \qquad\qquad\qquad 1 \quad 1 \overset{\displaystyle r = 1}{\swarrow}$$

$$n = 2 \qquad\qquad\qquad 1 \quad 2 \quad 1 \overset{\displaystyle r = 2}{\swarrow}$$

$$n = 3 \qquad\qquad\qquad 1 \quad 3 \quad 3 \quad 1 \overset{\displaystyle r = 3}{\swarrow}$$

$$n = 4 \qquad\qquad\qquad 1 \quad 4 \quad 6 \quad 4 \quad 1 \overset{\displaystyle r = 4}{\swarrow}$$

$$n = 5 \qquad\qquad 1 \quad 5 \quad 10 \quad 10 \quad 5 \quad 1 \overset{\displaystyle r = 5}{\swarrow}$$

$$n = 6 \qquad 1 \quad 6 \quad 15 \quad 20 \quad 15 \quad 6 \quad 1 \overset{\displaystyle r = 6}{\swarrow}$$

Fig. 9-3   Pascal's triangle.

two elements immediately above it in the $(n - 1)$st row.

$$\binom{n + 1}{r} = \binom{n}{r - 1} + \binom{n}{r}$$

Pascal's triangle is adequate for hand computations, where $n \leq 10$, but for much larger values of n, there is a better technique. We now derive this method because it is the basis of a useful algorithm to generate binomial coefficients on a computer. Suppose we wish to expand $(x + y)^n$ for a particular value of n. Consider the ratio of any two consecutive coefficients in the expansion.

$$\frac{\dbinom{n}{r + 1}}{\dbinom{n}{r}} = \frac{\dfrac{n!}{(r + 1)!(n - (r + 1))!}}{\dfrac{n!}{r!(n - r)!}}$$

$$= \frac{n!}{(r + 1)!(n - r - 1)!} \cdot \frac{r!(n - r)!}{n!}$$

$$= \frac{n - r}{r + 1}$$

Rewriting this, we have

$$\binom{n}{r + 1} = \frac{n - r}{r + 1}\binom{n}{r}$$

which expresses the $(r + 1)$st coefficient in terms of the rth coefficient. The principal advantage of this is that computing $\binom{n}{r} = \dfrac{n!}{r!(n - r)!}$ each time results in many multiplications when the factorials are evaluated. By avoiding many redundant multiplications, expensive computer time is saved. The flowcharts for both methods are shown in Figs. 9-4 and 9-5.

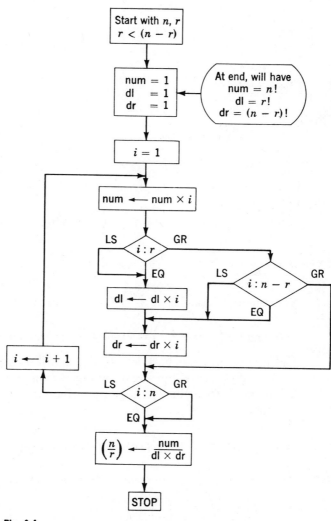

Fig. 9-4

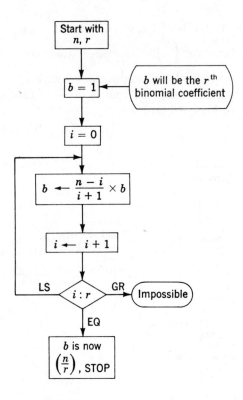

Fig. 9-5

EXERCISES

9-7.   The binomial coefficient $\binom{n}{r}$ has a prominent role in combinatorial mathematics, where $\binom{n}{r}$ is usually read "the number of subsets having r elements that can be taken from a set of n elements." Given a set having 10 elements, how many different subsets having 3 elements can be found? How many having 2 elements? At least 3 elements? 7 elements?

9-8.   The quantity 0! is defined to be 1. Knowing this, compute $\binom{n}{o}$ and $\binom{n}{n}$.

9-9.   Given a set of three elements, the total number of different subsets is

$$\binom{3}{0} + \binom{3}{1} + \binom{3}{2} + \binom{3}{3} = 8$$
$$= 2^3$$

Use the binomial theorem to expand $(1 + 1)^n$, and thus prove (why?) that the total number of subsets of a set having n elements is 2^n.

9-10. In a coin-flipping situation, let h be the probability of heads, and t the probability of tails. Assuming a balanced coin,

$$h = \tfrac{1}{2} \qquad t = \tfrac{1}{2}$$

If the coin is tossed three times, the number of ways that no heads can result is 1; one head is $\binom{3}{1}$; two heads is $\binom{3}{2}$; and three heads is 1. By expanding $(h + t)^n$ with the binomial theorem, can you see an easy way to find the probability of getting exactly r heads in n tosses ($r \leq n$)? (*Hint:* Use the exponents of h and t in the expansion.)

9-11. Suppose a coin is flipped seven times. What is the probability of getting 3 heads? Of getting 2 heads? Of at least 4 heads?

9-12. Make a flowchart to compute $n!$, where n is given.

9-13. Modify the flowchart in Fig. 9-5 for the special cases $\binom{n}{0}$ and $\binom{n}{n}$.

9-14. By using the identity $\binom{n}{r} = \binom{n}{n - r}$, the flowchart in Fig. 9-5 can be made even more efficient. Make this modification.

9-3 A BINARY SEARCH

Commercial data processing often encounters situations in which large quantities of data must be checked for some piece of information. When the data to be checked have certain properties, a very efficient technique can be used to decrease the search time. We will develop the binary search technique in general terms and simultaneously with a specific example.

The special property needed to apply the binary search technique is that the data must be a monotone sequence. There are four kinds of monotonicity possible for a sequence $\{x_i\}$. The sequence $\{x_i\}$ is

1. Monotonically increasing if $x_i < x_{i+1}$ for all i
2. Monotonically nondecreasing if $x_i \leq x_{i+1}$ for all i

Memory location	Part number	Quantity
1	100-01-2	370
2	100-01-3	25
3	100-01-5	112
.		
.		
.		
675	342-12-6	18
676	345-08-2	167
.		
.		
.		
5000	391-16-9	182
.		
.		
.		
7116	432-23-4	347
.		
.		
.		
7500	640-17-5	26
.		
.		
.		
7518	641-02-3	73
.		
.		
.		
7527	646-18-7	94
7528	646-19-1	118
7529	646-19-3	167
.		
.		
.		
7532	650-02-8	183
.		
.		
.		
7537	657-13-2	14
.		
.		
.		
7575	694-03-7	182
.		
.		
.		
7651	702-13-5	306
.		
.		
.		
7812	727-09-3	41
.		
.		
.		
8750	747-14-6	602
.		
.		
.		
10,000	748-13-5	181

Fig. 9-6

3.   Monotonically nonincreasing if $x_i \geq x_{i+1}$ for all i
4.   Monotonically decreasing if $x_i > x_{i+1}$ for all i

We shall consider strictly monotonic sequences (either $x_i < x_{i+1}$ or $x_i > x_{i+1}$) and develop the special cases for weak monotone sequences in the exercises.   As a concurrent example, let us consider an inventory problem for a manufacturing situation.   We are concerned with the available quantities of many (say, 10,000) different component parts.   Each part has a part number, but the part numbers do not necessarily run from 1 to 10,000.   The restriction on the part numbers is that they are arranged in a monotonically increasing sequence.   This arrangement may be physically manifested in several ways; for example, the part numbers might be written one per index card and then filed in (part-number) order.   A more automated way would be to have the part numbers and corresponding inventory information stored in consecutive memory locations in a computer.

The inventory problem is, given a specific part number, how many are presently available?

An elementary search would be to examine the first location to see if the part numbers match, and if they do, read out the available quantity; if they do not match, then check the next location; and so on.   This simple method will clearly work, but the higher the part number is, the longer the search will take. The binary search exploits the monotonicity of the part numbers.   We conclude our development of the binary search in more general terms.   To do this, we need the concept of the *greatest integer function*.   For any real number s, the greatest integer function of s is the greatest integer n such that $n \leq s$.   Symbolically, this is written

$$[s] = n$$

where the brackets denote the greatest integer function.

Now suppose that $\{x_i\}$ is a monotonically increasing sequence of M terms. We define a function on the integers 1, 2, . . . , M by

$$f(n) = x_n \qquad \text{for } n = 1, 2, \ldots, M$$

Since $\{x_i\}$ is monotonically increasing, if $k < m$, then we must have $f(k) < f(m)$.   The binary-search problem, stated in this context, is:

Given the value A of some element in $\{x_i\}$, find k such that $A = f(k) = x_k$. We state the algorithm to find k in flowchart form (see Fig. 9-7).

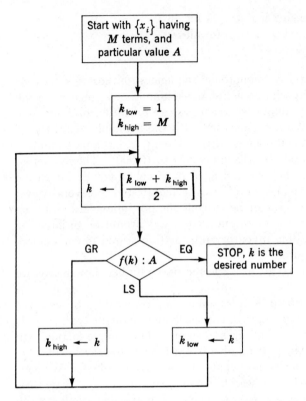

Fig. 9-7 Flowchart for binary search where $\{x_i\}$ is monotonically increasing.

EXERCISES

9-15. Make up your own examples of monotonically increasing and decreasing sequences (one each). Then make up examples of sequences that are

a. Nondecreasing but not strictly increasing
b. Nonincreasing but not strictly decreasing

Make each sequence have at least five elements.

9-16. For each of the four sequences in Exercise 9-15, define the function

$$f(i) = x_i$$

and graph the ordered pairs $\langle i, f(i) \rangle$ for each sequence. The differences between the four types of sequences can be easily seen when the points on the graph of each sequence are connected with straight lines.

9-17. Follow the algorithm in Fig. 9-7 for the example in Fig. 9-6. List the
memory locations tested and the results of each test, when the algorithm
is used to find part number 646-19-1.

9-18. Make a flowchart similar to the one in Fig. 9-7, but for the case where
$\{x_i\}$ is monotonically decreasing.

9-19. Discuss the similarities between a binary search and the binary-chopping
square-root algorithm.

9-20. In monotonically nonincreasing (and nondecreasing) sequences it is
possible that $x_i = x_{i+1}$ for some i. When this is the case, the general
statement of the binary-search problem is:
Given a value A of some element in $\{x_i\}$, find the integers k_1, k_2,
. . . , k_m such that

$$A = f(k_1) = f(k_2) = \cdots = f(k_m)$$

Revise the flowchart in Fig. 9-6 to apply to monotonically nondecreasing
sequences.

9-4 MATRIX INVERSION

The most common application for the inverse of a matrix is in the solution of a
system of simultaneous linear equations. Such a system can be written as the
matrix equation

$$A \cdot X = B$$

where A is an n by n (square) matrix, and X and B are n-element column
matrices. If the matrix A is nonsingular (det $A \neq 0$), then the solution can
be obtained using the inverse A^{-1} of the matrix A.

$$A^{-1}AX = A^{-1}B$$
$$IX = A^{-1}B$$
$$X = A^{-1}B$$

We now give an algorithm to find the inverse of a given matrix A. The
student is strongly advised to work out the exercises for this section because
they point out several improvements to the algorithm.

Given an n by n matrix A, form the n by $2n$ matrix AI, where columns 1
to n of AI are identical with A, and columns $n + 1$ to $2n$ of AI are identical
with the nth-order identity matrix. Now, by row operations only, reduce the
left half of AI to an nth-order identity matrix, applying each row operation to
the whole matrix AI. When this is done, the right half of AI (columns $n + 1$

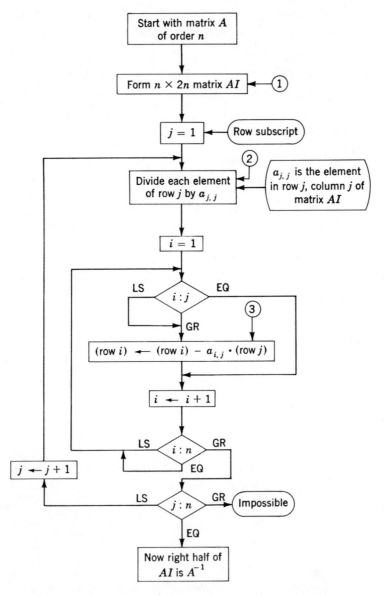

Fig. 9-8   Flowchart for matrix inversion by Gaussian elimination.

to 2n) is identical with A^{-1}.   The reduction of the left half of AI to an identity matrix is accomplished by the sweep-out process described in the flowchart for the algorithm (see Fig. 9-8).   This process is commonly referred to as Gaussian elimination, after the German mathematician Gauss.

As an example, we will use matrix inversion to solve the system of equations

$$2x_1 - 3x_2 + 6x_3 = 10$$
$$x_1 - 3x_2 \qquad = 5$$
$$3x_1 - 4x_2 - 2x_3 = 9$$

We start with the matrix A and form AI.

$$A = \begin{bmatrix} 2 & -3 & 6 \\ 1 & -3 & 0 \\ 3 & -4 & -2 \end{bmatrix}$$

$$AI = \begin{bmatrix} 2 & -3 & 6 & 1 & 0 & 0 \\ 1 & -3 & 0 & 0 & 1 & 0 \\ 3 & -4 & -2 & 0 & 0 & 1 \end{bmatrix}$$

Following the flowchart, the matrix AI goes through the changes below. The values of j and i are noted at each step.

$j = 1: i = 1:$

$$AI = \begin{bmatrix} 1 & -\frac{3}{2} & 3 & \frac{1}{2} & 0 & 0 \\ 1 & 3 & 0 & 0 & 1 & 0 \\ 3 & -4 & -2 & 0 & 0 & 1 \end{bmatrix}$$

$j = 1, i = 2:$

$$AI = \begin{bmatrix} 1 & -\frac{3}{2} & 3 & \frac{1}{2} & 0 & 0 \\ 0 & -\frac{3}{2} & -3 & -\frac{1}{2} & 1 & 0 \\ 3 & -4 & -2 & 0 & 0 & 1 \end{bmatrix}$$

$j = 1, i = 3:$

$$AI = \begin{bmatrix} 1 & -\frac{3}{2} & 3 & \frac{1}{2} & 0 & 0 \\ 0 & -\frac{3}{2} & -3 & -\frac{1}{2} & 1 & 0 \\ 0 & \frac{1}{2} & -11 & -\frac{3}{2} & 0 & 1 \end{bmatrix}$$

$j = 2, i = 4:$

$$AI = \begin{bmatrix} 1 & -\frac{3}{2} & 3 & \frac{1}{2} & 0 & 0 \\ 0 & 1 & 2 & \frac{1}{3} & -\frac{2}{3} & 0 \\ 0 & \frac{1}{2} & -11 & -\frac{3}{2} & 0 & 1 \end{bmatrix}$$

$j = 2, i = 1:$

$$AI = \begin{bmatrix} 1 & 0 & 6 & 1 & -1 & 0 \\ 0 & 1 & 2 & \frac{1}{3} & -\frac{2}{3} & 0 \\ 0 & \frac{1}{2} & -11 & -\frac{3}{2} & 0 & 1 \end{bmatrix}$$

$j = 2, i = 3:$

$$AI = \begin{bmatrix} 1 & 0 & 6 & 1 & -1 & 0 \\ 0 & 1 & 2 & \frac{1}{3} & -\frac{2}{3} & 0 \\ 0 & 0 & -12 & -\frac{5}{3} & \frac{1}{3} & 1 \end{bmatrix}$$

$j = 3,\ i = 4$:

$$AI = \begin{bmatrix} 1 & 0 & 6 & 1 & -1 & 0 \\ 0 & 1 & 2 & \frac{1}{3} & -\frac{2}{3} & 0 \\ 0 & 0 & 1 & \frac{5}{36} & -\frac{1}{36} & -\frac{1}{12} \end{bmatrix}$$

$j = 3,\ i = 1$:

$$AI = \begin{bmatrix} 1 & 0 & 0 & \frac{1}{6} & -\frac{5}{6} & \frac{1}{2} \\ 0 & 1 & 2 & \frac{1}{3} & -\frac{2}{3} & 0 \\ 0 & 0 & 1 & \frac{5}{36} & -\frac{1}{36} & -\frac{1}{12} \end{bmatrix}$$

$j = 3,\ i = 2$:

$$AI = \begin{bmatrix} 1 & 0 & 0 & \frac{1}{6} & -\frac{5}{6} & \frac{1}{2} \\ 0 & 1 & 0 & \frac{1}{18} & -\frac{11}{18} & \frac{1}{6} \\ 0 & 0 & 1 & \frac{5}{36} & -\frac{1}{36} & -\frac{1}{12} \end{bmatrix}$$

Now, according to the algorithm, the inverse of our original matrix A is

$$A^{-1} = \begin{bmatrix} \frac{1}{6} & -\frac{5}{6} & \frac{1}{2} \\ \frac{1}{18} & -\frac{11}{18} & \frac{1}{6} \\ \frac{5}{36} & -\frac{1}{36} & -\frac{1}{12} \end{bmatrix}$$

and the solution is

$$X = A^{-1}B = \begin{bmatrix} \frac{1}{6} & -\frac{5}{6} & \frac{1}{2} \\ \frac{1}{18} & -\frac{11}{18} & \frac{1}{6} \\ \frac{5}{36} & -\frac{1}{36} & -\frac{1}{12} \end{bmatrix} \begin{bmatrix} 10 \\ 5 \\ 9 \end{bmatrix}$$

$$= \begin{bmatrix} 2 \\ -1 \\ \frac{1}{2} \end{bmatrix}$$

or

$$x_1 = 2 \qquad x_2 = -1 \qquad x_3 = \frac{1}{2}$$

EXERCISES

9-21. Make more detailed flowcharts for the boxes labeled 1, 2, and 3 in the matrix-inversion flowchart, and incorporate these into the main flowchart. This illustrates the concept of *modularity*. Often, large programs are organized into functional modules. The advantage of this is that if a more efficient method is found for one of the modules, only that module need be changed, rather than the whole program.

9-22. Use the algorithm to find the inverse of

$$A = \begin{bmatrix} 2 & 0 & 4 & -6 \\ 4 & -1 & 3 & 0 \\ 0 & 2 & 1 & -3 \\ 1 & 3 & 0 & 5 \end{bmatrix}$$

9-23. Name your computed matrix B, and find the matrix product AB. Using the definition of matrix product, $c_{ij} = \sum_{k=1}^{n} a_{ik} b_{kj}$, make a flowchart for matrix multiplication.

9-24. Follow the matrix-inversion flowchart carefully for

$$A = \begin{bmatrix} 1 & 0 & 4 & -1 \\ 3 & 0 & 1 & 2 \\ 0 & -2 & 5 & -3 \\ 2 & -2 & 3 & 1 \end{bmatrix}$$

What difficulty occurs when $j = 2$? Revise the flowchart to include a test for this situation and a remedy (your own).

9-25. If the matrix A is singular (det $A = 0$), the inverse of A does not exist. The difficulty mentioned in Exercise 9-24 is related to singularity. If, for some $j \le n$, there is no nonzero a_{kj}, where $j < k \le n$, then the matrix is singular. Revise the change made in Exercise 9-24 to include a test for singularity.

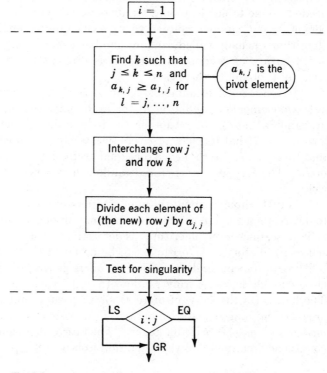

Fig. 9-9

9-26.   In Chap. 10 we will see that unusual results are sometimes obtained
        when arithmetic is done on computers. These are particularly evident
        in matrix inversion. One way to avoid much of this error is to use a
        process called *pivoting*. To include pivoting, we could replace box 2 of
        our first matrix-inversion flowchart with Fig. 9-9.

        By the nature of computer computation, if the pivot element is
        less (in absolute value) than 10^{-10}, the matrix is *ill-conditioned*, which,
        due to computing constraints, is the same as singular. Make a more
        detailed flowchart of the change above to allow pivoting and a test for
        singularity (and ill-conditioning).

9-5 RANDOM NUMBERS AND BUFFON'S NEEDLE PROBLEM

One very powerful use of digital computers is that of simulation and mathematical modeling. In this section we examine a classical problem of probability theory in the light of its mathematical model. We will then simulate
this problem using random, or more properly, pseudo-random, numbers.

Random numbers are most often used when statistical analyses are
performed on a computer. When this is done, a source of random numbers is
needed. One table of random numbers was created by listing the serial numbers of freight cars in a railroad yard. Now random numbers are computed by
algorithms, usually called random-number generators. Because of the "random" nature of random numbers, it is difficult to describe them except in
terms of probability theory.

Given a set A of numbers, a subset $B \subset A$ is a random subset of A if, for
any two elements a_1 and a_2 of A, the probability that $a_1 \epsilon B$ is the same as the
probability that $a_2 \epsilon B$. Another way to describe the subset B of random numbers is to say that its elements were selected by a nonpattern. That is to say
that there is no pattern; hence the equal probability to the selection of elements
of B. The freight-car-generated random numbers fit this requirement quite
well.

A little thought about the nonpattern requirement shows that any attempt
to devise an algorithm to generate random numbers is doomed to failure. This
is because, once any "algorithm" is determined, it is itself a pattern, and hence
self-contradictory. Algorithms can be designed that satisfy the equal-proba-
bility requirement, and the sets of numbers generated by such algorithms are
close enough to being truly random to make them an acceptable substitute.
The better (in the sense of more random) pseudo-random-number generators
are based on congruence arithmetic. Two integers m, n are said to be *congruent
modulo* p if $(m - n)/p$ is an integer. The integer p is called the modulus of the
congruence relation, and the usual notation is

$$m \equiv n \ (\text{mod } p)$$

Another way to state this relation is "*m* is congruent to its remainder *n* upon division by *p*." Now we can state the general form of two pseudo-random-number generators.

Our first algorithm is based on the Fibonacci series, and is essentially an additive congruential method. We choose two starting constants, k_1 and k_2, and then generate pseudo-random values r_i, using

$$r_0 = k_1$$
$$r_1 = k_2$$
$$r_{i+1} \equiv r_i + r_{i-1} \bmod (m)$$

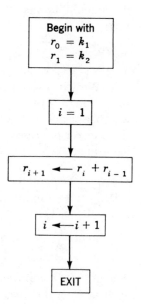

Fig. 9-10 Fibonacci random-number generator.

The sequence $\{r_i\}$ is a Fibonacci sequence, when $k_1 = 0$ and $k_2 = 1$; these are the usual choices for computing as well. On a binary machine of word length *n*, the best choice of the modulus *m* is $m = 2^n$. On a word machine choose $m = 10^d$, where *d* is the word size (the differences between these types of computers will be discussed in Chap. 10). A second, and statistically better, method is the multiplicative congruential generator

$$r_1 = k_1$$
$$r_{i+1} \equiv k_2 r_1 \bmod (m)$$

The choice of *m* is the same as for the Fibonacci method; for a binary machine choose k_1 to be any odd integer and k_2 the largest odd power of 5 less than *m*;

on a word machine, choose k_1 to be any integer not divisible by 2 or 5, and k_2 any integer in the set

$$\{3,11,13,19,21,27,29,37,53,59,61,67,69,77,83,91\}$$

By a convenient peculiarity of computer arithmetic, when the modulus m is the word size of the machine, the usual computer arithmetic is identical with the congruence arithmetic required.

The Buffon needle problem is concerned with dropping a needle onto a surface marked with parallel lines. If the distance between the lines is h and the length of the needle is l, then it can be shown that, once the needle is dropped, the probability that it will intersect one of the parallel lines is

$$P_{\text{cross}} = \frac{2l}{\pi h}$$

We will use random numbers to simulate dropping the needle onto the surface many times. Each time the needle is "dropped," we shall test to see whether or not it crossed a line. By keeping track of the number of drops and the number of crosses, we can approximate the probability of the needle crossing a line. Knowing this, we can compute the number π by

$$\pi = \frac{2l}{h} \cdot \frac{\text{number of drops}}{\text{number of crosses}}$$

or

$$\pi = \frac{2l}{hP}$$

The use of a computer and random numbers to simulate a real-world situation, such as we are doing, is known as Monte Carlo analysis.

We will generate two random numbers to simulate each "drop." These random numbers, r_1 and r_2, refer to the position of the needle between two lines. Knowing its position and the length of the needle and the distance between the lines, we can determine whether or not it crossed a line.

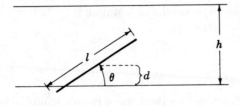

d : distance from midpoint of needle to nearer line

l : length of needle

h : distance between lines

θ : acute angle between needle and nearer line

Fig. 9-11

With the parameters as defined in Fig. 9-11, we can derive conditions to determine whether or not the needle crosses a line. The position of the needle is completely determined (except for symmetries) by r_1 and r_2, defined by

$$r_1 = \sin \theta$$

$$r_2 = \frac{d}{h/2}$$

Since $0 \le \theta \le 90°$, we will have

$$0 \le r_1 \le 1$$

The ratio $d/(h/2)$ is used for r_2 in order to ensure that

$$0 \le r_2 \le 1$$

If the needle happened to fall with its midpoint closer to the top line, we have a case exactly symmetric (mirror image) of the situation shown in Fig. 9-11. Similarly, we can restrict θ to an acute angle, rather than $0 \le \theta \le 180°$, by a reflective symmetry. These restrictions are more convenient than necessary: it is somewhat easier to generate (pseudo) random numbers in the interval from 0 to 1; hence the bounds on r_1 and r_2. Suppose, now, that we have generated specific random values for r_1 and r_2. Since we have then simulated a drop, we want to see whether or not the needle crosses a line. Due to trigonometric definitions, if we know the length s of the hypotenuse of a right triangle, and one of the acute angles, ϕ, then the other two sides of the triangle are as shown:

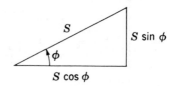

The distance of the end of the needle nearer a line is shown below to be $d - \frac{l}{2} \sin \theta$.

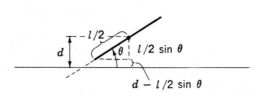

In order to cross the line, we must have

$$d < \frac{l}{2} \sin \theta$$

Since $r_2 = d/(h/2)$, then $d = (h/2)r_2$; so the crossing condition is

$$\frac{h}{2} r_2 < \frac{l}{2} r_1$$

or

$$hr_2 < lr_1$$

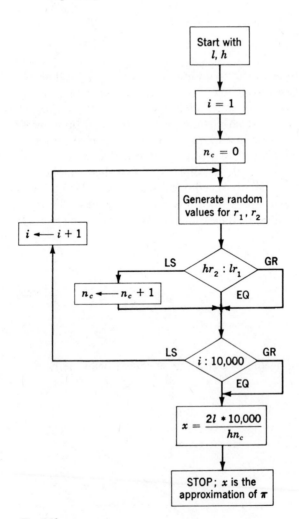

Fig. 9-12

If the length of the needle is greater than the separation between the lines, the needle could cross two lines in one drop. The condition for a second crossing is

$$h(2 - r_2) < lr_1$$

We could continue to derive conditions for three or more crossings, but this becomes tedious, and makes an otherwise interesting problem boring. We shall assume, then, that $l < h$, and then need only the first condition. Now our model of a real-world situation is complete: by generating random values for r_1 and r_2, we simulate a drop of the needle. By testing the "drop" according to the condition

$$hr_2 < lr_1$$

we can determine whether or not the simulated drop resulted in a crossing. The Monte Carlo simulation proceeds by generating hundreds of drops and keeping track of the number of crossings. A flowchart for the computer model of the Buffon needle problem is shown in Fig. 9-12. The process is allowed to simulate 10,000 drops.

EXERCISES

9-27. Practice the following congruence relations:

a. $18 \equiv$ _____ (mod 7)   b. $13 \equiv$ _____ (mod 7)
c. $11 \equiv$ _____ (mod 7)   d. $7 \equiv$ _____ (mod 4)
e. $3 \equiv$ _____ (mod 4)   f. $3 \equiv$ _____ (mod 2)
g. $5 \equiv$ _____ (mod 2)   h. $3 \equiv$ _____ (mod 1)

9-28. In Exercise 9-27 you saw that it is possible for several numbers to be congruent to the same number. If n is the modulus of a specific congruence relation, then the set of integers $\{0,1,2, \ldots , n - 1\}$ is known as the *complete set of residues modulo n*. List the complete set of residues modulo 7; modulo 8.

9-29. Given a complete set of residues A, we can define sets of numbers congruent to the elements of A:

$$R_1 = \{n:n \equiv a_1 \pmod{n}\}$$
$$R_2 = \{n:n \equiv a_2 \pmod{n}\}$$
$$\cdot \cdot \cdot \cdot \cdot \cdot \cdot \cdot \cdot \cdot \cdot \cdot \cdot \cdot \cdot$$
$$R_n = \{n:n \equiv a_n \pmod{n}\}$$

where $A = \{a_1, a_2, \ldots , a_n\}$ is the complete set of residues modulo n. Now if I is the set of all integers, is the following equality true?

$$I = R_1 \cup R_2 \cup R_3 \cup \cdots \cdots \cup R_n$$

9-30. Using the pseudo-random-number generator

$$r_1 = 3$$
$$r_{i+1} = 2r \pmod{19}$$

generate (in order) the first 20 numbers in the sequence $\{r_i\}$.

9-31. Apply the pseudo-random numbers from Exercise 9-30 to the Buffon needle-problem simulation. To get random numbers between 0 and 1, divide each by 19. How many crosses are there if $l = h/2$?

9-6 THE GAME OF NIM

Nim is an ancient Japanese game that lends itself to an interesting solution algorithm involving Boolean algebra concepts. The game is played by two players and several groups of objects. In his turn, a player may remove as many objects as he wants from one group. The player removing the last object is the winner. The game can be played with any number of groups and any number of objects in each group. Below is a sample game showing the moves of players A and B. Player A is using the winning algorithm.

After player A's third move, it is clear that he will win: if B removes two objects from a group, A removes the two in the other group in his next turn and wins; if B removes only one object, as in Fig. 9-13, then A removes only one

```
Start:
                        1  1  1
                     1  1  1  1  1
                  1  1  1  1  1  1  1

        A1                              B1
        1  1  1
     1  1  1  1  1                    1  1  1  1  1
  1  1  1  1  1  1                 1  1  1  1  1  1

        A2                              B2
     1  1  1  1  1                 1  1
     1  1  1  1  1                 1  1  1  1  1

        A3                              B3
        1  1                          1
        1  1                          1  1

        A4                              B4
        1                               1
        1
  A5  (wins)
```

Fig. 9-13

object from the other group, and wins on his next move.   While it is apparent
that A will win after his third move, actually, A won the game by his first move.

The algorithm to win Nim is based on the binary representations of the
number of objects in the groups.   These binary numbers are found and then
combined with the Boolean EXCLUSIVE-OR operation.   If the EXCLU-
SIVE-OR sum is zero, the game is said to be in the *even state*.   If the EXCLU-
SIVE-OR sum is nonzero, the game is in the *odd state*.   To play Nim by the
winning algorithm, a player first determines whether the game is in the even
or the odd state.   The object is to move so that the game is in an even state.
If the game is already in an even state, the player must make a random move,
and hope that his opponent leaves the game in the odd state after his move.
If the game is in the odd state when he gets his turn, he moves in such a way as
to create an even state.   The details of this will be explained in a general form
after the example below.   In this example, the game in Fig. 9-13 is analyzed
at each step.

```
Start:
                        1   1   1              011
                    1   1   1   1   1          101
                1   1   1   1   1   1   1      ⊕111
                                               ───
                                               001    odd state

 A1:                    1   1   1              011
                    1   1   1   1   1          101
                1   1   1   1   1   1          ⊕110
                                               ───
                                               000    even state

 B1:                                           000
                    1   1   1   1   1          101
                1   1   1   1   1   1          ⊕110
                                               ───
                                               011    odd state

 A2:                                           000
                    1   1   1   1   1          101
                    1   1   1   1   1          ⊕101
                                               ───
                                               000    even state

 B2:                                           000
                    1   1                      010
                    1   1   1   1   1          ⊕101
                                               ───
                                               111    odd state

 A3:                                           000
                    1   1                      010
                    1   1                      ⊕010
                                               ───
                                               000    even state
```

$B3$:			000	
	1		001	
	1	1	$\oplus 010$	
			011	odd state

$A4$:		000	
	1	001	
	1	$\oplus 001$	
		000	even state

$B4$:		000	
		000	
	1	$\oplus 001$	
		001	odd state

$A5$: (wins)	000	
	000	
	$\oplus 000$	
	000	even state

To state the winning algorithm in general terms, we first define

n_i = number of objects in ith group
m = number of groups

The EXCLUSIVE-OR sum of the binary representations of the n_i are found by

$$\text{EORSUM} = (((n_1 \oplus n_2) \oplus n_3) \oplus \cdots) \oplus n_m).$$

Now, if EORSUM is zero, the game is in the even state, and a random move must be made. If EORSUM $\neq 0$, the game is in the odd state, and we must determine (1) how many objects should be removed and (2) from which group. A flowchart of the algorithm up to this point is shown in Fig. 9-14.

To create an even state from a given odd state, it is necessary to define a new (binary) number for each group. Thus, we define

$$k_i = (n_i) \wedge (\text{EORSUM})$$

for each group. We then find the greatest power of 2, calling it 2^j, such that

$$2^j \leq \text{EORSUM}$$

Using this binary number, 2^j, we examine the k_i and find the first value of i, calling it i_0, such that

$$k_{i_0} \geq 2^j$$

This tells us which group should be changed. Now the i_0 group is changed by

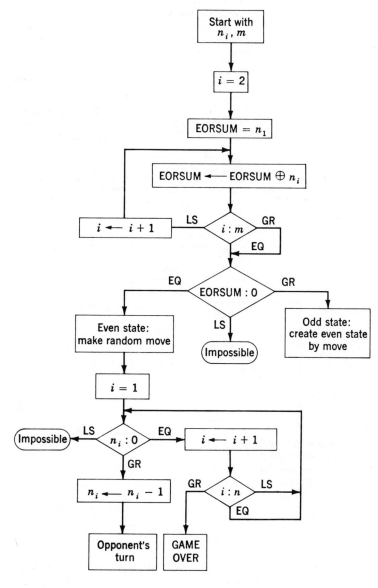

Fig. 9-14

the replacement

$$n_{i_0} \leftarrow (n_{i_0}) \oplus (\text{EORSUM}).$$

While this is a complicated procedure for a person to execute, it is easily done on computers, especially since computers operate in a binary mode and have

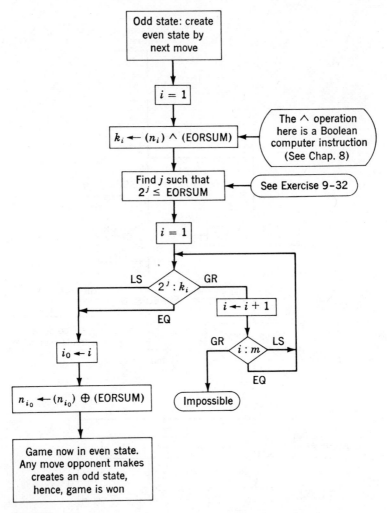

Fig. 9-15

Boolean instructions as part of their repertoire.   The flowchart for this part of the algorithm is Fig. 9-15.

EXERCISES

9-32.   Develop an algorithm and make a flowchart for the box in Fig. 9-15. (*Hint:* Assume the following characteristic of a machine division instruction: If n is a binary number, then

$$n \div 2 = [n/2]$$

where $\div$ denotes machine division, / denotes the usual arithmetic division, and [ ] is the greatest-integer function.)

9-33. Player B in the game shown in Fig. 9-13 did not play using the winning algorithm. Show the moves that players A and B would make if they both moved according to the algorithm.

9-34. Follow the flowchart in detail for the first two moves player A made in Fig. 9-13. Compute EORSUM, and find the k_i and j, and then i_0.

9-7 SOLUTION OF SIMULTANEOUS LINEAR EQUATIONS

Chapter 5 discussed the solution of a system of simultaneous linear equations. A system of the form

$$
\begin{aligned}
a_{11}x_1 + a_{12}x_2 + \cdots + a_{1n}x_n &= b_1 \\
a_{22}x_1 + a_{22}x_2 + \cdots + a_{2n}x_n &= b_2 \\
\cdot \cdot \cdot \cdot \cdot \cdot \cdot \cdot \cdot \cdot \cdot \cdot \cdot \cdot \cdot \\
a_{n1}x_1 + a_{n2}x_2 + \cdots + a_{nn}x_n &= b_n
\end{aligned}
\tag{9-1}
$$

can, by straightforward computation, be transformed into an equivalent system

$$
\begin{aligned}
a_{11}x_1 + a_{12}x_2 + \cdots + a_{1n}x_n &= b_1 \\
a'_{22}x_2 + \cdots + a'_{2n}x_n &= b'_2 \\
\cdot \cdot \cdot \cdot \cdot \cdot \\
a'_{nn}x_n &= b'_n
\end{aligned}
\tag{9-2}
$$

where the prime on a'_{ij} indicates the effect of the transformation on the coefficients.

Once a system of simultaneous linear equations has been reduced to the second form, the solution is easily obtained by a process known as back substitution. In this process, the nth equation is solved for x_n.

$$
x_n = \frac{b'_n}{a'_{nn}}
$$

When this value of x_n is substituted back into the $(n-1)$st equation, x_{n-1} is the only unknown, and can be found:

$$
a'_{n-1,n-1}x_{n-1} + a_{n-1,n}x_n = b'_{n-1}
$$

Since $x_n = b'_n/a'_{nn}$, we get

$$
a'_{n-1,n-1}x_{n-1} + a_{n-1,n}\left(\frac{b'_n}{a'_{nn}}\right) = b'_{n-1}
$$

or

$$
x_{n-1} = \frac{b'_{n-1} - a_{n-1,n}(b'_n/a'_{nn})}{a'_{n-1,n-1}}
$$

At each step in the back substitution, we use previously computed solutions to solve for the next one, until we substitute the (known) values of x_2, x_3, . . . , x_n into the first equation to solve for x_1. Once this step is complete, we have found the solution to the original system of equations (9-1).

This process is simple enough to make one ask why the subject is treated again in this chapter. The answer is that certain peculiarities occur when the process is executed on a digital computer. Because of inherent limitations of computers, the process of back substitution does not necessarily result in the true solution to a system of equations. These limitations are due to the finite precision of computer arithmetic, and are considered more thoroughly in Chap. 10. For the present, we can say that if the matrix

$$X = \begin{pmatrix} x_1 \\ x_2 \\ \cdot \\ \cdot \\ \cdot \\ x_n \end{pmatrix}$$

is the exact solution of the system (9-1), written in matrix form

$$A \cdot X = B$$

then the solution X' obtained from back substitution may not satisfy

$$X = X'$$

Another way to state this is: If we substituted the "solution" back into the original system of equations, we would get

$$A \cdot X' = C$$

where, possibly,

$$B \neq C$$

While this is a dismaying situation, there are ways of improving a solution; and that is the topic of this section. We must first extend the notion of a sequence introduced in the beginning of this chapter. Recall that we said that an iterative technique may result in a sequence $\{x_i\}$ of real numbers, where the sequence hopefully converges to a limit x. Now we must consider the elements in the sequence to be matrices. In this context, we will consider a sequence $\{X_i\}$ of matrices that converges to the solution matrix X. This extension is easier to visualize if we consider elements of the sequence to be coordinates of points. In the case of a sequence of real numbers, the elements are coordinates of points on the real-number line. For sequences of matrices, a particular element

$$X_i = \begin{pmatrix} x_{i1} \\ x_{i2} \\ \cdot \\ \cdot \\ \cdot \\ x_{in} \end{pmatrix}$$

can be considered to be the coordinates of a point in n-dimensional space.

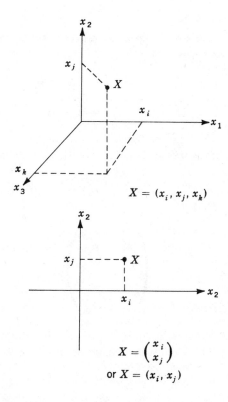

Fig. 9-16 Matrices as coordinates of points.

In describing the algorithm to compute elements in the sequence $\{X_i\}$, we will do all our computations using matrices. Remember that we are looking for a sequence $\{X_i\}$ that converges to a matrix X, where

$$A \cdot X = B \tag{9-3}$$

In the first iteration we use transformations that reduce A to the form (9-2), and then with back substitution, we get our first trial solution,

$$X_1 = \begin{pmatrix} x_{11} \\ x_{12} \\ \cdot \\ \cdot \\ \cdot \\ x_{1n} \end{pmatrix}$$

By substituting these values back into the original system of equations, we form the matrix product

$$A \cdot X_1 = B_1 \tag{9-4}$$

The next step is to subtract the system (9-4) from the system (9-3). Doing this, we get

$$A \cdot X - A \cdot X_1 = B - B_1$$

or

$$A \cdot (X - X_1) = B - B_1 \tag{9-5}$$

Let us pause to examine the meaning of the system (9-5). We know the matrices A, X_1, B, and B_1. By defining

$$E_1 = X - X_1$$

that is,

$$E_1 = \begin{pmatrix} x_1 - x_{11} \\ x_2 - x_{12} \\ \cdot \\ \cdot \\ \cdot \\ x_n - x_{1n} \end{pmatrix}$$

we now have an expression for the error in the first trial-solution matrix X_1. This makes it reasonable now to solve the system

$$A \cdot E_1 = C_1 \tag{9-6}$$

where $C_1 = B - B_1$. If we name the elements of E_1 by

$$e_{11} = x_1 - x_{11}$$
$$e_{12} = x_2 - x_{12}$$
$$\cdot \cdot \cdot \cdot \cdot \cdot \cdot \cdot$$
$$e_{1n} = x_n - x_{1n}$$

we can now solve the system (9-6) for the error terms e_{ij}. When we do this, we know, approximately, the values of the entries of E_1. This tells us that

$$x_1 = x_{11} + e_{11}$$
$$x_2 = x_{12} + e_{12}$$
$$\cdots \cdots \cdots$$
$$x_n = x_{1n} + e_{1n}$$

or in matrix form,

$$X = X_1 + E_1$$

In other words, the matrix E_1 is a correction to X_1, the first trial solution. Since there is still the possibility of error in the solution for E_1, all we have is a better trial solution. Thus we define

$$X_2 = X_1 + E_1$$

and complete the first iteration. For the second iteration, we proceed as before.

We first substitute X_2 back into the original system and form the matrix product

$$A \cdot X_2 = B_2 \tag{9-7}$$

Subtracting the system (9-7) from the original system (9-3), we get

$$A \cdot X - A \cdot X_2 = B - B_2$$

or

$$A \cdot (X - X_2) = C_2$$

where

$$C_2 = B - B_2$$

Defining

$$E_2 = X - X_2$$

we have the new correction term. Again we solve the system

$$A \cdot E_2 = C_2$$

for the elements of E_2. Once we have them, we can further refine our trial solution by the fact that

$$X = X_2 + E_2$$

We still cannot assume that E_2 was an exact solution; so all we really have is a new trial solution

$$X_3 = X_2 + E_2$$

The process should now be pretty clear. Each iteration produces a correction to the previous trial solution. If the sequence $\{X_i\}$ converges to the true solution X, then the elements of the correction matrices E_i should get smaller. Thus we have a stopping criterion for the iterative process: at the end of each iteration, we check the magnitude of the elements in the correction matrix. If they are greater than a predetermined tolerance, we iterate again; otherwise we have reached an adequate trial solution.

We conclude the section with a flowchart of the iterative process and exercises showing various facets of the process.

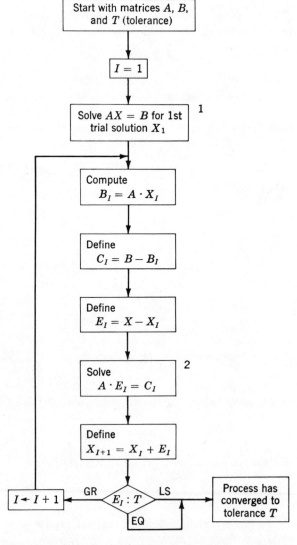

Fig. 9-17 Iterative solution of simultaneous linear equations.

EXERCISES

9-35. The process of transforming a system of equations of form (9-1) into form (9-2) is very similar to the matrix-inversion algorithm of Sec. 9-4. Referring to that section, make a flowchart for the transformation of a system of equations from form (9-1) to form (9-2), and then solution by back substitution. This flowchart would replace boxes 1 and 2 in Fig. 9-17.

9-36. Follow the iteration algorithm for the system

$$3x_1 - 4x_2 = 1$$
$$37x_1 - 50x_2 = 11$$

Use two-digit decimal arithmetic.
The exact solution is $x_1 = 3$, $x_2 = 2$.

chapter ten

COMPUTER COMPUTATION AND ERROR ANALYSIS

A certain amount of error is unavoidable when arithmetic is performed on a computer. This error is attributable to the finite memory of computers, and is clearly seen when the development of the real-number system is understood. Once the source of error is known, it can be studied, and then reduced as much as possible, in the light of this new knowledge.

10-1 HISTORICAL DEVELOPMENT OF THE REAL-NUMBER SYSTEM

When man first began to count, the beginnings of arithmetic were formed. The *natural numbers* are the numbers

0, 1, 2, 3, 4, . . .

Natural numbers were useful for counting and comparing quantities. With natural numbers it is possible to perform addition and multiplication, where multiplication of natural numbers is, essentially, repeated addition.

As man began to develop mathematically, the shortcomings of the natural-number system became noticeable. Questions like "How many?" and "Do you have as many as I?" can be answered in the natural-number system. A question like "How many more do you have?" cannot be answered with natural numbers. Such a question requires the notion of subtraction. If one person has m sheep and a second person has n sheep, when the first person asks how many more sheep does the second man have, he is phrasing the equation

$$m + x = n$$

The solution is easy.

$$x = n - m$$

But notice that subtraction is required to answer the question. As long as the second man has more sheep than the first, i.e., as long as

$$n > m$$

there is no difficulty. If, however, the first man had more sheep, then $n - m$ is a negative number. Due to situations like this, the need for a larger number system was realized, and as a consequence, the *integer* number system evolved. The set of integers includes the natural numbers as subset:

$$I = \{. \ . \ . \ , -3, -2, -1, 0, 1, 2, 3, \ . \ . \ .\}$$

In much the same way that solution of the equation

$$x + m = n \tag{10-1}$$

necessitated the extension from natural numbers to integers, solution of the equation

$$x \cdot a = b \tag{10-2}$$

requires another extension. If b happens to be an integral multiple of a, then Eq. (10-2) has a solution within the set of integers. It is easy to pick values of a and b so that Eq. (10-2) has no solution in the set of integers. For instance,

$$x \cdot 2 = 3$$

has no integral solution. In order to be able to solve equations of the form

$$px = q$$

where p and q are integers, it is necessary to expand from the set of integers to a more comprehensive set, the set of *rational* numbers. The set of rational numbers can be described by

$$R = \left\{ x : x = \frac{p}{q}, \ p \ \epsilon \ I, \ q \ \epsilon \ I, \ q \neq 0 \right\}$$

where I is the set of integers.   Notice how the motivation for rational numbers in the solution of

$$px = q$$

appears in the definition of the set of rational numbers.

We have seen that number systems have expanded to allow solution of more complicated equations.   The rationals were necessary to solve

$$px = q$$

where p and q are integers.   This extension process can be carried another significant step.

Suppose you have a can of paint that will cover 75 square feet.   If you ask how long is the side of the largest square that the paint will cover, your question demands the solution of

$$x^2 = 75 \tag{10-3}$$

where x is the length of the side of the square.   One solution of Eq. (10-3) is

$$
\begin{aligned}
x &= \sqrt{75} \\
  &= \sqrt{25 \times 3} \\
  &= \sqrt{25} \times \sqrt{3} \\
  &= 5 \times \sqrt{3}
\end{aligned}
$$

Another solution is $x = -5 \times \sqrt{3}$, but a square with negative length sides is meaningless in this context.   The importance of the solution $x = 5 \times \sqrt{3}$ is that the number $5 \times \sqrt{3}$ is not a rational number.   That is, there are no integers p and q such that

$$5 \times \sqrt{3} = \frac{p}{q}$$

Again we have the situation where a larger number system is needed to be able to solve an equation.   This next system, the *real-number system*, is most easily described in terms of the decimal representation of rational numbers.

The decimal representation of an integer is simply that integer followed by a decimal point, and then 0's, until we get tired of writing them.   The decimal representation of the integer -3 is

$$-3.0000000 \ldots$$

Instead of writing many zeros, we can indicate repetition of decimal digits to the right of the decimal sign by a bar over the digits that repeat.   The decimal representation of -3 is then

$$-3.\overline{0}$$

Decimal representations of rational numbers are of two types: terminating and nonterminating. The rational numbers $\frac{1}{4}$ and $\frac{1}{7}$ exhibit these types:

$$\frac{1}{4} = 0.25$$
$$\frac{1}{7} = 0.14\overline{14}$$

In a trivial way, any rational number can be considered to have a nonterminating decimal representation because it is always possible to append zeros on the right:

$$\frac{1}{4} = 0.25\overline{00}$$

Thus the rational numbers are those numbers that either have terminating decimal representations or decimal representations that repeat infinitely after some point. It is this characteristic that allows description of real numbers that are not rational numbers. These real numbers, sometimes called irrational numbers, are numbers that have a *nonterminating, nonrepeating* decimal representation. One such irrational number is the number

$$\pi = 3.141592 \ . \ . \ .$$

The number π has been computed to an excess of 100,000 digits with no repetition. This alone does not assure that there will be no repetition. It is possible to prove, however, that the decimal representation of π is nonrepeating and nonterminating.

At this point, it may seem that we are rather far astray from the topic of this chapter, namely, errors in computer computation. The reason for discussing the various number systems is that both the number systems developed in order to solve different equations and the types of equations in which computer errors commonly occur are those which require the real-number system.

The crux of errors in computer computation is that irrational numbers cannot be represented within a computer; they can only be approximated by a rational number. Once this approximation is made, error in the computations with "irrational" numbers can never be avoided. In order to understand this source of error more fully, it is necessary to know how numbers are represented within a computer.

10-2 REPRESENTATION OF NUMBERS WITHIN COMPUTERS

There are two basic types of memory organizations for computers: the character approach and the word approach. The adjectives character and word refer to the way numbers are represented in the computer's memory unit. A memory word can be pictured as a string of devices, called bits, which can have values of either 1 or 0. Memory words are always finite, and seldom exceed 64 bits. Some special computers have been built with 80-bit words, but they are engineering curiosities, and not in general use. On both types of computers, numbers can have two forms: fixed-point and floating-point. The *fixed-point form* is the mode of representing integers; the *floating-point form* is used for representing rational numbers.

Character machines represent numbers using 10 as the number base. A fixed-point number, or integer, is stored in up to 20 memory locations, one decimal digit per location. (The maximum number of locations may vary from one computer manufacturer to the next.) When a rational number is stored in a computer, it is stored in floating-point form. On a character machine, floating-point form closely corresponds to scientific notation. The number

$$.\text{DDDDD} \times 10^{\text{EE}}$$

where the D's and E's are decimal digits, would appear in memory as

$$\text{DDDDD|EE}$$

with each decimal digit occupying one memory location. Again there is a maximum number of digits (which varies, depending upon the manufacturer); this maximum is usually 20. The exponent of the floating-point number cannot exceed 99.

If we have a character-oriented computer in which 20 is the maximum number of digits that either a fixed- or a floating-point number can have, what numbers can be represented? The set of integers that can be stored in fixed-point form is

$$I_{\text{fix}} = \{i\!:\!-(10^{19} - 1) \le i \le (10^{19} - 1) \text{ and } i \text{ is an integer}\}$$

The set of rational numbers that can be exactly represented in floating-point form is

$$R_{\text{float}} = \{x\!:\!x = f \times 10^e, \text{ where } f \text{ is an 18-decimal-digit fraction,}$$
$$-1 < f < 1, \text{ and } e \text{ is an integer } -100 < e < 100\}$$

The importance of the set R_{float} is that not all rational numbers are members of R_{float}; hence these numbers cannot be represented within the computer.

In a word-oriented computer (as in a character machine), the memory word contains a fixed number of bits. The two types of number representations, fixed- and floating-point, occupy one and two memory-storage locations, respectively. The number of bits in the memory word determines what numbers can be represented. For the remainder of the chapter, we shall consider a 16-bit word-oriented computer. We do this for two reasons: Similar conclusions will apply to character-oriented machines, and longer word lengths only complicate the discussion. Figure 10-1 shows a schematic representation of a memory location in a sixteen-bit word machine.

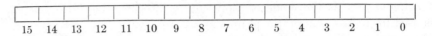

15   14   13   12   11   10   9   8   7   6   5   4   3   2   1   0

Fig. 10-1 A 16-bit memory word.

Each bit has the binary property of being either a 1 or a 0, and for this reason integers are stored in a word machine in binary form. For convenience, the bits in a memory word are numbered, in our case from 0 to 15, going from right to left. The right part of a word is called the low-order end, and the left part, the high-order end, consistent with the bit-position numbers. It is fairly easy to see how positive integers are represented in a word machine. The bits are 1 or 0, depending on whether the digits in the binary representation of the positive integer are 1 or 0. Some decimal numbers, their binary equivalents, and their computer-memory representation are shown in Fig. 10-2.

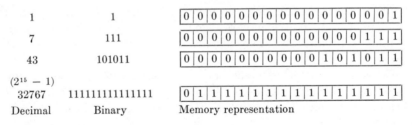

1	1
7	111
43	101011
$(2^{15} - 1)$ 32767	111111111111111
Decimal	Binary	Memory representation

Fig. 10-2

Obviously, not all integers can be represented in a word machine; also, we have said nothing about negative integers. Since we have 16 bits, each of which is 1 or 0, we can form 2^{16} different bit patterns, or binary numbers. This means we can represent only 2^{16} different integers. Usually, we want to be able to work with negative as well as positive integers, so that we can subtract, for example. In order to represent negative numbers, a special convention, called *two's-complement form*, is used.

In two's-complement form, the high-order bit (bit 15) is used to indicate whether the integer is positive (bit 15 = 0) or negative (bit 15 = 1). The two's-complement form of a positive integer is its binary representation. To form the two's complement of a negative binary number, the 0's are changed to 1's, the 1's are changed to 0's, and then 1 is added to the result of the change. As an example, the two's-complement form of -3 is shown for 16-digit binary numbers.

```
3:                  0  0  0  0  0  0  0  0  0  0  0  0  0  0  1  1
Complement:         1  1  1  1  1  1  1  1  1  1  1  1  1  1  0  0
                                                               +1
Two's complement:   1  1  1  1  1  1  1  1  1  1  1  1  1  1  0  1
```

Notice that adding the 16-digit binary representation of 3 to the 16-digit two's-complement form of -3 results in zero:

```
(3)     ¦ 0  0  0  0  0  0  0  0  0  0  0  0  0  1  1
(-3)    ¦ 1  1  1  1  1  1  1  1  1  1  1  1  1  0  1
      1 ¦ 0  0  0  0  0  0  0  0  0  0  0  0  0  0  0
```

The carry from the addition in the fifteenth position results in a 1 in bit position 16; but the memory word contains only bits for positions 0 to 15; so the last carry is lost. Some examples of storage representation of negative integers are shown in Fig. 10-3.

Decimal   Internal (memory) form

Decimal	Internal (memory) form
-3	1 1 1 1 1 1 1 1 1 1 1 1 1 1 0 1
-4	1 1 1 1 1 1 1 1 1 1 1 1 1 1 0 0
-11	1 1 1 1 1 1 1 1 1 1 1 1 0 1 0 1

Fig. 10-3

Using two's-complement form, the set of integers that are representable by 16 binary digits is

$$I_{\text{fix}} = \{i : -2^{15} \leq i < 2^{15}\}$$

Floating-point numbers occupy two memory words of storage. The general form of the floating-point mode is

$$\pm F \times 2^{E}$$

where F is a binary fraction

$$0 \leq F < 1$$

and E is a signed binary integer. We shall decide to allocate the two memory words between F and E as in Fig. 10-4.

First word:

$\pm$		F_{high}
15	14	0

Second word:

F_{low}	$\pm$	E
15	9 8 7	0

Fig. 10-4

Notice that the fraction portion occupies more than one word. The part of F in the first memory word, F_{high}, is the high-order, or most significant, part of the fraction. The low-order, or least significant, part of the fraction is contained in the second word. Altogether, the fraction is a 22-bit binary fraction between 0 and 1. Bit 15 of the first word is the sign bit for the fraction: if bit 15 is 0, the fraction is positive, and if bit 15 is 1, the fraction is negative. The exponent also has a sign bit, bit 8 of the second word. Bits 0 to 7 of the second word contain a binary-integer exponent. We are now is a position to describe the set of rational numbers that can be exactly represented with this floating-point scheme.

To make the discussion simpler, let us assume that the fraction F is a 22-bit binary fraction, and ignore the fact that it is split into two words. Now F is shown in Fig. 10-5. As a further simplification, let us restrict our-

F

±																						

22 21 20 19 18 17 16 15 14 13 12 11 10 9 8 7 6 5 4 3 2 1 0

⋮ Binary point

Fig. 10-5

selves to positive rationals, because their negatives are easily obtained via two's complements. Now consider what rationals can be represented exactly by

$$F \times 2^E$$

where $E = 0$. By setting just one bit in F to 1, we can get the fractions indicated in Fig. 10-6. Setting more than one bit to 1 means that the fractions corresponding to those bits are added. Since any or all of the 22 bits

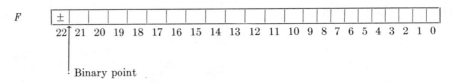

$\frac{1}{2}$ | 0 | 1 | 0 | 0 | 0 | 0 | 0 | 0 | 0 | 0 | 0 | 0 | 0 | 0 | 0 | 0 | 0 | 0 | 0 | 0 | 0 | 0 | 0 |

$\frac{1}{4}$ | 0 | 0 | 1 | 0 | 0 | 0 | 0 | 0 | 0 | 0 | 0 | 0 | 0 | 0 | 0 | 0 | 0 | 0 | 0 | 0 | 0 | 0 | 0 |

$\frac{1}{8}$ | 0 | 0 | 0 | 1 | 0 | 0 | 0 | 0 | 0 | 0 | 0 | 0 | 0 | 0 | 0 | 0 | 0 | 0 | 0 | 0 | 0 | 0 | 0 |

·   ·
·   ·
·   ·

22 21 20 19 18 · · ·   1 0

$\frac{1}{2}^{22}$ | 0 | 0 | 0 | 0 | 0 | 0 | 0 | 0 | 0 | 0 | 0 | 0 | 0 | 0 | 0 | 0 | 0 | 0 | 0 | 0 | 0 | 0 | 1 |

Fig. 10-6

in F can be set to 1, we can exactly represent 2^{22} rational numbers in the interval from 0 to 1. One important consequence of this is that when any number between 0 and 1 is to be represented, we know that if we cannot represent it exactly, the maximum error will be $\frac{1}{2}^{23}$.

Now suppose the exponent E has the value 1. F can have the same values as before; only now E is no longer zero in

$$F \times 2^E$$

so now the numbers

$$1, 1\frac{1}{2}, 1\frac{1}{4}, 1\frac{1}{8}, \ldots, 1\frac{1}{2}^{21}$$

and any sum of the fractions are represented. Thus, in the interval from 1 to 2, we can exactly represent 2^{21} rational numbers, and the maximum error for any other number is $\frac{1}{2}^{22}$. For $E = 3$, the numbers that can be exactly represented are

$$2, 2\frac{1}{2}, 2\frac{1}{4}, 2\frac{1}{8}, \cdots, 2\frac{1}{2^{20}}, 3, 3\frac{1}{2}, 3\frac{1}{4}, 3\frac{1}{8}, \cdots, 3\frac{1}{2}^{20}$$

and any sum of the fractional parts. Now only 2^{20} rationals are represented between 2 and 3, and 2^{20} are between 3 and 4. We see that as E increases, the difference between exactly representable numbers, and hence the maximum error, increases. Let h be the difference between the "closest" representable numbers in any interval determined by E. The intervals determined by E are shown on the number line in Fig. 10-7. In the interval from 0 to 1,

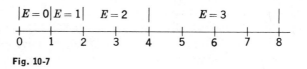

Fig. 10-7

h is $\frac{1}{2}^{22}$. Suppose that some number x is to be represented, and suppose that

$$0 < x < \frac{1}{2}^{22}$$

Then the number x falls somewhere in between the points 0 and $\frac{1}{2}^{22}$; so it cannot be represented exactly. We can see in Fig. 10-8, however, that the

Fig. 10-8

maximum error is $h/2$. Now we see that, knowing h for each interval, we also know the maximum error. Figure 10-9 shows part of the real-number

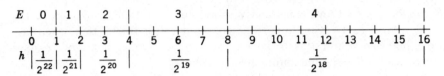

Fig. 10-9

line and how h increases with E.   Notice that, as E increases, h also increases; and hence the "distance" between representable numbers becomes greater.

Up to now, we have said nothing about the possibility of E having negative values. When E has a positive value, the binary point is shifted to the right E places.   By analogy, then, we might expect negative values of E to shift the binary point to the left $|E|$ places, and indeed this is the case.

Negative values of E, then, allow us to make finer divisions on the line of representable numbers.   For instance, if $F = \frac{1}{2}{}^{22}$ and $E = -1$, we represent the number

$$F \times 2^E = \frac{1}{2^{22}} \times 2^{-1}$$

$$= \frac{1}{2^{22}} \times \frac{1}{2}$$

$$= \frac{1}{2^{23}}$$

Thus, for $E = -1$, we represent 2^{22} numbers between 0 and $\frac{1}{2}$; for $E = -2$, we represent 2^{22} numbers in the interval from 0 to $\frac{1}{4}$; and so on.

We can finally appreciate one of the most serious problems of a digital computer: only a subset of the rational numbers can be exactly represented in a computer memory.   Even though this subset is quite large, it is not large enough to provide exact representations of the solution to many common problems, for example, the solution of

$$x^2 - 2 = 0$$

We must be aware of this inherent error, and try to reduce its effect as much as possible.   We consider below ways of doing this.

10-3 ACCURACY AND ERROR

We have established that a certain amount of error is unavoidable in computer computation.   We next consider how to reduce the effect of this error in our computations.   To do this, we must first define two qualities related to accuracy: precision and significance.   These terms apply primarily to situations in which calculations are performed on data from some type of measurement, rather than from data obtained through counting.   We may generalize further and assume that the data are taken from a graduated scale, such as a ruler.   This is no serious restriction, because almost any measured quantity, volts, pounds, seconds, inches, is indicated on some sort of scale (see Fig. 10-10).

Fig. 10-10   A measuring scale.

Precision is related to the gradation on a measuring scale as the number of graduations between two units increases.   Thus one has greater precision when using a scale graduated in 64ths than when using a scale graduated in 16ths.   *Precision*, then, refers to how small a change can be measured on a scale.

On digital computers, precision has a meaning fairly similar to its use in measurement.   The number of bits available to represent a number (say, in floating-point form) is the *precision* of the computer.   In our hypothetical 16-bit-word machine under our floating-point scheme, we have 22 bits to represent a fraction.   We thus have 22-digit binary precision.   Below, we show a way to determine the decimal-digit precision.

Let n be the number of binary bits of precision, and m the number of decimal digits of precision.   We solve

$$10^m = 2^n$$

for m.   We have $n = 22$; so

$$10^m = 2^{22}$$
$$m \log_{10} 10 = 22 \log_{10} 2$$
$$m = 22 \ (0.30103)$$
$$= 6.6$$

So we have almost seven decimal digits of precision.

Where precision may be considered a theoretical limit on the accuracy of a measurement, significance becomes a practical limit on the accuracy of a measurement.   Suppose we want to measure the length of a bar that we know to be exactly $3\frac{1}{3}$ inches long and that we are using a ruler graduated in tenths of an inch.   The bar and the ruler are shown in Fig. 10-11.   We see that the end of the bar is between the third and fourth gradation past the 3-inch mark; so we can say that the bar is between 3.3 and 3.4 inches long.   We can also see that the end of the bar is closer to the 3.3 mark; so, using this ruler, we would have to say that the bar is 3.3 inches long.   This measurement, 3.3, has two significant digits.   A *significant digit* is a digit in a measured

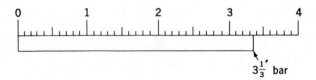

Fig. 10-11

number that we are "sure of." We know that the length of the bar is closer to 3.3 than it is to 3.4. The accepted convention for indicating significant digits is to write only the significant digits. Thus we would say that the bar is 3.3 inches long; we would not write the length as 3.300. Suppose there was a mark on the bar exactly $2\frac{1}{4}$ inches from the end. If we were to measure this distance, what would we call the length? The mark falls exactly halfway between 2.2 and 2.3 on the scale. Here the real difficulty of significant digits is seen. Do we say that the bar is 2.2 inches long because we are sure that it is at least that long, or do we round upward and call it 2.3 inches? In such cases, it is often helpful to consider the purpose of the measurement. If someone is to cut lengths of steel rod to the length of the mark on the original, it would be better to call it 2.3 inches.

There is an interdependence between precision and significance. If the ruler in Fig. 10-11 were graduated in hundredths of an inch, the greater precision would allow us more significance. We could then say that the length of the rod is 3.33 inches and that the distance of the mark from the end is 2.25 inches. Each of these measurements has three significant digits. We see, then, that increased precision allows more significance. The converse of this cannot be achieved through computation. As an example, suppose that 2.25 and 3.33 are the measured lengths of the sides of a rectangular surface. If we compute the area of this surface, we might write

$$
\begin{array}{r}
2.25 \\
3.33 \\
\hline
675 \\
675 \\
675 \\
\hline
7.4925
\end{array}
$$

and say that the area is 7.4925 square inches. In the light of significant figures, claiming 7.4925 to be the measured area is asserting that we made the measurements with an instrument having sufficient precision to allow five significant digits, when in fact we could measure only three significant digits. This is an all-too-common fallacy of computations based on measured data, and must be carefully avoided. The general principle that governs computation with significant digits is that the result of the computation cannot have more significant digits than the original measurements.   A more specific statement of this principle is:

The number of significant digits in the result of computation with measured numbers is the number of digits in the original number having the fewest significant digits.

As an example, in the computation

$$\frac{(2.25)^2 \times 3.368}{1.2005}$$

the result can have only three significant digits.   If this is done by hand, the quotient, after carrying one extra zero in the numerator (17.04950000), is 14.2009, which rounds to 14.201.   Since one of the original terms (2.25) only has three significant digits, the answer, in terms of significant digits, is 14.2.

When computations are performed with concern for significance, the number having the fewest number of significant digits should be found.   Next round all the numbers involved in the computation to one more than this number of significant digits.   That is, if the number with the fewest significant digits has n significant digits, round all numbers to $n + 1$ significant digits.   Then the final result is rounded to n digits.   When rounding a number, for example,

$$d_1d_2d_3d_4 \cdot \cdots \cdot d_nd_{n+1} \cdots$$

to n significant digits, the following rule applies:

If $6 \le d_{n+1} \le 9$, add 1 to d_n.
If $1 \le d_{n+1} \le 4$, delete (or truncate) all digits to the right of d_n.

There are two conventions for the case where d_{n+1} is 5.   The easier rule is to add 1 to d_n if d_{n+1} is 5.   From a statistical viewpoint, a better rule is:

If $d_{n+1} = 5$, then add 1 to d_n if d_n is an odd number and leave d_n unchanged if it is even.

We have mentioned rounding and truncation as they relate to hand calculation using significant digits.   When arithmetic operations are performed on a computer, roundoff and truncation often occur, due to the fixed word length of the computer.   (Newer computers allow the user to specify the number of digits desired, but even then, roundoff and truncation occur.) *Roundoff error* is the difference between a true number and that number rounded to some number of significant digits.   When the rule for rounding is examined, we see that rounding produces an error of at most half of the last significant digit.   If we round 2.71828 to five significant digits, 2.7183, the roundoff error

$$2.71828 - 2.7183 = -0.00002$$

is less than half a unit in the ten-thousandths place.

When a number is *truncated* to n significant digits, all digits to the right of the nth digit are deleted. Thus *truncation error*, the difference between a true number and that number truncated to n digits, can be almost one unit in the nth place. For example, if 2.53999 . . . is truncated to three digits, the result is 2.53, and the truncation error is

$$2.53999 \ . \ . \ . \ -2.53 = 0.00999 \ . \ . \ .$$

which is almost a 1 in the hundredths place. We have already noticed that only some rational numbers can be exactly represented in floating-point form in a computer. If a number cannot be exactly represented, it is truncated to the next lowest exactly representable number.

We see, then, that the finite-word-length restriction of computers necessitates roundoff and truncation; hence roundoff and truncation error is a consequence. The only consolation the computer user has is that, in most cases, roundoff and truncation affect digits to the right of his least significant digit. It is only when these errors propagate that he must be concerded. To study error propagation, we need the concept of *absolute* and *relative error*. For convenience, we agree to write a true value as a lowercase letter and an approximation to that value as the same letter with a bar above it. Thus, if we are considering

$$x = \tfrac{1}{3}$$

the number closest to $\tfrac{1}{3}$ that can be stored in floating-point form is

$$\bar{x} = 0.010101010101010101010101$$

With these notation conventions, absolute and relative error are defined by

$$e_A = |x - \bar{x}| \qquad \text{absolute error}$$
$$e_R = \frac{|x - \bar{x}|}{\bar{x}} = \frac{e_A}{\bar{x}} \qquad \text{relative error}$$

One might ask why relative error is not defined by

$$e_R = \frac{|x - \bar{x}|}{x} = \frac{e_A}{x}$$

The reason is that, in situations where relative error is important, such as data obtained from measurement, the true value x is not really known.

10-4 ERROR PROPAGATION

Our final topic is the propagation of error and how it may be reduced. We shall consider all the types of error in an approximation $\bar{x}$ to a true value x to be in the error term e_x, where

$$e_x = x - \bar{x}$$

Inherent error (perhaps due to measurement), truncation error, and roundoff error are at once denoted in the error term e_x. We shall derive expressions for error propagation when two true values x and y are operands for the four arithmetic operations.

$$x = \bar{x} + e_x$$
$$y = \bar{y} + e_y$$

The absolute-error terms for addition and subtraction are easy.

$$\begin{aligned}
x + y &= (\bar{x} + e_x) + (\bar{y} + e_y) \\
&= (\bar{x} + \bar{y}) + (e_x + e_y) \\
x - y &= (\bar{x} + e_x) - (\bar{y} + e_y) \\
&= (\bar{x} - \bar{y}) + (e_x - e_y)
\end{aligned}$$

For multiplication and division, we make the assumption that the error terms e_x and e_y are very small in relation to $\bar{x}$ and $\bar{y}$, respectively. The reason for this will be clear in the following discussion.

$$\begin{aligned}
xy &= (\bar{x} + e_x)(\bar{y} + e_y) \\
&= \bar{x}\bar{y} + \bar{x}e_y + \bar{y}e_x + e_x e_y
\end{aligned}$$

Since $e_x e_y$ is extremely small, we drop that term and get

$$xy \approx \bar{x}\bar{y} + (\bar{x}e_y + \bar{y}e_x)$$

For division,

$$\begin{aligned}
\frac{x}{y} &= \frac{\bar{x} + e_x}{\bar{y} + e_y} \\
&= \frac{(1/\bar{y})(\bar{x} + e_x)}{1 + (e_y/\bar{y})} \\
&= \left(\frac{\bar{x}}{\bar{y}} + \frac{e_x}{\bar{y}}\right) \frac{1}{1 + (e_y/\bar{y})} \frac{1 - (e_y/\bar{y})}{1 - (e_y/\bar{y})} \\
&= \left(\frac{\bar{x}}{\bar{y}} + \frac{e_x}{\bar{y}}\right) \frac{1 - (e_y/\bar{y})}{1 - (e_y/\bar{y})^2}
\end{aligned}$$

Since e_y is small in relation to $\bar{y}$, we can consider $(e_y/\bar{y})^2$ to be nearly zero; hence

$$\frac{x}{y} \approx \left(\frac{\bar{x}}{\bar{y}} + \frac{e_x}{\bar{y}}\right) \frac{1 - (e_y/\bar{y})}{1}$$

$$\approx \frac{\bar{x}}{\bar{y}} + \frac{e_x}{\bar{y}} - \frac{\bar{x}e_y}{\bar{y}^2} - \frac{e_x e_y}{\bar{y}^2}$$

The term $e_x e_y/\bar{y}^2$ is so small, we can ignore it; then we have

$$\frac{x}{y} \approx \frac{\bar{x}}{\bar{y}} + \left(\frac{e_x}{\bar{y}} - \frac{\bar{x}e_y}{\bar{y}^2}\right)$$

The expressions for absolute-error propagation are

$$e_{x+y} = e_x + e_y$$
$$e_{x-y} = e_x - e_y$$
$$e_{xy} \approx \bar{x}e_y + \bar{y}e_x$$
$$e_{x/y} \approx \frac{e_x}{\bar{y}} - \frac{\bar{x}e_y}{\bar{y}^2}$$

From these we can easily get relative-error propagation expressions:

1. $\dfrac{e_{x+y}}{\bar{x} + \bar{y}} = \dfrac{e_x + e_y}{\bar{x} + \bar{y}} = \dfrac{\bar{x}}{\bar{x} + \bar{y}}\left(\dfrac{e_x}{\bar{x}}\right) + \dfrac{\bar{y}}{\bar{x} + \bar{y}}\left(\dfrac{e_y}{\bar{y}}\right)$

2. $\dfrac{e_{x-y}}{\bar{x} + \bar{y}} = \dfrac{e_x - e_y}{\bar{x} - \bar{y}} = \dfrac{\bar{x}}{\bar{x} - \bar{y}}\left(\dfrac{e_x}{\bar{x}}\right) - \dfrac{\bar{y}}{\bar{x} - \bar{y}}\left(\dfrac{e_y}{\bar{y}}\right)$

3. $\dfrac{e_{xy}}{\bar{x}\bar{y}} \approx \dfrac{\bar{x}e_y + \bar{y}e_x}{\bar{x}\bar{y}} = \dfrac{e_x}{\bar{x}} + \dfrac{e_y}{\bar{y}}$

4. $\dfrac{e_{x/y}}{\bar{x}/\bar{y}} \approx \dfrac{\bar{y}}{\bar{x}}\left(\dfrac{1}{\bar{y}}e_x - \dfrac{\bar{x}}{\bar{y}^2}e_y\right)$

   $\approx \dfrac{e_x}{\bar{x}} - \dfrac{e_y}{\bar{y}}$

The relative-error propagation expressions are written in the more complicated form for addition and subtraction to show more clearly the effect of these operations on the relative error in their operands. Some of the exercises at the end of this chapter illustrate other consequences of error propagation.

Error-propagation Trees

We borrow the notion of a tree from a very powerful and growing field of interest, linear graph theory. Graph theory is concerned with structures consisting of points and lines, or in graph-theory terminology, nodes and branches. The power of graph theory lies in the freedom to give specific interpretations to the meanings of "node" and "branch." We will be concerned with a special type of linear graph called a *tree*. The formal definition of a tree is topological in nature, and will only introduce confusion at this point. Rather than define a tree, we give a few examples

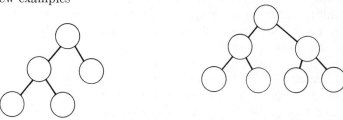

The circles are *nodes*, and they are connected by *branches*. These trees will enable us to have an easily visualized tool for our study of error propagation. We will start this by defining operation trees.

The arithmetic operations addition, subtraction, multiplication, and division are all *binary operations*, that is, each operation has two operands. Negation is an example of an operation that is not binary; having only one operand, negation is a *unary operation*. The operation trees for each of the four arithmetic operations are

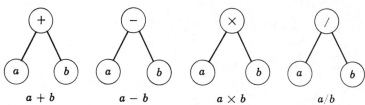

These elementary operation trees can be concatenated to express any arithmetic expression. For example, the tree for

$$a(b + c) - (d/(e - f))$$

is

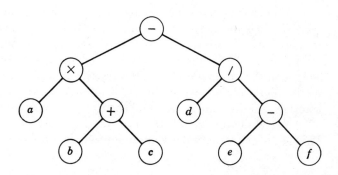

By adopting a suitable interpretation of nodes and branches, we will have our tool for studying error propagation. In calculations performed on digital computers, relative error, rather than absolute, is propagated. In each expression on p. 330, the propagated error is expressed in terms of the relative error of each operand. In addition (and subtraction) the relative errors are multiplied by a coefficient, and then added (subtracted), and similarly for multiplication and division, except that, for these operations, the coefficients are 1. We are now ready to give special meaning to the nodes and branches, or error-propagation trees.

In an error-propagation tree, nodes correspond to the total relative error accumulated from lower connected nodes. Branches in an error-propagation tree correspond to the multiplicative coefficients in the error-propagation expressions. Below we give the error-propagation trees for each arithmetic operation. We abbreviate the relative error in the operands $\bar{x}$ and $\bar{y}$, with a and b. That is,

$$a = \frac{e_x}{\bar{x}}$$

$$b = \frac{e_y}{\bar{y}}$$

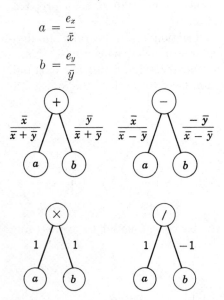

Now, to find the accumulated relative error at any node, we first find the relative error in the two nodes immediately below, and connected to, the node in question. The relative errors in these nodes are multiplied by the branch coefficients. The sum of these two products is the total relative error propagated to the original node. This algorithm applies to each of the four arithmetic operations, because the subtraction required in two operations (subtraction and division) is accomplished by the negative branch coefficient.

We wish to examine the propagation of error in adding four numbers. It is necessary to consider rounding after each operation because the roundoff error will also be propagated. To facilitate this, we write a number in the operation nodes to indicate the order in which operations are performed. This number is also used as a subscript for the roundoff-error terms. Thus the roundoff error from the nth operation will be denoted r_n.

Let
$$y = A + B + C + D$$

$$a = \frac{e_A}{A} \qquad b = \frac{e_B}{B} \qquad c = \frac{e_C}{C} \qquad d = \frac{e_D}{D}$$

One operation tree for this sum is

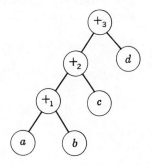

Inserting the branch coefficients, we have

$$
\frac{A+B+C}{A+B+C+D} \; \overset{+_3}{} \; \frac{D}{A+B+C+D}
$$

$$
\frac{A+B}{A+B+C} \; \overset{+_2}{} \quad d
$$

$$
\frac{A}{A+B} \; \overset{+_1}{} \quad c \quad \frac{C}{A+B+C}
$$

$$
a \qquad \frac{B}{A+B} \qquad b
$$

Now, computing the error propagated to each node, at $\;+_1\;$ the total error is

$$\frac{A}{A+B}a + \frac{B}{A+B}b + r_1 = \frac{e_A + e_B}{A+B} + r_1$$

The total error at $\;+_2\;$ is

$$\frac{A+B}{A+B+C}\left(\frac{e_A+e_B}{A+B} + r_1\right) + \frac{C}{A+B+C}c + r_2$$

$$= \frac{e_A + e_B + (A+B)r_1}{A+B+C} + \frac{e_C}{A+B+C} + r_2$$

Similarly, at $\bigoplus_3$, the total propagated error is

$$\frac{A + B + C}{A + B + C + D} \left[\frac{e_A + e_B + e_C + (A + B)r_1 + (A + B + C)r_2}{A + B + C} \right]$$
$$+ \frac{D}{A + B + C + D} d + r_3$$
$$= \frac{e_A + e_B + e_C + (A + B)r_1 + (A + B + C)r_2}{A + B + C + D} + \frac{e_D}{A + B + C + D} + r_3$$

This result will yield an interesting consequence about commutativity and associativity of addition on computers.   First, we let

$$r = \max (r_1, r_2, r_3)$$

and then, since $r \geq r_i$ for $i = 1, 2, 3$, we can write

$$\frac{e_y}{y} \leq \frac{e_A + e_B + e_C + e_D}{A + B + C + D}$$
$$+ \frac{(A + B)r + (A + B + C)r + (A + B + C + D)r}{A + B + C + D}$$

Consider the roundoff-error term

$$\frac{(A + B)r + (A + B + C)r + (A + B + C + D)r}{A + B + C + D}$$

We may rewrite this

$$\frac{3Ar + 3Br + 2Cr + Dr}{A + B + C + D}$$

or

$$\frac{(3A + 3B + 2C + D)r}{A + B + C + D}$$

This shows that the order in which A, B, C, and D are added affects the magnitude of the roundoff-error term.   Obviously, the best order is to arrange the numbers so that

$$A \leq B \leq C \leq D$$

a result that is quite surprising.

Another surprising result is a consequence of performing the sum

$$y = A + B + C + D$$

in a different way.   This time we shall use the operation tree

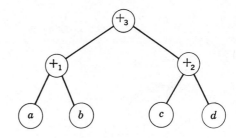

The branch coefficients are

The error at $\boxed{+_1}$ is

$$\frac{A}{A + B} a + \frac{B}{A + B} b + r_1 = \frac{e_A + e_B}{A + B} + r_1$$

Similarly, at $\boxed{+_2}$, the error is

$$\frac{C}{C + D} c + \frac{D}{C + D} d + r_2 = \frac{e_C + e_D}{C + D} + r_2$$

At $\boxed{+_3}$ we get

$$\frac{A + B}{A + B + C + D}\left(\frac{e_A + e_B}{A + B} + r_1\right) + \frac{C + D}{A + B + C + D}\left(\frac{e_C + e_D}{C + D} + r_2\right) + r_3$$

$$= \frac{e_A + e_B + (A + B)r_1}{A + B + C + D} + \frac{e_C + e_D + (C + D)r_2}{A + B + C + D} + r_3$$

$$= \frac{e_A + e_B + e_C + e_D}{A + B + C + D}$$

$$+ \frac{(A + B)r_1 + (C + D)r_2 + (A + B + C + D)r_3}{A + B + C + D}$$

If we again let

$$r = \max\ (r_1, r_2, r_3)$$

we have

$$\frac{e_y}{y} \le \frac{e_A + e_B + e_C + e_D}{A + B + C + D}$$

$$+ \frac{(A + B)r + (C + D)r + (A + B + C + D)r}{A + B + C + D}$$

The roundoff-error term now is

$$\frac{(2A + 2B + 2C + 2D)r}{A + B + C + D}$$

Notice that when the four numbers are added in the new order, it is not necessary to arrange them in order of increasing magnitude. Finally, if A, B, C, and D are approximately equal, adding them in this second order $[(A + B) + (C + D)]$ results in a smaller roundoff-error term. In other words, addition on a computer is not associative. Whenever a series of computations is to be performed, the type of analysis done for the above example can be used to determine the most accurate way.

10-5 SOME GENERAL RULES FOR ERROR REDUCTION

1. Whenever it is possible, normalize numbers on which arithmetic operations are to be performed. Suppose the numbers x_1, x_2, . . . , x_n are to be used. To normalize them, first find

$$a = \min_i (x_i)$$
$$b = \max_i (x_i)$$

The normalized numbers (indicated with a prime) are

$$x_i' = \frac{x_i - a}{b - a} \qquad \text{for } i = 1, 2, \ldots, n$$

This puts all the numbers in the range from -1 to $+1$, where the floating-point representation is most dense. A normalizing process such as this is often used in matrix-inversion programs. When this is done, it is called *pivoting*.

2. When adding numbers of varying magnitudes, they should be arranged

$$x_1 \le x_2 \le \cdots \le x_n$$

and then added. This reduces roundoff error.

3. When adding approximately equal numbers (i.e., numbers varying by two or three powers of 10), it is best to group the numbers as follows:

$$y = x_1 + x_2 + \cdots + x_n + x_{n+1} + \cdots + x_{2n} + x_{2n+1} + \cdots + x_{n^2}$$
$$= (x_1 + \cdots + x_n) + (x_{n+1} + \cdots + x_{2n}) + \cdots$$
$$+ (x_{n^2-n+1} + \cdots + x_{n^2})$$

If n^2 numbers are to be added, group them into n groups of n numbers per group, sum each group, and then add these sums together.

4. Subtraction of nearly equal numbers should be avoided if possible, and if unavoidable, the subtraction should be the last operation. This is because many significant digits can be lost through subtraction.

$$.63572 \times 10^4$$
$$-.63567 \times 10^4$$
$$\overline{.00005 \times 10^4}$$

5. Often the distributive laws do not hold when errors are considered. Calculations such as $x(y - z)$ and $(y - z)/x$ can be rewritten $xy - xz$ and $y/x - z/x$. If y and z are nearly equal, performing the subtraction first will reduce the roundoff error.

6. Since roundoff occurs with each operation, the distributive laws can be used to reduce the number of operations, and hence the number of roundings, in a computation.

7. If possible, use numbers that are exactly representable. This can often be done when designing an experiment.

EXERCISES

10-1. What are largest and smallest integers that can be represented on the 16-bit-word machine? Show computer (two's-complement) representations of these.

10-2. Referring to the discussion on p. 324:
    a. Express h in terms of E.
    b. When does $h = 1; 2; 8$?
    c. What is the greatest representable number?
    d. How does the value of E affect the position of the binary point in a represented number?

10-3. Referring to the discussion on p. 324:
    a. Examine the behavior of h from 0 to 1 as E decreases.
    b. What is the smallest positive number that can be exactly represented?

c. How many numbers can be exactly represented between 0 and 1? Between 2 and 4?

10-4. Write $\frac{1}{3}$ as a binary floating-point number.

Hint: The binary expansion of $\frac{1}{3}$ is

0.010101 . . .

so truncation must occur. What is $\frac{1}{3}$ truncated to?

10-5. Show the binary floating-point form of the numbers below. Use the 6-bit floating-point scheme shown in Exercise 10-6.

      a. $\frac{1}{2}$ b. $1\frac{3}{4}$ c. $2\frac{1}{2}$
      d. 100 (possible since $2^7 = 128$)   e. $\frac{1}{4}$
      f. 0.45   g. $-\frac{1}{2}$ h. $3\frac{7}{8}$

10-6. What numbers are represented by the binary floating-point forms below?

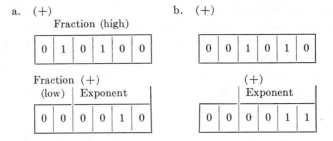

10-7. What is the greatest possible positive number that can be exactly represented? The smallest positive number? (Use the scheme of Exercise 10-6.)

10-8. The binary equivalent of $\frac{1}{5}$ is the repeating, nonterminating number

    $\frac{1}{5} = .0011\ 0011\ 0011\ \ldots$

We could store this on our hypothetical computer as

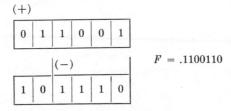

                          $F = .1100110$

where we take $E = -2$ to give us more accuracy.   (If we took $E = 0$, we would have $F = .0011001$, which is not as accurate.)   What is the actual *fraction* that $\frac{1}{5}$ is represented by?   Express this as a fraction, where the denominator is 64.

10-9. Since $E = -2$, in Exercise 10-8, $1/5$ is actually represented by $F \times 2^{-2}$, or $n/64 \times 1/4$, which is $n/256$.   (n is your answer to Exercise 10-8.) What is the absolute error in this representation?   What is the relative error?

10-10.   The area of the shaded portion of this figure is given by

$$A_1 = \pi R_1{}^2 - \pi R_2{}^2$$

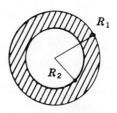

Two other mathematically equivalent expressions are

$$A_2 = \pi(R_1{}^2 - R_2{}^2)$$
$$A_3 = \pi(R_1 + R_2)(R_1 - R_2)$$

The error-propagation tree for A_1 is

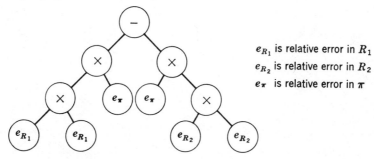

e_{R_1} is relative error in R_1
e_{R_2} is relative error in R_2
e_π is relative error in π

Make the error-propagation trees for A_2 and A_3; include the branch coefficients (purposely omitted above).

10-11.   Using your error-propagation tree for

$$A_3 = \pi(R_1 + R_2)(R_1 - R_2)$$

compute the total propagated relative error for the following values:

$$\bar{R}_1 = 2.00 \qquad e_{R_1} = 0.0025$$
$$\bar{R}_2 = 1.00 \qquad e_{R_2} = 0.005$$
$$\bar{\pi} = 3.14 \qquad e_\pi = 0.007$$

10-12.   The figure below corresponds to the Pythagorean theorem, which says
         that, for the right triangle shown, $c^2 = a^2 + b^2$. Since each term is
         squared, this corresponds to finding the areas of the squares S_a, S_b, and
         S_c. Suppose we know the values of b and c, and we wish to find the
         area of the square S_a. Two expressions to do this are $S_a = c^2 - b^2$ and
         $S_a = (c + b)(c - b)$. Make the error-propagation trees for these two
         expressions.

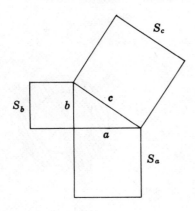

PART THREE

chapter eleven

CHARACTERISTICS OF PROGRAMMING LANGUAGES

In Parts 1 and 2 of this text we were concerned with the mathematics of digital computing. We have seen that digital computers have the capacity to solve problems of great magnitude and complexity; we have not yet seen, however, how a man can make a machine solve a problem. This question is the theme of Part 3.

In very general terms, a man has certain information, and digital computers have the capacity to process this information in a meaningful way. The crux of the matter is: How does the man communicate his information to the machine, and how can he interpret information produced by the machine? In this context, information includes not only data, but an algorithm to process the data. We shall see that the concept of a programming language bridges the man-machine communication gap, and that this is the real key to exploiting the power of a digital computer. This whole area of thought and activity is sometimes referred to as information processing, rather than the more limited notion of data processing. It is the power of programming languages, in conjunction with the power of digital computers, that makes the statement

Information is power

a good summary of the current impact of computers on our society.

11-1 MACHINE INSTRUCTIONS

We have made references in the Introduction and in the text to machine instructions, but these must be more fully understood, to appreciate the power of programming languages. Every digital computer has a set of machine instructions that it can execute. A computer program is actually a sequence of these machine instructions. The instruction set of a digital computer is usually partitioned into subsets of functionally similar instructions. These subsets include arithmetic instructions, logical instructions, decision-making (comparison) instructions, input-output instructions, register instructions, and flow-control instructions. When a program (sequence of machine instructions) is loaded into a computer's memory unit, all the information necessary to the execution of that program must be present. This includes not only raw data and what to do with the data, but also where the data are (in the memory unit) and where the sequence of instructions is. The instructions that make up a program must include all this information. As an example, a typical segment of a program is shown in Fig. 11-1. This little program takes the number in memory location 1000_8 and copies it into a register known as the accumulator. The second instruction causes the contents of location 1001_8 to be added to the number in the accumulator. The third instruction causes the number in the accumulator (the sum of the numbers formerly in locations 1000_8 and 1001_8) to be stored back in location 1000_8.

Instruction	Location
0 7 6 0 1 0 0 0	200
0 5 5 0 1 0 0 1	201
0 3 5 0 1 0 0 0	202

Fig. 11-1

The instructions in Fig. 11-1 have the appearance of ordinary binary numbers (written as octal numbers for brevity), which in fact they are. The computer that executes these instructions is electronically capable of interpreting the binary numbers as instructions to be executed and as addresses of the data to be used in the execution. The computer can do this because it expects instructions to have a definite format. One such format is shown in Fig. 11-2.

23	2120	1514	0
Label	Operation	Address of operand	

Fig. 11-2

Each of the subset types of the instruction set may have its own format, and this format may vary from one computer to the next. In Fig. 11-2, the instruction has three fields: a label field, an operation field, and an operand address field. The binary digits in the operation field are, actually, the binary number of the type of action to be performed. For the instructions in Fig. 11-1, the *operation codes* have the following meanings:

76 Load accumulator register
55 Add to accumulator
35 Store (contents of) accumulator

When these instructions are executed, the computer decodes them, notes the addresses of the operands, and then executes them sequentially. This process seems complicated, and it is, but the complication is necessary because the computer is only a machine. If we want a computer to do something, we must express it in the computer's terms.

In the early computers, programs had to be written in machine-language instructions. Programmers had to memorize all the operation codes of the instruction set (or else constantly refer to charts), and it was necessary to assign memory locations both to data and to instructions. This type of programming is tedious, and because of the monotony, programming became an unpleasant task. Programmers began to notice that the actual machine-language coding was a mechanical task, the kind of problem that a computer could do if it were properly programmed. This notion led to the development of *assembly language.* Assembly languages have alphabetic abbreviations for the operations and allow symbolic names for memory locations. Referring to the little program in Fig. 11-1, let SUM be the variable name of the number in memory location 1000_8, and let TERM be the name of the number in location 1001_8. For operation names, let us use LAM for "load accumulator from memory," AAM for "add accumulator from memory," and SAM for "store accumulator in memory." In assembly language, the program would be

```
LAM     SUM
AAM     TERM
SAM     SUM
```

Now, a person who knew the instruction abbreviations (or mnemonics, as they are usually called) could look at the assembly language and more easily understand the program. The programs written to translate assembly-language programs into machine-language instructions are called *assemblers.* An assembler is a program that accepts data in the form of assembly-language statements and generates the proper machine-language instructions that correspond to the input statements. The advent of assemblers made programming a much easier task. Programmers no longer needed to memorize operation codes and build their own tables of memory-location contents, because now the computer, and the assembler program, did all this. Being thus relieved of the mechanical aspects of machine-language programming, programmers were able to write much more complicated programs.

The main advantage of assembly language is that the programmer is relieved of the monotony of machine-language instructions. A second advantage is that assembly-language programs, since they employ mnemonic and symbolic names, are easier to understand and write than machine-language programs. Another advantage of assembly-language programming is that the programmer dictates exactly what the computer should do; so he has complete control over the instructions that the computer executes. The greatest drawback of assembly-language programming is that the programmer is still very "close" to the computer, and hence must always be aware of the computer's constraints. Also, assembly-language programming has some of the monotony of machine-language programming. These, and other more complicated drawbacks, motivated the evolution of more sophisticated programming systems.

11-2 PROBLEM-ORIENTED PROGRAMMING LANGUAGES

As programmers made more and more use of assembly languages in various applications, they began to notice that certain sequences of instructions were used repeatedly. An example of such a sequence is shown above. This little program is sometimes referred to as a *replacement*. The number in location 1000_8 is replaced by the sum of the number in location 1001_8 and the previous number contained in 1000_8. This replacement would appear in flowchart form as the box below.

$$\downarrow$$
$$\boxed{\text{SUM} \leftarrow \text{SUM} + \text{TERM}}$$
$$\downarrow$$

If we look at a few such replacements:

$$\text{SUM 1} \leftarrow \text{SUM 1} + \text{A}$$
$$\text{SUM 2} \leftarrow \text{SUM 2} + \text{B}$$
$$\text{C} \leftarrow \text{C} + \text{SUM 2}$$

we can see that they are all of the form

$$\text{variable}_1 \leftarrow \text{variable}_1 + \text{variable}_2 \tag{11-1}$$

It is not to difficult to see that the only differences in the machine-language instructions to perform the three replacements above will be the addresses of the different variable names.   The operation fields of the instructions will be the same for all three replacements.   Knowing this, it would seem reasonable to supply only the particular variable addresses whenever a replacement of the form (11-1) is needed in a program.

This observation, and many similar ones, led to the development of more sophisticated programming languages, known now as *problem-oriented languages*. Problem-oriented programming languages are programming systems in which one statement may be equivalent to several machine-language instructions. We shall consider the functions and common terminology of problem-oriented languages in this chapter, and of specific problem-oriented languages in sequel chapters.

The evolution of problem-oriented languages is seen in terms of instructions actually executed by computers.

System	*Statement*	*Execution*
Machine language	Machine instruction	Executed immediately
Assembly language	Symbolic instruction	Translated to machine equivalent and then executed
Problem-oriented language	Symbolic statement	Translated to equivalent sequence of machine instructions, which are then executed

In much the same way that assemblers are programs to generate the machine-instruction equivalents of assembly-language statements, problem-oriented languages use a program to generate *sequences of machine instructions* that are functionally equivalent to problem-language statements.   These translation programs for problem-oriented languages are called *compilers*.   The term problem-oriented stems from the development of different languages for particular types of computer applications.   The FORTRAN language is directed toward algebraic problems, as its name (FORmula TRANslation) implies.   COBOL (from COmmon Business-Oriented Language) is designed for use in commercial applications.

The problem-oriented languages are made possible by their compiler programs.   Compiler programs are able to accept a variety of types of statements and produce the machine-language instructions that are equivalent (functionally) to the input statement.   Input-language statements are actually data to a compiler program, and the output of a compiler program is a machine-language program that will execute the programmer's intention.   The replacement operation that we have used as an example thus far, when stated within the FORTRAN programming language, is

$$SUM = SUM + TERM.$$

This statement is even easier to understand than its assembly-language equivalent sequence

LAM   SUM
AAM   TERM
SAM   SUM

The main advantage of problem-oriented languages, then, is that the programmer is removed from the single-instruction constraint.   He can specify functions and not be concerned with what (or even how many) machine instructions are needed to execute the function.   This step has made computers available to many more people, because it is no longer necessary for them to become familiar with the computer's instruction set.   Another desirable consequence is that a problem-oriented program (sequence of problem-oriented-language statements) can be executed by a different type of computer once it has been compiled by a compiler for the second computer.   This makes it possible for a program written by one company for its computer to be used by another company on a different computer, with very little change.

Problem-oriented languages, while they increase the usability of computers, do have drawbacks.   Different computers require different compilers, because their instruction sets are not identical.   Second, compilers are *programs* and, as such, can accept only certain forms of statements.   These forms are more easily understood by people, but programmers are still restricted by them.   If a programmer includes a statement in his program that is not of a form acceptable to the compiler, it will not be translated into its machine-language equivalent sequence, and the programmer will have to make a correction.   This restriction is the subject of the next section.

11-3 PROCESSORS

Programs that translate language statements into machine instructions are called *processors*.   There is a spectrum of processors that is based on the complexity of the translation to be performed.   At the one end, there is the assembler; at the other end, there are the problem-oriented compilers (see Fig. 11-3).

Fig. 11-3 The processor spectrum.

Between these extremes are processors of varying power.   The power, or strength, of a processor is most easily described by the variety of statement forms that it has the capacity to translate into machine language.   Each processor, or language—the two terms are almost synonymous—has a finite number of statement forms that it can translate.   Input-language statements that conform to these forms are, in a sense, understandable to the processor. We may ask: What makes a statement understandable to a processor? This question applies to all languages, programming and natural. In a natural language, such as English, understandable statements are sentences or sentence fragments that convey meaning. Someone may ask what it is about a sentence that allows meaning to be conveyed. We begin our answer in a negative way. It is pretty clear that the sentence

Is is is the is the the man man man

has no meaning, while the sentence

The man is

does have meaning. The essential difference between these two statements is that the second conforms to the syntax of the English language, while the first does not. It is the syntax, or rules of formation, that makes it possible to determine whether or not a statement "makes sense" or has meaning within a language. "The man is" is a statement that has a subject and a verb, and hence conforms to English syntax. The other statement has four identical verbs and three identical subjects, and this, together with the word order, does not conform to English syntax; hence there is no meaning. In order to have meaning within a language, a statement must conform to the syntax of that language.

The specification of the syntax of a language completely determines what statements will be meaningful within that language. Obviously, the more complicated syntax a language has, the more complicated the concepts that can be stated meaningfully within that language. The notion of syntax also allows description of a hierarchy of languages. If the set of forms allowed by the syntax of one language is a subset of the set of forms allowed by the syntax of a second language, then every statement that has meaning within the first language also has meaning within the second language. The converse of this is not necessarily true: there may be meaningful statements of the second language that have no meaning within the first language. As an example of this, let us consider ordinary algebra as a language within English. The sentence

$$c^2 = a^2 + b^2$$

has meaning both in algebra and in English, because the syntax that it conforms to in algebra is part of the syntax of English. The English sentence

Descartes said "I think, therefore I am"

has meaning in English, but is nonsense when viewed as an algebraic statement. If a statement is of a form permitted by the syntax of a language, we will call it a *well-formed statement*. Statements that do not conform to the syntax of a language, then, are not well-formed. Thus we avoid the ambiguity of referring to "statements that have meaning within a language." Indeed, it is possible to discuss statements which have no inherent meaning, yet do have a syntactic structure. We did this in our discussion of Boolean algebra, when we specifically avoided giving any "meaning" to Boolean algebra statements. The positive result of this was a body of facts that applied not only to Boolean algebra itself, but also, with suitable interpretations, to set theory, logic, and switching circuits.

The reason for the term well-formed is that the syntax of a language is most easily phrased in terms of *rules of formation*. These rules of formation should be an effective procedure (see Chap. 9) for determining whether or not a given statement is well-formed. In programming languages the need for an effective procedure is necessary, because the compiler program must be capable of determining well-formedness. Before we discuss the way in which the syntax of a programming language is specified, we must first establish the vocabulary commonly used in programming languages.

11-4 STRUCTURAL ELEMENTS OF PROGRAMMING LANGUAGES

We all have a vague notion of the structure of the English language. Sentences (well-formed) should have subject and predicate clauses and, optionally, objective clauses. Subject clauses usually contain nouns, predicates contain verbs, and so on. Our purpose here is to develop terms analogous to those of English grammar. Since we are concerned with programming languages, these terms will be more precise, and hence more limited, than their English-grammar analogs.

Every programming language must have a *character set*. The character set of a programming language is the set of letters, numerals, and special signs (such as $+$, $\$$, $=$) that can be used. All other entities of the language are built up as strings of these characters. Words in English, for example, are actually strings of letters; numbers are strings of digits. A *character string* consists of the juxtaposition of elements of the character set, and a character string is indicated simply by writing the particular characters next to each other. The character string

$$A \ B \ 1 \ C + D \ \$ \ . \ ) \ , = 2$$

is an example.

A *constant* is a string of digits (or numerals 0, 1, 2, . . . , 9) that represents a number. Since we most probably would like to represent rational numbers as well as integers in a programming language, a constant can include a . to indicate the decimal point. We would also like to indicate whether a constant is positive or negative; so the symbols $+$ and $-$ must be allowed in character strings for constants. These conventions allow the constants 123, $+123$, -12.3.

Perhaps the most useful element of a programming language is the *identifier*. An identifier is a name for an entity in the language. There are three common types of identifiers, the first of which is the *scalar identifier*. A scalar identifier is a character string that is a symbolic name for some number. The scalar identifiers of a programming language are used in the same way that the letters a, b, x, y are used in algebra to indicate numbers. Usually, scalar identifiers can consist of letters and digits, with the restriction that a scalar identifier must begin with a letter. Possible examples of scalar identifiers include

SUM, TERM, TERM1, TERM2

An *array identifier* is a more complicated feature of programming language. An array identifier is a name for a sequence of scalars, and the usage exactly parallels the common mathematical convention of naming a sequence with a letter. The sequence

$$A = \{a_1, a_2, \ldots, a_n, \ldots\}$$

would be represented in a programming language by the array identifier A. Like scalar identifiers, array identifiers may consist of more than one letter, and can include digits. Thus SEQ1 could be the name of a sequence in a programming language. Particular elements of the sequence are usually indicated by subscripts; thus the second element would be specified by SEQ1(2). The third type of identifier, the *subprogram identifier*, is much more limited in scope. As the term implies, a subprogram identifier is the name of a subprogram. A subprogram to compute the square root of a number might be named by the subprogram identifier SQRT. If this subprogram were used in a program (written in some programming language), the reference would be accomplished via the subprogram identifier.

Once the notions of constants and identifiers are established, these become building blocks of the language. The next level in the development of a language is concerned with connectives and punctuation. Connectives function similarly to verbs in English, and the use of punctuation is usually analogous to the notion of grouping in algebra. Connectives are used to indicate what happens to constants and identifiers. The most common connectives, then, are the arithmetic operations $+$, $\times$, $-$, $\div$. Having these connectives, we can make "phrases" out of constants and identifiers:

TERM1 + SUM

Usually, the only punctuation symbols are parentheses and commas. Parentheses are used to indicate the order in which operations are to be performed. In most programming languages, the use of parentheses to indicate order exactly parallels standard mathematical usage. Connectives and parentheses, used together with constants and identifiers, allow the construction of what is perhaps the most useful programming-language entity—the expression.

An *expression* in a programming language is a string of characters that indicates a sequence of computations. In order to do this, an expression must contain a connective, and the presence of a connective implies the presence of operands for the connective. These operands are usually constants or scalar identifiers. Thus an example of an expression is

$$PI \times (R1-R2) + 3.67$$

Again, expressions within programming languages employ the same conventions as expressions within mathematics. This applies particularly to the order in which operations are performed when there are no parentheses to indicate order. The convention is that multiplication and division precede addition and subtraction, and exponentiation precedes multiplication and division. The hierarchy of operations within a programming language is always specified in the documentation describing the language. There is a degenerate case of expressions that is largely a matter of convenience. We said that an expression indicates a sequence of computations, and hence has at least one connective. An identifier or a constant standing alone is also considered to be an expression. In this case, we might say that the expression indicates a sequence of no operations, or possibly an *empty* sequence of operations. This all sounds pretty artificial, but it does make the description of available options more concise. We shall see this later in the chapter when we discuss Backus normal form.

There are three other terms common to many programming languages: list, block, and subprogram. A *list* is a linguistic device that describes a sequence of items to the compiler of the language. These items can be constants, scalar or array identifiers, or possibly expressions. Lists require parentheses to indicate the beginning and end of the sequence, and commas to separate the items in the sequence. The most common use of lists is to specify a number of items that are output. That is, items in an *output list* are those that the computer will eventually communicate to the outside world, possibly by printing them or punching them on cards. The remaining two terms, block and subprogram, are related to each other. A *block* is a sequence of statements of a programming language. Blocks can have names in programming languages, and if they do, these names are another type of identifier. Naming blocks allows easy reference to several programming-language statements. If these statements are the representation (within the language) of a common sequence of calculations, then reference to that block is equivalent (in a linguistic sense) to reference to the whole sequence of calculations. A *subprogram* is also a sequence of programming-language statements that represent some sequence of calculations. Subprograms (and blocks) can include other computer functions, such as reading magnetic tape or printing output. The primary difference between a block and a subprogram is that blocks are usually a part of a program, while subprograms are external (in a sense that need not be explained here) to a program.

There are several other common programming-language terms, but they are not common to all programming languages. These terms usually refer to special features and functions of specific languages, and hence are different for different languages. The notion of replacement is an excellent example of this. The example from the first part of this discussion

$$\text{SUM} \leftarrow \text{SUM} + \text{TERM}$$

is expressed one way in some languages and another way in others. In FORTRAN, this replacement would be written as

$$\text{SUM} = \text{SUM} + \text{TERM}.$$

Here the = sign is used to indicate replacement, not equality. This usage is at first confusing, because we usually assume that the presence of the = sign indicates that the quantity to its left is identical with the quantity to its right.

Another linguistic function that differs from one language to the next is that of flow control. In our use of flowcharts (see Chap. 9), it was often necessary to make a decision and, depending on the outcome of this decision, go to one of several *blocks* of instructions. We indicated this in flowcharts simply by arrows pointing to the blocks to be executed. When these flow-charts are expressed in terms of some programming language, that language must have the capacity for describing the "flow" of the program.

A final, and perhaps most difficult, language function is that of input and output. The terms *input* and *output* refer to information that must be presented to a computer and information the computer presents to its user. Computer-programming languages must be able to specify the input and output to a program. This specification includes what variables are input data, the physical form (punched cards, magnetic tape, etc.), and how the data are arranged on the input medium. Similarly, output specification must include what information is to be transmitted to the outside world and where it should appear (magnetic tape, printer, card punch). The input-output features of programming languages vary widely from one type of a computer to the next. Each computer manufacturer implements input-output state-ments in a different way, partly because the computers themselves are different, and partly because each tries to find the most efficient input-output approach. Because the input-output features of programming languages are so variable, we will not discuss the topic as thoroughly as other more computational-oriented features. This is fairly reasonable, because whenever any program-ming language is to be used on a specific computer, documentation of the language *for that computer* must be consulted regarding the particular features present in its implementation.

11-5 BACKUS NORMAL FORM

Backus normal form is the widely accepted means of specifying the syntax of a programming language. This acceptance is due to the succinct way in which the options of a language can be described, and to the fact that the description itself indicates how the compiler for that language can be organized. We will discuss the conventions of Backus normal form, and use them to specify a simple language. We will use Boolean algebra as an example throughout, because it is fairly familiar, and it is simple enough (as a language) so that its linguistic features are easily recognizable.

It will be necessary to distinguish between words that are part of a programming language and words used to describe the language (which are *not* part of the language). For example, we may wish to specify the identifiers permitted in a language. In this description, the word "identifier" describes part of the language. When used in this sense, we indicate this by writing

$\langle$identifier$\rangle$

Backus normal form, as a descriptive tool, requires the notion of replacement that we have discussed before. To indicate a replacement of one linguistic entity by another we use the symbol

$::=$

A third convention of Backus normal form is the way to specify options. The symbol | is used to indicate an option, and may be interpreted as a *linguistic or*. Finally, there is the notion of *concatenation*. Concatenation is indicated by juxtaposition; that is, the order in which linguistic entities may occur is indicated by the order in which they are written.

Before proceeding with the Backus normal form development of Boolean algebra as a language, we will illustrate the conventions defined above with the Backus normal form definition of constants. We wish to describe formally that any of the following forms

$$123 \quad +123 \quad +12.3 \quad -123 \quad -12.3$$

are permissible constants. Numbers to facilitate line reference are included.

$$\langle\text{digit}\rangle ::= 0|1|2|3|4|5|6|7|8|9 \tag{1}$$
$$\langle\text{decimal point}\rangle ::= . \tag{2}$$
$$\langle\text{arithmetic sign}\rangle ::= +|- \tag{3}$$
$$\langle\text{natural number}\rangle ::= \langle\text{digit}\rangle|\langle\text{natural number}\rangle\langle\text{digit}\rangle \tag{4}$$
$$\langle\text{integer}\rangle ::= \langle\text{natural number}\rangle|\langle\text{arithmetic sign}\rangle\langle\text{natural number}\rangle \tag{5}$$
$$\langle\text{constant}\rangle ::= \langle\text{integer}\rangle\langle\text{decimal point}\rangle|\langle\text{integer}\rangle|$$
$$\langle\text{integer}\rangle\langle\text{decimal point}\rangle\langle\text{natural number}\rangle \tag{6}$$

Line (1) defines permissible digits to be any of the digits 0, 1, 2, . . . , 9, and shows the use of | to indicate the *linguistic or*. Notice that this allows decimal numbers. If we wanted to specify octal constants, the symbols 8 and 9 would not be allowed as digits. Lines (2) and (3) specify the symbols used for indicating decimal points and plus and minus signs. Line (4) illustrates concatenation, and also the notion of a recursive definition. The second alternative, ⟨natural number⟩⟨digit⟩, is recursive, in the sense that the linguistic entity ⟨natural number⟩ is used in the definition of ⟨natural number⟩. This at first seems circular, but it is not, because we can apply the definition to ⟨natural number⟩ on the right side of the ::= sign and know that it is either a single digit or a natural number. If it is a digit, we have finished; if not, we apply the definition again. This repeated application in effect removes one digit from the natural number each time, as illustrated below.

$$(1234) ::= (123)(4)$$
$$(123) ::= (12)(3)$$
$$(12) ::= (1)(2)$$

so

$$(1234) ::= (1)(2)(3)(4)$$

Concatenation is shown by writing ⟨natural number⟩⟨digit⟩. This means that, in a natural number, a digit may follow a natural number. The combination of recursive definition and concatenation allows the definition of a natural number as a string of digits written next to each other. Line (5) specifies the difference between natural numbers and integers as linguistic entities. Basically, line (5) says that natural numbers are integers and that integers can also be signed natural numbers. Finally, line (6) indicates all the possibilities for constants. Below are examples of the options that are allowed by the definition of a constant.

123	123.45
+123	+123.45
−123	−123.45
123.	
+123.	
−123.	

The definitions in lines (2) and (3) are superficial, and possibly their only contribution is confusion. To avoid this unnecessary complication, some primitive symbols are *defined by* their *usage*. If we decided to define the symbols +, −, and . by usage, the development of constants would be

⟨digit⟩ ::= 0|1|2|3|4|5|6|7|8|9
⟨natural number⟩ ::= ⟨digit⟩ | ⟨natural number⟩⟨digit⟩
⟨integer⟩ ::= ⟨natural number⟩ | +⟨natural number⟩ | −⟨natural number⟩
⟨constant⟩ ::= ⟨integer⟩ | ⟨integer⟩ . | ⟨integer⟩ . ⟨natural number⟩

In the above definition, the usage of the symbols $+$, $-$, and . defines where they can appear. Definition by usage makes Backus normal form descriptions shorter and easier to understand, and is particularly useful when grouping symbols are expressed. If we could not define parentheses by their use, we would be forced into awkward statements like

⟨left grouping symbol⟩⟨expression⟩⟨right grouping symbol⟩

instead of

((⟨expression⟩))

11-6 BACKUS NORMAL FORM DESCRIPTION OF BOOLEAN ALGEBRA

Boolean algebra may be regarded as a language. When we specify the syntax of Boolean algebra, we define the form of meaningful Boolean algebra statements. There is a subtle difference between the syntax and the semantics of a language. Syntax is essentially form, or structure. Specification of syntax does not *give* meaning to statements. The semantics of a language is the *meaning* of statements within the language that conform to its syntax. In the specification of the syntax of Boolean algebra, we do not specify the semantics, or the meanings, of linguistic entities. We depart from the notation in Chap. 8 when we define T and F to be the Boolean constants. This is done to avoid confusion between the 0 and 1 of Chap. 8, and the 0 and 1 as digits in subscripts of Boolean variables.

$$\begin{array}{lr}
\langle\text{constant}\rangle ::= \text{T} \mid \text{F} & (1) \\
\langle\text{digit}\rangle ::= 0|1|2|3|4|5|6|7|8|9 & (2) \\
\langle\text{letter}\rangle ::= A|B|C|D & (3) \\
\langle\text{natural number}\rangle ::= \langle\text{digit}\rangle|\langle\text{natural number}\rangle\langle\text{digit}\rangle & (4) \\
\langle\text{variable}\rangle ::= \langle\text{constant}\rangle|\langle\text{letter}\rangle|\langle\text{letter}\rangle\langle\text{natural number}\rangle & (5) \\
\langle\text{connective}\rangle ::= +|\cdot|'|\equiv & (6) \\
\langle\text{expression}\rangle ::= \langle\text{variable}\rangle|\langle\text{variable}\rangle'| & \\
\quad\quad (\langle\text{variable}\rangle+\langle\text{variable}\rangle)| & \\
\quad\quad (\langle\text{variable}\rangle\cdot\langle\text{variable}\rangle)| & \\
\quad\quad (\langle\text{expression}\rangle)'| & \\
\quad\quad (\langle\text{expression}\rangle+\langle\text{expression}\rangle)| & \\
\quad\quad (\langle\text{expression}\rangle\cdot\langle\text{expression}\rangle) & (7) \\
\langle\text{statement}\rangle ::= \langle\text{expression}\rangle \equiv \langle\text{expression}\rangle & (8)
\end{array}$$

We could omit line (6) and define the Boolean connectives by usage. The reason for specifically defining them is that all the connectives of the language can be seen at a glance. If we defined them by usage, statements (7) and (8) would have to be examined to find all the permitted connectives.

The first three lines, together with line (6), define the primitive symbols of Boolean algebra. Line (4) indicates the recursive construction of natural numbers from digits. These will be used as subscripts on Boolean variable names, as seen in line (5). Line (7) shows how expressions can be constructed from variables and connectives, and also how the grouping symbols (and) are used. Finally, line (8) indicates the construction of Boolean statements of equivalence.

We can show the constructive nature of Backus normal form with the character string

$$(A + B) \equiv (A \cdot B)$$

This satisfies the definition of a statement if $(A + B)$ and $(A \cdot B)$ are expressions. When we check the definition of expressions, we see that $(A + B)$ and $(A \cdot B)$ are indeed expressions if A and B are variables. Since one of the options in the definition of a variable permits a single letter, we will have variables if A and B are permitted letters; and line (3) guarantees this. When we apply the Backus normal form description to a specific example, we see its treelike structure. This is the key to the concise descriptive capability of Backus normal form.

While it is true that the statement

$$(A + B) \equiv (A \cdot B)$$

conforms to the syntax of Boolean algebra, we know from Chap. 8 that the expressions $(A + B)$ and $(A \cdot B)$ are not equivalent. Here we see the difference between syntax and semantics. Just because a statement conforms to the syntax of a language, it does not necessarily conform to the semantics of that language. The relation between syntax and meaning is that if a statement has meaning, then it conforms to the syntax. An equivalent, and more useful, way to say this is: If a statement does not conform to the syntax of a language, then it does not have meaning within the language. The question of meaning for statements compatible with the syntax of a language depends on the semantics of the language. When this is applied to programming languages, the semantics of a programming language depends on the purpose of the language and, to some extent, on the computer that will eventually execute a program written in the language. Our concern here is the syntax, not the semantics, of programming languages.

The definitions made in the Backus normal form specification of a language are sometimes called *productions*, because they show how one linguistic entity can be produced from more primitive entities. When a specific linguistic entity is traced through all the productions necessary for its construction, the sequence of productions is called the *derivation* of the entity. We saw that the statement

$$(A + B) \equiv (A \cdot B)$$

is permitted by the syntax of Boolean algebra. Below we give a derivation of this statement:

$$A, B, (A + B), (A \cdot B), (A + B) \equiv (A \cdot B)$$

We will have two concluding problems to illustrate the concept of syntax as defined by Backus normal form.

Problem 1

Derive the Boolean statement

$$(F \cdot (((A + B) \cdot C)' + D1)) \equiv (((A1 + D2) \cdot C1') + T)$$

derivation:

F, T	(1)
A, B, C, D	(3)
$1, 2$	(2)
$A1, C1, D1, D2$	(5)
$(A + B), ((A + B) \cdot C), ((A + B) \cdot C)'$	
$(((A + B) \cdot C)' + D1), (F \cdot (((A + B) \cdot C)' + D1))$	
$(A1 + D2), C1'$	
$((A1 + D2) \cdot C1'), (((A1 + D2) \cdot C1') + T)$	(7)
$(F \cdot (((A + B) \cdot C)' + D1)) \equiv (((A1 + D2) \cdot C1') + T)$	(8)

Each line in the derivation above is part of the derivation sequence. The numbers in parentheses refer to the production used in that line. This derivation guarantees that the Boolean statement conforms to the syntax of the Boolean algebra language. Compilers must also be able to determine whether or not input statements are syntactically correct. In a syntax check, a compiler would, essentially, execute the above derivation. It is in this way that the Backus normal form description of a programming language describes the organization of the compiler for that language. Our second problem shows how a syntax error can be detected.

Problem 2.

Do the expressions

    a. $((A + B) \cdot C + D)$
    b. $(((AA + B) \cdot C) + D)$
    c. $((A \oplus B) \cdot C)$

conform to the syntax of Boolean algebra?

solution: a. If $((A + B) \cdot C + D)$ is an expression, it must use the production

$$\langle\text{expression}\rangle ::= (\langle\text{expression}\rangle + \langle\text{expression}\rangle)$$

(The other options are omitted for clarity.) Certainly, D is an expression, because D is an acceptable variable, and one option for expressions is a variable standing alone. We must now check whether or not

$$((A + B) \cdot C$$

is an expression. It is not, because the productions using the connective $\cdot$ also use left and right parentheses. If we had

$$(((A + B) \cdot C) + D)$$

we would have had a syntactically correct expression. Thus our syntax detects punctuation errors in the use of parentheses.

b. We can immediately see that

$$(((AA + B) \cdot C) + D)$$

does not commit the parenthesis error that the first character string did. Rather than repeat the above line of reasoning, we continue, examining

$$((AA + B) \cdot C)$$

to see if it is an expression. If it is, it must satisfy the form

$$(\langle\text{expression}\rangle \cdot \langle\text{expression}\rangle)$$

C is an expression, and the parentheses are correct; so now we examine $(AA + B)$. Again, we satisfy the form

$$(\langle\text{expression}\rangle + \langle\text{expression}\rangle)$$

if AA is an expression. Here the string fails, because the production for variable names does not permit concatenation of letters. This demonstrates that our syntax specification can detect errors in variable names.

c. The character string

$$((A \oplus B) \cdot C)$$

satisfies the production form

$$(\langle\text{expression}\rangle \cdot \langle\text{expression}\rangle)$$

only if $(A \oplus B)$ is a valid expression. We can see that it is not, because the connective $\oplus$ (EXCLUSIVE-OR) is not defined as a permissible connective. We see by this that our syntax can also detect errors in the use of connectives.

11-7 CONCLUSION

Programming languages, in bridging the man-machine communication gap, still comply with the strict limitations of digital computers regarding explicitness. Although Boolean algebra is an elementary example of a language, the same notions of syntax and Backus normal form apply to more sophisticated programming languages. We can see that Backus normal form will enable us to describe complicated linguistic structures and still satisfy the explicit nature of digital computers. One of the other characteristics (see Chap. 1) of a digital computer, its capacity for repetition, is also employed in the syntax check that compilers must perform. Once a compiler has established that a given statement is syntactically correct, the statement is then translated into its equivalent in terms of machine instructions. It is this translation that provides the semantics of a programming language.

EXERCISES

11-1. If a computer manufacturer produces a series of increasingly powerful (in terms of instruction sets and possibly memory size) computers, where assembly-language programs that can be executed on one machine can also be executed on all the more powerful machines in the series, the series of computers is said to be *upward compatible*. What is the relation between instruction sets in an upward-compatible line of computers? Use this relation to define upward compatibility in terms of set theory.

11-2. Apply the Backus normal form definition of constants to the following character strings to determine whether or not they conform to the specified syntax.

a.	1234	b.	± 1234
c.	-12.34	d.	$12.3E + 03$
e.	968TE (base 12)	f.	37A2CD (base 16)
g.	$+.123$	h.	$+0.123$

11-3. Determine whether or not the character strings below are permitted by the syntax of Boolean algebra. Give the reason for each decision.

a.	$A + B$	b.	$(A + B)$
c.	B'	d.	$(B)'$
e.	$((A + B))$	f.	$(A1 > B1)$
g.	$(((A + B) \cdot C1) + ((A1 \cdot B1) + C)))$		

11-4.   A production in Backus normal form has the general form

⟨linguistic entity⟩ ::= ⟨linguistic entity⟩ | · · · | ⟨linguistic entity⟩

where the | denotes a *linguistic-or*. If we did not allow this symbol, all the options indicated in the production would have to be specified by as many separate productions of the form

⟨linguistic entity⟩ ::= ⟨linguistic entity⟩

Suppose we did this, and then defined the syntax of a language to be a *set of productions*. BASIC is a programming language that includes the more common features of FORTRAN, and as such is often referred to as a *subset* of FORTRAN. What does it mean to say one language is a subset of another?

11-5.   We have seen that, for programming languages, if a statement has meaning in the language, it must conform to the syntax of that language. We can conceive of statements that might not have meaning in one language but do have meaning in higher (superset) languages. (If *A* is a subset of *B*, *B* is a superset of *A*.) Consider the English language as having a fixed syntax (set of productions). If English is the only language we understand, then we can understand only statements that conform to its syntax. Think about the possibility of statements that have meaning in a language that is a superset of English but do not have meaning in English. This is a problem that some linguists are investigating today. In particular, it is felt that there may be scientific truths that are not expressible within English, and hence can never be explained or understood within English; thus our language partially determines the extent of our understanding in much the same way that the syntax of a programming language determines the extent of problems that can be programmed in that language.

chapter twelve

FORTRAN

The FORTRAN programming language is one of the most widely used and easily understood of all the languages currently in use. Although it is designed for algebraic-oriented problems, and hence ideally suited for scientific and mathematical programming, it is also widely used in nonscientific applications. Many of its options are available in other languages, such as ALGOL (ALGOrithmic Language) and PL/1. FORTRAN has four types of statements: arithmetic, control, declaration, and input-output. We will illustrate these with examples taken from Chap. 9, with more emphasis on the first three types. Input-output statements differ widely from one compiler to the next; so they will be discussed only briefly here. The similarity between conventional mathematics notation and FORTRAN notation should be noticed. The similarity is intended, because FORTRAN is designed to be as compatible as possible with usual mathematical notation.

Throughout our study of the FORTRAN programming language, we must remember two important uses of the language: it is a vehicle that enables us to tell a digital computer what to do, and it has the facility to give instructions to the compiler program. The arithmetic and control statements fall into the first category; the declaration statements are used to give directions to the FORTRAN compiler. These two features allow the FORTRAN programmer to completely specify (to the compiler and to the computer) what he wants his program to do. In this way, the nonintuitive nature of digital computers is overcome.

12-1 ARITHMETIC STATEMENTS

The arithmetic statements are all of the replacement type that we discussed in Chap. 11. Specifically, they are of the form

variable ← expression

where "variable" is the symbolic name for a memory location, and the right side of the replacement can be any expression permitted by FORTRAN syntax. The symbol to denote this replacement in FORTRAN is the = sign, rather than the arrow (←) commonly used in flowcharts. To specify the types of expressions permitted in FORTRAN, we must first discuss constants and identifiers.

FORTRAN has two modes of arithmetic and memory-storage allocation, fixed-point or floating-point, depending on whether integral or rational numbers are used.

The *fixed-point mode* is used when all the data for a problem are integers. Fixed-point arithmetic is faster than floating-point arithmetic because a fixed-point number (an integer) is stored in one memory location, and hence the machine-language arithmetic instructions can be used. We will often encounter a "trade-off" between alternatives available in digital computing. One such trade-off is between speed and accuracy: fixed-point arithmetic is faster than floating-point arithmetic, but floating-point arithmetic is more accurate. This is because *floating-point arithmetic* is performed on rational numbers that are stored in two memory locations (see Chap. 10). Use of fixed- or floating-point mode is specified by the constants and identifiers that are used in a FORTRAN program.

The digits 0, 1, 2, . . . , 9 can be used to construct constants in FORTRAN. Notice that this precludes duodecimal or hexadecimal constants. Other symbols that can appear in a FORTRAN constant are $+$, $-$, ., and E. The decimal point indicates whether a constant is to be fixed- or floating-point. Integers (fixed-point) have no need of a decimal point; so when a constant does not have one, it is considered to be fixed-point. The fixed-point constants permitted in FORTRAN are defined by the following Backus normal form productions.

$\langle$digit$\rangle$ ::= 0 | 1 | 2 | 3 | 4 | 5 | 6 | 7 | 8 | 9   (1)

$\langle$natural number$\rangle$ ::= $\langle$digit$\rangle$ | $\langle$natural number$\rangle$$\langle$digit$\rangle$ (2)

$\langle$integer$\rangle$ ::= $\langle$natural number$\rangle$ | $+$ $\langle$natural number$\rangle$ | $-$ $\langle$natural number$\rangle$

(3)

Examples of fixed-point constants allowed are

    1637 -1637 $+134829$

One slight difference in FORTRAN is that commas are not permitted in either fixed- or floating-point constants. Thus we would have to write

    123456789

instead of the more readable

    123,456,789

There is also a maximum number of digits for fixed-point constants. This is determined by the word size of the computer being used, and is always specified in documentation supplied by the computer manufacturer.

    Rational numbers must be written in floating-point form. One way corresponds exactly to the decimal representation of a rational number; a second way is very similar to scientific notation. If we wanted to write Avogadro's number, 6.02×10^{23}, as a FORTRAN constant, we would write

$$6.02E + 23$$

where the letter E has the meaning "times 10 raised to the power . . . ," and the exponent is the integer following the E. The full description of floating point constants is

    ⟨rational number⟩ ::= ⟨integer⟩. | .⟨integer⟩ | + ⟨integer⟩. | — ⟨integer⟩.|
               ⟨integer⟩.⟨natural number⟩ |
               ⟨integer⟩.E⟨integer⟩|
               ⟨integer⟩E⟨integer⟩|
               ⟨integer⟩.⟨natural number⟩E⟨integer⟩   (4)

All the constants below are permitted in the floating-point mode:

    $+123.$ $—1.23$ 123.45   123.E$—$02   123.E$+$02   .68E$+$07   6.02E$+$23

The use of the letter E is an excellent example of the semantics-syntax situation described in Chap. 11. We define E as part of the syntax of FORTRAN, and semantically give it the meaning "times 10 raised to the power." This is necessary because the usual notation 6.02×10^{23} requires a spatial interpretation. We know that the 23 written above and to the right of the 10 means that the number 10 is raised to the 23d power. A digital computer does not have this spatial sense, however; so we must replace it with something more definite; hence the E notation. As in the case of fixed-point constants, a maximum number of digits is allowed in floating-point constants. This is greater than the maximum for fixed-point constants because the floating-point mode uses two memory locations to store a number. There is also a maximum number of digits, almost always two, allowed as the exponent following E. Being confined to numbers between $\pm 10^{99}$ is not too unrealistic a restriction.

Identifiers in FORTRAN are also either of the fixed- or the floating-point mode. Fixed-point identifiers always begin with one of the letters I, J, K, L, M, N. An identifier beginning with any other letter is a floating-point identifier. Identifiers are used in FORTRAN as names for scalars (constants), arrays, functions, and subprograms. The possible identifiers are defined by the productions:

$$\langle\text{letter}\rangle ::= A \mid B \mid C \mid D \mid E \mid F \mid G \mid H \mid I \mid J \mid K \mid L \mid M \mid N \mid O \mid$$
$$P \mid Q \mid R \mid S \mid T \mid U \mid V \mid W \mid X \mid Y \mid Z \quad (5)$$
$$\langle\text{alphanumeric string}\rangle ::= \langle\text{letter}\rangle \mid \langle\text{digit}\rangle \mid \quad\quad\quad\quad\quad (6)$$
$$\langle\text{letter}\rangle\langle\text{alphanumeric string}\rangle \mid$$
$$\langle\text{digit}\rangle\langle\text{alphanumeric string}\rangle \quad (7)$$
$$\langle\text{identifier}\rangle ::= \langle\text{letter}\rangle \mid \langle\text{letter}\rangle\langle\text{alphanumeric string}\rangle \quad (8)$$

Line (7) merely allows the construction of any sequence of letters and digits, for example

$$\text{S2FT3A, 10FBZ6, 1A2B3C}$$

An identifier, then, is a sequence of letters and digits that begins with a letter. Again, a maximum number of characters is allowed, and this depends on the computer's memory word size. When identifiers are used as names for constants, they are called scalar identifiers. Identifiers are also used to name arrays and subprograms as shown in (10) and (13) below:

$$\langle\text{subscript list}\rangle ::= (\langle\text{integer}\rangle) \mid (\langle\text{integer}\rangle,\langle\text{integer}\rangle) \mid$$
$$(\langle\text{integer}\rangle,\langle\text{integer}\rangle,\langle\text{integer}\rangle) \mid \ldots \ldots \quad (9)$$

[process continues up to the maximum number of subscripts allowed]

$$\langle\text{array identifier}\rangle ::= \langle\text{identifier}\rangle\langle\text{subscript list}\rangle \quad (10)$$

The difference between scalar and array identifiers is that a subscript list follows an array identifier.

Some possible array identifiers are

$$\text{SUM(\quad), SUM2(\quad), S34BA(\quad)}$$

where the subscripts are omitted.   The identifier part of an array identifier
is often referred to as the *array name*.   The array names of the array identifiers
above are SUM, SUM2, and S34BA.

The last type of identifier, the subprogram identifier, uses the definitions
of scalar and array identifiers because both are permitted as arguments.

$$\langle\text{argument list}\rangle ::= (\langle\text{identifier}\rangle) \mid (\langle\text{identifier}\rangle,\langle\text{identifier}\rangle) \mid$$
$$(\langle\text{identifier}\rangle,\langle\text{identifier}\rangle,\langle\text{identifier}\rangle) \mid \ . \ . \ . \ . \qquad (11)$$

[process continues up to the maximum number of arguments allowed]

$$\langle\text{subprogram identifier}\rangle ::= \langle\text{identifier}\rangle \mid \langle\text{identifier}\rangle\langle\text{argument list}\rangle \quad (12)$$

Notice that an argument list is actually a sequence of either scalar or array
identifiers.   Subprograms are used in FORTRAN to specify smaller, commonly
used programs within a main program.   One special type of subprogram is the
FUNCTION subprogram.

The FUNCTION programs in FORTRAN are intended to allow an analog
of the mathematical usage

$$y = f(x)$$

where f is some specific function of the variable x.   FUNCTIONS can be fixed-
or floating-point in mode and can have more than one argument.   Several
common functions are "built into" the FORTRAN language, and can be used
by a replacement of the form

$$\langle\text{identifier}\rangle :: = \langle\text{function identifier}\rangle\langle\text{argument list}\rangle \qquad (13)$$

A table of the more common functions follows.

Function identifier and argument list	Value returned
ALOG (X)	$\log_e x$
EXP (X)	e^x
SIN (X)	$\sin x$
COS (X)	$\cos x$
SQRT (X)	$\sqrt{x}$
ATAN (Y,X)	$\arctan \dfrac{y}{x}$
ABS (X)	$|x|$
AMAX (X,Y)	$\max{(x,y)}$
AMIN (X,Y)	$\min{(x,y)}$
MOD (N,M)	$k \equiv n \text{ modulo } m$
INT (X)	$[x]$ (greatest integer function)
MAX (M,N)	$\max{(m,n)}$
MIN (M,N)	$\min{(m,n)}$

As an example of the use of these functions, if we wanted to express

$$y = \sqrt{\sin x + \log_e x}$$

we could write, in FORTRAN,

$$Y = SQRT\ (SIN(X) + ALOG(X))$$

When the machine-language instructions corresponding to this statement are executed, the desired result will be in the memory locations (two, since Y is a floating-point variable) assigned to Y. We are now ready to characterize the types of expressions allowed in FORTRAN.

FORTRAN expressions can use any of the arithmetic operations shown in the following table.

Operation symbol	Function	Example
+	Addition	A + B
−	Subtraction	A − B
*	Multiplication	A/B
/	Division	A∗B
**	Exponentiation	A∗∗B

These operations, or more generally connectives, are used to build expressions, as shown by the productions

$$\langle connective \rangle ::= +|-|*|/|** \tag{14}$$
$$\langle constant \rangle ::= \langle integer \rangle | \langle rational\ number \rangle \tag{15}$$
$$\langle variable \rangle ::= \langle constant \rangle | \langle identifier \rangle |$$
$$\langle array\ identifier \rangle \langle subscript\ list \rangle |$$
$$\langle subprogram\ identifier \rangle \langle argument\ list \rangle \tag{16}$$
$$\langle expression \rangle ::= \langle variable \rangle |$$
$$\langle variable \rangle \langle connective \rangle \langle variable \rangle |$$
$$(\langle variable \rangle \langle connective \rangle \langle variable \rangle) |$$
$$\langle variable \rangle \langle connective \rangle (\langle expression \rangle) |$$
$$(\langle expression \rangle) \langle connective \rangle \langle variable \rangle \tag{17}$$

Production (17) is truly powerful in the variety of expressions it permits. Some examples of permissible expressions are

$$(6.02E+23*X) + Y**2$$
$$SQRT\ (X**2 + Y**2)$$
$$(X(I) + Y(I))/(X(I) - Y(I))$$
$$(X(1) + Y(2)) * (3.14159)$$
$$(2.71828 * 3.14159) + 76.087$$

These expressions correspond to the following algebraic expressions:

$(6.02 \times 10^{23})x + y^2$

$\sqrt{x^2 + y^2}$

$\dfrac{x_i + y_i}{x_i - y_i}$

$(x_1 + y_2) \cdot 3.14159$ or $(x_1 + y_2)\pi$

$(2.71828 \times 3.14159) + 76.087$ or $e\pi + 76.087$

We are now able to write a simple FORTRAN program. In any program, all the information must be present, because neither the computer nor the compiler intuitively will recognize what we are trying to accomplish. If we wanted to compute the area of a circle with a radius of 2, we could not just write

$$A = \pi*2**2$$

because the computer does not know the numerical value of the number π. We could write

$$PI = 3.14159$$
$$A = PI*2.**2$$

and once the compiler-produced instructions corresponding to these statements are executed, the (approximate) area of the circle would be stored in the memory locations assigned (by the compiler) to the variable A. We will use the pseudo-random number generator discussed in Chap. 9 as the subject of our first program. All the statements in the program are replacements of the form

$$variable = expression$$

where the expression is evaluated by the computer and then stored in the memory locations assigned to the variable to the left of the equal (replacement) sign.

IR(1) = 0	(1)
IR(2) = 1	(2)
I = 2	(3)
IR(I + 1) = IR(I) + IR(I − 1)	(4)
I = I + 1	(5)

Lines (1) and (2) of the program assign the values 0 and 1 to the *array* variables IR(1) and IR(2). These are fixed-point constants (no decimal point), and the array name is also a fixed-point name. The reason for using the fixed-point mode, rather than floating-point, is that when statement (4) is executed, the arithmetic the computer performs is, actually, the congruence arithmetic required by the algorithm, where the modulus is the greatest integer that can be stored in one memory location.

As it stands, this program would generate pseudo-random numbers on a binary computer. (The reader may refer to Chap. 10 for a more complete discussion of binary computers.) We could also program this algorithm as follows:

$$R(1) = 0. \tag{1}$$
$$R(2) = 1. \tag{2}$$
$$I = 2 \tag{3}$$
$$MODULUS = (2**16) - 1 \tag{4}$$
$$TEMP = R(I) + R(I-1) \tag{5}$$
$$R(I+1) = AMOD \ (TEMP, \ MODULUS) \tag{6}$$
$$I = I + 1 \tag{7}$$

In this program, we use the floating-point mode of arithmetic, which does not automatically perform congruence arithmetic. Statement (4) defines the modulus to be the greatest integer stored in one word on a 16-bit binary machine. In statement (5) we compute $r_i + r_{i-1}$ and temporarily store this sum in the locations assigned to TEMP. Statement (6) uses a FUNCTION subroutine named AMOD, and it is this subroutine that actually performs the congruence arithmetic. (The AMOD subroutine is available in almost all FORTRAN systems.) Finally, the subscript variable I is incremented so that the next pseudo-random number generated is computed from r_2 and r_3. This is important, because if we did not increment the subscript, we would always compute the same number, and then clearly lose the "randomness." There are a few other flaws in this program, but we will discuss them later in the chapter. One of them is that the difference between a subroutine name and an array name must be made clear. How does the compiler know, for example, that AMOD is the name of a FUNCTION subprogram, rather than a two-dimensional array? The second major flaw is fairly subtle. If the reader examines the Backus normal form productions for array variables and subscript lists, he will see that these are violated in both programs. Specifically, we used expressions $I + 1$ and $I - 1$ as subscripts, but production (9) allows only integers as subscripts. Actually, production (9) is a weaker statement than is actually allowed. FORTRAN does permit fixed-point-mode expressions as subscripts for array variables, and some implementations of FORTRAN permit floating-point expressions as subscripts.

The arithmetic statements we have discussed thus far enable the FORTRAN programmer to tell the computer what calculations to perform. In practice, the programmer must be sure that his arithmetic statements actually describe the desired calculation. The computer has no intuition, and it will execute instructions without question, even if they are nonsensical. A particularly irritating example of this is the following:

$$T1 = 1.$$
$$T2 = 2.$$
$$T3 = 3.$$
$$AVG = (T1 + T2 + T3)/N$$

This looks like a program to compute the average of the variables T1, T2, and T3, whose values are assigned in the first three statements. The "bug" in the program is that the value of the variable N is not defined in a statement. When we look at the last statement, we can see that the value of N should be 3, because then the last statement will compute the average of T1, T2, and T3, and this is what the variable name AVG implies. We drew this conclusion from our past experience. However, digital computers have no recollection of past experience; so the computer would just use whatever number happened to be present in the memory location assigned to N. In fact, on some computers, undefined variables (such as N above) have the value zero; so in this little program we would actually be dividing 6 by 0, which is meaningless. This is the kind of detail which must be specified, via the FORTRAN language, to the computer. Attention to this level of detail is probably the greatest difficulty for beginning programmers. It can be avoided by always bearing in mind that the computer must be told everything; it cannot think for itself.

12-2 CONTROL STATEMENTS

The FORTRAN programming language has several types of statements that allow the programmer to specify the order of execution of arithmetic statements, and also their repetition. A FORTRAN program is a sequence of FORTRAN statements. These statements are executed (more properly, the machine instructions corresponding to the statements are executed) sequentially, that is, in the order in which they appear. The exception to this is that some statements themselves can change the order in which the statements in the program are executed. Before discussing and illustrating these, we will digress to the physical form of the statements.

The most common physical form of FORTRAN statements is holes on tabulating cards. A programmer writes his FORTRAN statements on a coding form such as the one in Fig. 12-1. These forms are then key-punched, one line per tabulating card. This is necessary because the computer can more easily accept and interpret these cards. There are input devices that can read coding forms directly, but these are not in general use. The tabulating cards have 80 columns, which correspond to columns on the coding form. In FORTRAN, only the first 72 columns are used, but this is not of great importance here. Most statements begin in the seventh column. The first six

FX-0897 (5/62)

Program _____

Coded By _____

Checked By _____

FORTRAN CODING FORM

Identification
73   80

Date _____

Page _____ of _____

C FOR COMMENT

STATEMENT NUMBER		FORTRAN STATEMENT	
1 5	6 7	36	72
C		EXAMPLE OF A COMMENT CARD.	
C		THE STATEMENTS BELOW ARE AN EXAMPLE OF	
C		HOW FORTRAN STATEMENTS SHOULD APPEAR ON	
C		A CODING FORM	
C			
C			
C		SAMPLE STATEMENTS:	
		PI = 3.14159	
		R = 2.0	
10		AREA = PI*R**2	
C		NOTE STATEMENT LABEL "10" ABOVE.	

Fig. 12-1

columns have a special use. One use is that a comment card (statement) may be inserted into a program. Comments are never executed; they are present only for the programmer's convenience and to convey nonprogram information. To specify that a statement is a comment, the programmer inserts a C in the first column. This is a signal to the compiler program that everything else on the card (statement) is just a comment.

A second use for the first five columns is that statement numbers may appear there at the programmer's option. Statement numbers, or labels, as they are sometimes called, are the key to controlling the flow of statement execution.

In situations where decisions are made during the execution, flow depends upon the outcome of these decisions. Statement numbers are used in conjunction with the control statements to indicate which statement should be executed. Many of the flowcharts in Chap. 9 included decision boxes of the form

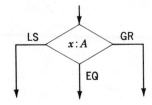

In a FORTRAN program, the decision itself would be made with an IF statement (to be discussed in this section). The three possible outcomes have different instructions associated with them, and the FORTRAN statements for these would have statement numbers. The use of statement numbers will become clear as the various control statements are considered. The three most important control statements are GO TO, IF, and DO. The next four are much easier to understand: CONTINUE, PAUSE, RETURN, and STOP. Finally, we will briefly examine some of the less frequently used control statements. In our discussion of control statements we shall use N_1, N_2, N_3, . . . to indicate statement numbers.

GO TO N_1

The GO TO statement is the simplest transfer-control instruction. If this statement is in a program, when it is executed, the sequence of instructions is altered by this statement. The GO TO statement in a program is analogous to the arrows connecting boxes in flowcharts. In a program for the flowchart below, the transfer from the last box to the second box would be accomplished with a GO TO N_1 statement, where N_1 is the label on the first statement in the coding for the second box.

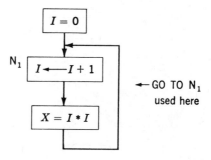

After we discuss the IF statement, we will illustrate the use of GO TO and IF with an example.

IF ($\langle$expression$\rangle$) N_1, N_2, N_3

The IF statement finds the value of the FORTRAN expression in parentheses, and then compares this value to zero. If the value of the expression is less than zero, the statement with the label N_1 is executed next; if the expression is equal to zero, statement N_2 is the next statement executed; and if the expression is greater than zero, the next statement to be executed is the one with the statement number N_3. The IF statement actually compares the value of the expression within the parentheses to zero.   It can compare any two numbers by using the property of subtraction shown below.

Let x and a be real numbers.

$$x > a \Leftrightarrow x - a > 0$$
$$x = a \Leftrightarrow x - a = 0$$
$$x < a \Leftrightarrow x - a < 0$$

The student should keep this in mind, because it is very often used in FORTRAN programming.

As an example to illustrate the GO TO and IF statements, as well as several arithmetic statements, we will write a FORTRAN program for the square-root algorithm (see Sec. 9-1).   The flowchart is repeated for convenient reference.

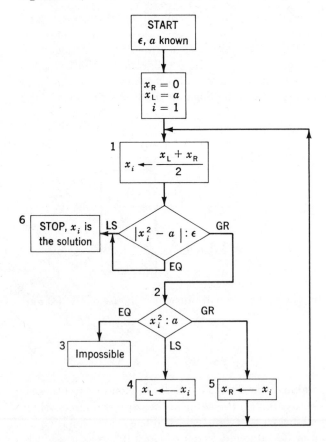

We will assume that the values of the variables EPS and A, corresponding to ϵ and a in the flowchart, are already in the computer.

```
C     PROGRAM FOR BINARY CHOPPING SQUARE ROOT ALGORITHM.   (1)
C     VALUES OF EPS AND A ARE PRE-DEFINED.                  (2)
C                                                           (3)
      XL = 0.                                               (4)
      XR = A                                                (5)
      I = 1                                                 (6)
    1 XI = (XL + XR)/2.                                     (7)
      IF(ABS(XI*XI—A)—EPS) 6,6,2                            (8)
    2 IF(XI*XI—A) 4,3,5                                     (9)
    3 STOP                                                  (10)
C     COULD HAVE ERROR RETURN AT 3.                         (11)
    4 XL = XI                                               (12)
      GO TO 1                                               (13)
    5 XR = XI                                               (14)
      GO TO 1                                               (15)
    6 CONTINUE                                              (16)
C     AT 6, THE VALUE OF XI IS THE APPROXIMATE SQUARE ROOT OF A. (17)
```

The first three statements in this program are simply explanatory comments. The next three statements define values for the variables XL, XR, and I. (Even though we did not use I in this program, we will want to use it later.) Statement (7) has a label, the statement number 1, and corresponds to the third box in the flowchart. It has a statement label because it must be executed again after the value of either XL or XR has been changed. Statement (8) is the IF statement that corresponds to the first decision box in the flowchart. ABS is a FUNCTION subprogram that computes the absolute value of its argument, in this case, XI*XI — A. The value of EPS is then subtracted from this, and the result is compared with zero by the IF statement. This is an example of two quantities being compared, rather than just one quantity compared with zero. Notice that two of the statement labels are the same in the first IF statement. If we look at the flowchart, we see that both the LS (less) and the EQ (equal) branches lead to the end of the program (statement labeled 6). We can accomplish this by giving the same statement label to the "less than" and the "equal to" positions of the IF statement. In line (9) we have the IF statement that corresponds to the second decision box. The only way this statement can be executed is by having control passed to it from the first IF statement. When executed, it compares XI*XI with A (actually, XI*XI — A with zero) and then transfers control to statements labeled 4, 3, or 5, depending on the outcome of the test. If XI*XI — A equals zero, control goes to statement (3). This outcome is labeled impossible in the flowchart, because if XI*XI — A = 0, then, in the first IF test, control would have gone to statement (6). At lines (12) and (14) the values of XL or XR are changed, so that the next iteration can proceed with new intervals. Finally, lines (13) and (15)

show how the GO TO statement is used.   Line (16) is the last of our program.
Labeled 6, this line can be reached only by a transfer from the first IF statement.
At this point [statement (6)] the value of XI is within the tolerance EPS of the
square root of A.   The CONTINUE statement is there to indicate that nothing
more must be done to complete the algorithm.   If this algorithm were part of a
larger program, the CONTINUE statement would probably be replaced by a
statement (labeled 6!) that used the value of XI.   There are several other ways
the IF statement can be used, and they are summarized below.   Notice that the
choice of statement numbers can determine the effect of the IF statement.

Statement		*Effect*
IF (A)	1, 2, 3	Compare value of A to zero
IF (X — A)	1, 2, 3	Compare values of X and A
IF (A)	1, 2, 2	Test for $A \geq 0$
IF (X — A)	1, 2, 2	Test for $X \geq A$
IF (A)	1, 1, 2	Test for $A \leq 0$
IF (X — A)	1, 1, 2	Test for $X \leq A$
IF (A)	1, 2, 1	Test for $\neq 0$
IF (X — A)	1, 2, 1	Test for $X \neq A$

DO N₁ INDEX = LOW, MAX, INC

The DO statement is the third of the more powerful control statements, its
power coming from its ability to specify repetition.   The statement label N_1
refers to a statement that *follows* the DO statement somewhere later in the
program.   All the statements between the DO statement and the statement
labeled N_1 form a block (see Chap. 11) of statements known as a DO-*loop*.   The
index, a fixed-point variable name, is used to specify how many times the
statements in the DO-loop block are repeated.   The programmer can specify
the initial and final values of the index and the increment in the index for each
repetition.   A more complete description of the DO statement is its Backus
normal form production.

$$\langle \text{statement label} \rangle ::= \langle \text{digit} \rangle | \langle \text{digit} \rangle \langle \text{digit} \rangle |$$
$$\langle \text{digit} \rangle \langle \text{digit} \rangle \langle \text{digit} \rangle |$$
$$\langle \text{digit} \rangle \langle \text{digit} \rangle \langle \text{digit} \rangle \langle \text{digit} \rangle |$$
$$\langle \text{digit} \rangle \langle \text{digit} \rangle \langle \text{digit} \rangle \langle \text{digit} \rangle \langle \text{digit} \rangle \tag{18}$$
$$\langle \text{fixed point prefix} \rangle ::= I|J|K|L|M|N \tag{19}$$
$$\langle \text{fixed point identifier} \rangle ::= \langle \text{fixed point prefix} \rangle | \langle \text{integer} \rangle |$$
$$\langle \text{fixed point prefix} \rangle \langle \text{alphanumeric string} \rangle \tag{20}$$
$$\langle \text{do-statement} \rangle ::= \text{DO} \langle \text{statement label} \rangle \langle \text{fx.pt.id} \rangle = \langle \text{fx.pt.id} \rangle, \langle \text{fx.pt.id} \rangle |$$
$$\text{DO} \langle \text{statement label} \rangle \langle \text{fx.pt.id} \rangle = \langle \text{fx.pt.id} \rangle, \langle \text{fx.pt.id} \rangle, \langle \text{fx.pt.id.} \rangle \tag{21}$$

For the sake of completeness, we include the following:

$\langle$go-to statement$\rangle$ ::= GO TO $\langle$statement label$\rangle$ (22)

$\langle$if-statement$\rangle$ ::= IF ($\langle$expression$\rangle$)$\langle$st.label$\rangle$,$\langle$st.label$\rangle$,$\langle$st.label$\rangle$ (23)

The productions for the DO statement show that the specification of the increment for the index is optional. The index of the DO statement is a counter: it keeps track of how many times the statements in the DO-loop are executed. The first fixed-point identifier after the equal sign is the starting value of the index. After the first execution of the DO-loop, the index is incremented by the value of the third fixed-point identifier after the equal sign. After being incremented, the value of the index is compared with its final value, the second fixed-point variable after the equal sign. If this value has not been reached, the statements in the DO-loop are repeated again. If the increment is not specified, it is assumed to have the value 1. Below, we give several examples of DO statements, and then a program using DO-loops.

```
DO  1   I = 1, 10, 1
DO  1   I = 1, 10
DO 26 JX = I1, I6, 2
DO 37  K = 1, MAX, 3
DO 18  L = −3, LIMIT, 2
DO 66  M = 18, 1, −1
```

Various implementations of FORTRAN differ in their options permitted regarding the index and its limits. Some FORTRAN compilers even allow floating-point indices and limits, but these are special cases. As an example, the statements below show how a DO-loop might be used. The first two statements initialize the values of the variables MAX and ISUM. In the DO statement, J is the index variable, and MAX is the end value of J. Since no incre-

```
MAX = 10
ISUM = 0
DO 6 J = 1, MAX
6 ISUM = ISUM + J
```

ment is specified, the value of the increment is automatically 1. Each time statement (6) is executed, the value of J is increased by 1 and then compared with the value of MAX. Once J reaches MAX, the DO-loop is complete, and then the statement following statement (6) would be executed. In this example, once the value of J is 10, the loop is complete.

One of the convenient applications of DO-loops is in conjunction with subscripted arrays. The index can serve as the subscript of the array variable, and the number of elements in the array can be the limit for the DO statement. As an example of this, consider the following simple application. We wish to find the average of 200 plating thicknesses, where the ith plating thickness is denoted by x_i. If we define X to be an array variable (this process will be discussed later), then the sequence $\{x_i\}$ of plating thicknesses can be stored in the array X. Now, to find the average of these, the program below will suffice.

$$
\begin{aligned}
&\text{SUM} = 0 \\
&\text{DO 1 J} = 1,200 \\
1\quad&\text{SUM} = \text{SUM} + \text{X(J)} \\
&\text{AVG} = \text{SUM}/200.
\end{aligned}
$$

In this example of a loop, the index (J) is a subscript for the array X. The first time through the loop, SUM has the value x_1. The second time around, SUM has the value x_1 (from before) $+ x_2$. When J is 3, SUM is $x_1 + x_2 + x_3$, and so on. Finally, when J has the value 200, the value of SUM is the sum of $x_1, x_2, \ldots, x_{200}$. The next statement computes the average by dividing the sum by the number of variables. Notice how easily the formula for computing averages

$$
\mu = \frac{\sum_{i=1}^{200} x_i}{200}
$$

can be expressed in FORTRAN. If we wanted a more general program, we could replace 200 with a variable name, say, N, and define N before the loop was executed. Then we would have a program for the formula

$$
\mu = \frac{\sum_{i=1}^{n} x_i}{n}
$$

Another use of DO statements must be discussed. Recall that a DO-loop is a block of statements that is executed a certain number of times. There is no reason why this block of statements cannot be a part of another DO-loop. When this is done, the loops are said to be *nested*. Another example of the nesting concept is the sequence of intervals we produced in the binary-chopping square-root algorithm. In that sequence each interval was contained in the interval of the previous iteration. In much the same way, a DO-loop can be entirely contained (nested) in a second DO-loop. This will be our last example of DO-loops. In this example, we wish to program the formula

$$
k = 1! + 2! + 3! + \cdots + n!
$$

Our inner loop will compute the factorials

$$n! = 1 \cdot 2 \cdot 3 \cdot \cdots \cdot n$$

and our outer loop will sum the factorials.

For the sake of definiteness, we will initialize n to be 10, thus computing

$$k = 1! + 2! + 3! + \cdots + 10!$$

```
      K = 0
      NMAX = 10
      DO 2 N = 1, NMAX
      NFACT = 1
      DO 1 I = 1, N
    1 NFACT = NFACT * I
  C      AT THIS POINT, THE VALUE OF NFACT IS N FACTORIAL.
    2 K = K + NFACT
```

The inner loop is entirely contained within the outer loop. This example is a little unusual, because the index of the outer loop is the maximum value for the inner loop, which again illustrates the power of the FORTRAN language. The inner loop computes N!, where N is the index of the outer loop. Once the inner loop is complete, this value (NFACT) is added to K. By the time the outer loop has been executed NMAX times, K has the desired value. Notice the initialization of K and NFACT. K is initialized to be zero, so that the first time the outer loop is executed, we actually have

$$K \leftarrow 0 + NFACT$$

NFACT is initialized to be 1, because the first time the inner loop is executed, we actually get

$$NFACT \leftarrow 1 * I$$

If we initialized NFACT to be zero, we would always be multiplying by zero, and our final answer would be zero. Finally, notice that NFACT is reinitialized to be 1 before the inner loop is executed again. This is important, because otherwise we would be computing

$$K = 1! + 1!2! + 2!3! + 3!4! + 4!5! + \cdots + 9!10!$$

which is quite different from what we intended.

Nested DO-loops can have either of the forms shown below. The second form frequently appears in programs for matrix manipulations. We will have

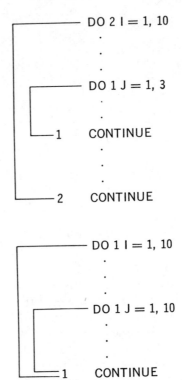

or

an example of this when we discuss arrays. The situation below is not per-mitted, and all FORTRAN compilers regard it as an error. The two loops are not really nested; they overlap.

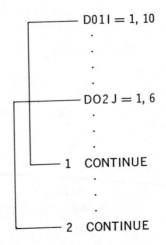

A little thought about this overlapping shows why it is an error. Which loop includes which loop? Do we execute the loop ending at 2 six times and then complete the loop ending at 1, or vice versa? This ambiguity cannot be handled either by a computer or a compiler program; hence the error.

CONTINUE

The CONTINUE statement is the first of four of the more common control statements that are easy to understand. When a CONTINUE statement is executed, no computations are performed. In this sense, it is a dummy, or do-nothing, statement. In our last example we showed the use of this statement. A CONTINUE statement having a label can be a target for a GO TO or an IF statement, and can be the last statement in a DO-loop. These are the main uses of the CONTINUE statement, although it can also be used in a similar way with the less common control statements. Some examples of the CONTINUE statement used as a target for other transfer-control statements are shown below. A CONTINUE statement that has no statement label has no effect on a program.

```
          GO TO 6
            .
            .
            .
   6      CONTINUE
          IF (X–A) 1, 2, 3
            .
            .
            .
   1      CONTINUE
            .
            .
            .
   2      CONTINUE
            .
            .
            .
   3      CONTINUE
            .
            .
            .
          DO 4 J = 1, 10
            .
            .
            .
   4      CONTINUE
```

PAUSE

The PAUSE statement has exactly the effect that its name implies. When a PAUSE statement is executed as part of a FORTRAN program, the computer comes to a halt. At this time, if the programmer is present, he can examine certain memory locations to see if his program is executing correctly. At the programmer's option, the program can be started again, and the statement following the PAUSE will be executed. This statement is primarily a debugging aid.

STOP

The STOP statement should be the last statement executed; it simply stops the computer. A STOP is more final than a PAUSE, however, because there is no option to execute an instruction following a STOP statement. The STOP statement, while it seems trivial, is actually needed, because it signals the end of a program.

RETURN

This statement is used to signal the end of a subprogram. When executed in a subprogram, the RETURN statement returns the execution flow back to the main program.

CALL ⟨Subroutine name⟩⟨argument list⟩

The CALL statement transfers execution from a main program to a subroutine. If we wrote a subroutine to invert a matrix, and named it INVERT, we could access this subroutine by the statement

CALL INVERT

If the subroutine used arguments (discussed later) from the main program, such as the name of the matrix to be inverted and its order, these variable names would appear in the call statement. For example, if the matrix we wished to invert has the array name A, and the variable N is the order of A, we would call the subroutine with

CALL INVERT (A, N)

When the RETURN statement in the subroutine INVERT is executed, the next statement that will be executed is the one that follows the CALL statement.

We conclude this section with four additional control statements, which are the less common ones. They are redundant in the sense that they add very little to the FORTRAN language, and they can be replaced by suitable use of the other statements in the language. We will discuss them in the order of their usefulness.   Other control statements appear in some of the implementations of FORTRAN, but we will not consider them here.   These are all easily understood because they are fairly similar to the control statements presented here.

Computed GO TO

The Computed GO TO statement is an extension of the GO TO statement.   If $N_1, N_2, \ldots$ are statement labels, then the Computed GO TO statement has the form

$$\text{GO TO } (N_1, N_2, \ldots, N_m)\langle\text{expression}\rangle$$

where the expression is in the fixed-point mode.   If the value of the expression is 1, the next statement to be executed is the one having the label N_1.   If the value of the expression is 3, the statement labeled N_3 will be executed next. The value of the expression corresponds to the statement label in the list that will be executed next.   An example is necessary to clarify a subtle point.

$$\text{GO TO } (10,\ 68,\ 29,\ 3)\ J$$

.

.

.

3   CONTINUE

.

.

.

68   CONTINUE

.

.

.

10   CONTINUE

.

.

.

57   CONTINUE

.

.

.

29   CONTINUE

Value of J	Label of next statement executed
1	10
2	68
2	29
4	3
5	(error)

The example and table above show that the order of the statement labels in the program does not have to correspond to their order in the GO TO list. Also, the value of J is not the statement label of the next statement executed; it merely tells which label in the list is the next to be executed. Finally, if the value of J is greater than the number of labels in the GO TO list, an error condition exists. Negative values of J have the same effect.

ASSIGN and Assigned GO TO

These two statements can be used to place small "subroutines" in a main program or in a subprogram. The Assigned GO TO statement has the form

$$\text{GO TO } \langle \text{variable} \rangle$$

where the value of the variable is the label of the statement that control is being transferred to. The ASSIGN statement has the form

$$\text{ASSIGN } \langle \text{integer constant} \rangle \text{ TO } \langle \text{variable} \rangle$$

The example below shows how these statements can be used to make a subroutine.

10	CSQ = A**2 + B**2	(1)
	DIST = SQRT (CSQ)	(2)
	GO TO BEGIN	(3)
	.	
	.	
	.	
	ASSIGN 3 TO BEGIN	(4)
	GO TO 10	(5)
3	CONTINUE	(6)
	.	
	.	
	.	
	ASSIGN 4 TO BEGIN	(7)
	GO TO 10	(8)
4	CONTINUE	(9)

Statements (1) to (3) compute

$$\text{dist} = \sqrt{a^2 + b^2}$$

for the current values of a (in A) and b (in B), and then transfer control to the statement whose label is the current value of BEGIN. Thus, at statement (4),

BEGIN is given the value 3 by the ASSIGN statement. The next statement, (5), transfers control to the statement labeled 10, which is the beginning of our "subroutine." When statement (3) is executed, since the value of BEGIN is now 3, the statement labeled 3 is the next one executed. Later in the program, BEGIN is assigned to be 4, and the GO TO 10 statement transfers back to the subroutine. By this time, A and B probably have different values; so a new DIST is computed, and then the program goes to statement (9) (labeled 4) because this is the new value of BEGIN. If an ASSIGN statement assigns a value of BEGIN that is not a statement label in the program, an error condition exists; so the programmer must check this possibility.

IF (SENSE SWITCH ⟨expression⟩) N₁, N₂

A SENSE SWITCH is an external switch that can be controlled while a program is executing. There are four of these switches, and the value of the expression indicates which switch is being tested by the statement. If the switch being tested is on, control goes to the statement labeled N_1; if it is off, the statement labeled N_2 is executed next. Since there are four switches, the value of the expression must be 1, 2, 3, or 4. Any other value will result in an error condition, because the computer will not know which switch to test. The main advantage of sense switches is that they can be manipulated while the program is executed. This can be used as a debugging aid, as shown in the example below. In this example, the variables A and B are intermediate values in a long computation. They are not the final result, but they can show the programmer whether or not the program is doing what he wanted it to do.

```
            .
            .
            .
        IF (SENSE SWITCH 3) 6, 10
      6   PRINT (A,B)
     10   X = A**2 + B**2
            .
            .
            .
```

If sense switch 3 is off, the values of A and B will not be printed; if the switch is on, they will be printed. If the programmer wanted to see what the values of A and B are, he could turn sense switch 3 on and let the program run. When the IF (SENSE SWITCH) statement is executed, it will transfer control to the PRINT statement, and the intermediate results will be printed out. After the printing, the next statement will be executed. When the program is fully debugged, it is executed with sense switch 3 off, and the intermediate results

never get printed.   Another good use for sense switches is to check whether an
iterative process is converging.   If such a process does not converge, the program will run forever (or at least until the computer is turned off).   By inserting a sense-switch test at the end of each iteration, this situation can be
controlled externally.

We have now completed the two main types of statements in FORTRAN,
arithmetic and control.   The arithmetic statements enable us to specify the
computations that the computer should perform, and the control statements
give us, as their name implies, a way to control our program, particularly
while it executes.   The third type of FORTRAN statement, the declaration,
is essentially a means of presenting information to the FORTRAN compiler.

12-3   DECLARATION STATEMENTS

The declaration statements in FORTRAN are needed because a FORTRAN
compiler is a program, and as such, it needs to know everything about a FOR-
TRAN program that is to be compiled.   When we first mentioned arrays and
functions, we hinted at the type of information that the declaration statements
can convey.   To repeat this here, consider the arithmetic statement

$$X = XN + ABSV(N)$$

Is ABSV an array name and N its subscript, or is ABSV a function identifier and
N the argument of the function?   Since compilers are programs, ambiguities
such as this one cannot be tolerated.   The declaration statements are used to
clarify situations like this.   We will discuss the six more common declaration
statements: DIMENSION, SUBROUTINE, FUNCTION, COMMON, EQUIVALENCE,
and END.   As with control statements, there are other declaration statements
in some FORTRAN systems.   We will discuss only the declaration statements
that are present in all FORTRAN systems.

DIMENSION

The DIMENSION statement is used for two purposes: it defines array names and
tells the compiler how many memory locations to reserve for the array.   It
also indicates how many subscripts an array variable has.   There are two
forms that a DIMENSION statement can have.   An example of the simpler
form is

DIMENSION A(100), X(100,50), I(28)

This statement tells the compiler that A, X, and I are array names, and that
references to A should have one subscript, references to X should have two
subscripts, and references to I should have one subscript.   The numbers in

the subscript position indicate the maximum value that a subscript can have, because that is the number of locations reserved for that array. For this statement, the compiler would reserve $100 \times 2 = 200$ locations for the array A (we multiplied the 100 by 2 because A is a floating-point variable name). The array X is described as having two subscripts, the first having a maximum value of 100 and the second having a maximum of 50. As a result of the DIMENSION statement, the compiler would reserve $100 \times 50 \times 2 = 10,000$ memory locations for the X array. An array may have more than just one subscript; the number of subscripts to be associated with an array is defined by the number of maximum values present (separated by commas) between the parentheses following the array name. The number of subscripts an array has is called the *dimension of the array*. Thus a one-dimensional array has one subscript, a three-dimensional array has three subscripts, and so on.

Suppose we define arrays A, B, and C by the statement

$$\text{DIMENSION} \quad A(15,15), \quad B(15,15), \quad C(15,15)$$

This statement tells the compiler that future references to A should have two subscripts (similarly for B and C). If we had a statement

$$X = A(I,J)$$

the computer would find the values I and J (suppose they are 8 and 12, for now) and then find the correct memory location for A(I,J), (here A(8,12)) and put that number (the value of A(8,12)) into the memory locations reserved for the floating-point variable X. One common error that occurs is referring to an array with subscripts whose values are greater than the maximums in the DIMENSION statement. Thus, if we said

$$X = A(I,J)$$

and the value of I is 17, we would commit an error. This type of error is fairly subtle because A(I,J) is compatible with the DIMENSION statement. Another common error is using more subscripts than defined by the DIMENSION statement. If we wrote

$$X = A(6,8,2)$$

we stay within the maximum values of the subscripts, but we used one too many subscripts. This error is not as serious, because the compiler can detect the wrong number of subscripts, and when it does, it prints out an error message.

Since DIMENSION statements permit the definition of multidimensional arrays, we have a convenient analog of algebraic variables having several subscripts. The most common occurrence of such variables is the elements of a matrix. Suppose we have two square matrices, A and B, where their elements are given by

$$A = (a_{i,j})$$
$$B = (b_{i,j})$$

and suppose we wish to form the matrix product

$$C = A \cdot B$$

To make the example simple let A, B, and C be 4 by 4 matrices. The elements of C are given by the formula

$$c_{i,j} = \sum_{k=1}^{4} a_{i,k}b_{k,j}$$

as we saw in Chap. 5. Below we give an example of how this could be programmed in FORTRAN. Notice how the subscripts are manipulated in the DIMENSION statements and in the nested DO-loops.

```
        DIMENSION A(4,4), B(4,4), C(4,4)
        DO 3 I = 1,4
        DO 2 J = 1,4
        C (I,J) = 0.
        DO 1 K = 1,4
    1   C (I,J) = C(I,J) + A(I,K) * B(K,J)
    2   CONTINUE
    3   CONTINUE
```

The outer loops (ending at 2 and 3) refer to the subscripts on the elements of the matrix C, which is stored in the array named C. The inner loop actually performs the sum

$$c_{i,j} = \sum_{k=1}^{4} a_{i,k}b_{k,j}$$

for the I and J in the outer loops. This again illustrates how the index of a DO-loop can be used as a subscript in an array. The innermost loop is executed four times for each value of J, and the middle loop (indexed by J) is executed four times for each value of I, where I is the index of the outermost loop. This ensures that all 16 elements of the matrix C are actually computed.

Some FORTRAN compilers allow the second form of the DIMENSION statement, which is shown below. These versions are common enough to warrant consideration here.

DIMENSION A(6/20), B(6/20, 10), C(−2/3, −10/−5)

In this example, the array A is one-dimensional, while B and C are two-dimen-

sional.   The slash separates the minimum and maximum values that a subscript can have.   The subscript on A can range from 6 to 20; if any value outside this range is used, an error is committed.   Being able to specify upper
and lower limits to the values of subscripts, and also negative subscripts, is
sometimes convenient, but this option is not often used.

Subroutine

A subroutine is actually a program that is used by a main program.   The
SUBROUTINE declaration statement is used at the beginning of a subroutine
to tell the compiler that the sequel instructions are part of a subroutine.
This is necessary because a FORTRAN compiler has no other way to dis-
tinguish between a main program and a subroutine.   The general form of the
SUBROUTINE statement is

SUBROUTINE ⟨identifier⟩ (⟨argument list⟩)

where the identifier is the name of the subroutine, and the argument list contains variables and constants that the subroutine will use.   Subroutines are
used in situations where the same type of computation is to be performed
many times.   The example below illustrates many features of subroutines.
   The program to compute the square root of a number by binary chopping
can be made into a subroutine.   At the time, we said that the values of the
variables EPS and A were predefined.   In our square-root subroutine we will
use EPS and A as arguments in the calling sequence.   The square root of the
number stored in A will be returned to the main program in the location assigned
to the variable SQRTA.   We will give the subroutine the name BCSQRT,
standing for *B*inary *C*hopping *SQ*uare *R*oo*T*.

```
C      BCSQRT IS A SUBROUTINE TO COMPUTE THE SQUARE ROOT OF A
C      WITHIN THE TOLERANCE EPS.
       SUBROUTINE BCSQRT (EPS, A, SQRTA)
       XL = 0.
       XR = A
1      XI = (XL + XR)/2.
       IF (ABS(XI*XI — A) — EPS) 6,6,2
2      IF (XI*XI — A) 4,3,5
3      STOP
4      XL = XI
       GO TO 1
5      XR = XI
       GO TO 1
6      SQRTA = XI
       RETURN
       END
```

Most of the statements in this subroutine are the same as we had in the earlier example. The main change is that now it is defined to be a subroutine, and we leave the value of the square root in a new location. The SUBROU-TINE statement tells the compiler that the statements following it make up a subroutine named BCSQRT. The argument list indicates to the compiler that EPS, A, and SQRTA are parameters from the main program (which uses the subroutine). We have used the END statement for the first time in this example. The END statement is a signal to the compiler that there will be no additional FORTRAN statements in the subroutine. In the statement labeled 6, the variable SQRTA is given the value currently in XI. We saw earlier that this point, XI, contained the approximate square root of the number in A. Since this is the whole purpose of the subroutine, we must return the computed approximation to the main program. The RETURN statement returns the flow of execution back to the main program. This subroutine could be called by any of the statements

CALL BCSQRT (EPS, A, SQRTA)
CALL BCSQRT (TOL, B, SQRTB)
CALL BCSQRT (O.OOO1, 64.7, B)

If the first call statement is used, the values of EPS and A must be defined previous to the call statement. The subroutine computes the value of SQRTA and returns it to the main program in the memory locations assigned to the variable SQRTA. To use this value in the main program, the variable name SQRTA must be used. The second call statement shows one of the features of subroutines. In the second call statement, different variable names are used. If we called BCSQRT with this statement, the number stored in TOL would be the value of EPS in the subroutine, and similarly, the value of B would be the value of A, and the square root of this number would be returned in the variable named SQRTB. The third statement defines the values of EPS and A in the subroutine literally. If we called the subroutine with this statement, when the subroutine executed, the value of EPS would be 0.0001 and the value of A would be 64.7. The approximate square root of 64.7 would be returned to the main program in the variable B.

Once a subroutine is defined, any calls to that subroutine must conform to the SUBROUTINE statement. The proper subroutine name must be used, and the correct number of arguments must be present in the argument list. Finally, the variables in the argument list must be of the same mode (fixed- or floating-point) and order as they appear in the SUBROUTINE statement. Each of the call statements below commits an error in calling our BSCQRT subroutine.

```
CALL BCSQRT (EPS, N, SQRTN)
CALL BCSQRT (K, 64, X)
CALL BCSQRT (TOL, A, B, X)
CALL BCHSQRT (EPS, A, SQRTA)
```

The argument list of a subroutine may contain array names. If it does, it is necessary to define the array names as arrays within the subroutine by a DIMENSION statement. As an example of this, we will make a subroutine out of our example of matrix multiplication.

```
      SUBROUTINE MTXMLT (A, B, C, N)
      DIMENSION A(10,10), B(10,10), C(10,10)
C     N IS THE SIZE OF THE MATRICES TO BE MULTIPLIED.
      DO 3 I = 1, N
      DO 2 J = 1,N
      C(I,J)   = 0.
      DO 1 K = 1,N
    1 C(I,J)   = C(I,J) + A(I,K) * B(K,J)
    2 CONTINUE
    3 CONTINUE
      RETURN
      END
```

Besides rewriting our previous program as a subroutine, there are two other changes. This subroutine will form the matrix product of any two square matrices up to order 10, where our old program operated just on 4 by 4 matrices. Since we have added this flexibility, we must also specify the order of the matrices being used, and this is accomplished using the variable N in the calling sequence. The second change is that the arrays A, B, and C are each defined as 10 by 10 arrays. If we actually wanted to form the product of two 4 by 4 matrices, they would have to be in the "upper left-hand corner" of the arrays A and B. That is, in the main program, the arrays A, B, and C must also be dimensioned as 10 by 10 arrays. If we use the subroutine to multiply two 4 by 4 matrices, they must be in the first four rows and columns of the 10 by 10 arrays in the main program. The rule that applies to the use of arrays in subroutines is that they must have identical DIMENSION statements, both in the subroutine and in a main program using the subroutine.

FUNCTION

The FUNCTION statement in FORTRAN is present to allow an easy analog of the mathematical notion of a function. In our discussion of expressions, we mentioned that almost all FORTRAN systems have some standard functions. The FUNCTION statement makes it possible for the FORTRAN user to define his own functions. These are subprograms that are very similar to subroutines, the differences being the way in which the FUNCTION is called and the way the result of the FUNCTION is returned. FUNCTION statements have the general form

FUNCTION ⟨identifier⟩⟨argument list⟩

The example below illustrates the difference between a FUNCTION and a SUBROUTINE.

Suppose we have a program that uses the factorial function often. The usual mathematical notation for this is

$$y = n!$$

However, we could equivalently write

$$y = f(n)$$

where

$$f(n) = n!$$

The FUNCTION declaration is intended to use the latter form. If f is any function of the variable x, we can write a FUNCTION analog of f. For the factorial example, we could write the FUNCTION subprogram below.

```
        FUNCTION NF(N)
        J = 1
        DO 1 I = 1, N
    1   J = J * I
        NF = J
        RETURN
        END
```

The most important difference between a FUNCTION and a SUBROUTINE is that a FUNCTION can return only one number, and this number is returned in the memory location(s) assigned to the FUNCTION identifier (name). Because of this, the name of the function must agree in mode (fixed- or floating-point) with its purpose. If a FUNCTION is to return an integer, it must have a fixed-point mode name, as our factorial function does. A FUNCTION can have any number of arguments, just as a SUBROUTINE can, and these arguments can be array identifiers. The function can return only one number, however.

If we used our NF FUNCTION in a main program, we could use any of the statements below.

$$NFACT = NF(N)$$
$$NFACT = I + NF(N)$$
$$K = NF(10)$$

If arrays are used in FUNCTION subprograms, they must be defined as arrays within the FUNCTION subprogram by a DIMENSION statement. The comments on arrays and DIMENSION statements in SUBROUTINES also apply to the use of arrays within FUNCTIONS.

END

The END statement is used to signify (to the FORTRAN compiler) the end of a subprogram or a main program. END statements allow a main program, subroutines, and functions to be compiled together. When used for this purpose, they act almost like parentheses, or possibly like semicolons in a *sequence* of FORTRAN statements. When SUBROUTINE or FUNCTION statements are used, these signify the beginning of a subprogram. The END statement is used to signify the end of such subprograms. This usage is shown below.

```
Main program using MTXMLT and NF
X = 1.
     .
     .
     .

END
SUBROUTINE MTXMLT (A, B, C, N)
     .
     .
     .

END
FUNCTION NF(N)
     .
     .
     .

END
```

The DIMENSION, SUBROUTINE, and FUNCTION declaration statements enable the compiler to properly classify identifiers as naming scalar quantities, arrays, or subprograms. The last two declaration statements, COMMON and

EQUIVALENCE, are directed toward storage allocation. When a FORTRAN compiler compiles a program, each time it encounters a new identifier, it allocates sufficient memory locations (to the identifier). This is the reason for defining the size of an array in a DIMENSION statement. Since storage is allocated to identifiers as they are encountered, the order of first appearance of identifiers in a program determines their order of storage in the memory unit. The last two declaration statements, COMMON and EQUIVALENCE, allow the FORTRAN programmer to partially control the storage allocation for his program.

COMMON

The COMMON statement is used to specify that certain memory locations should be available (or common to, hence the name) both a main program and subprograms used by the main program. The following sample program will make our discussion of COMMON much easier.

```
C   MAIN PROGRAM
    DIMENSION A(10,10), B(15)
    COMMON A, B, N
    N = 100
         .
         .
         .

    CALL SUBR (X, Y)
         .
         .
         .

    END
    SUBROUTINE SUBR (XX, YY)
    DIMENSION A (10,10), B (15)
    COMMON A, B, N
         .
         .
         .

    END
```

In this example, the main program uses a subroutine SUBR that has two scalar identifiers as arguments. By defining A and B to be array identifiers both in the main program and in SUBR, and then by declaring them with the COMMON statement, the array variables A and B can be used by SUBR. The COMMON statement also makes the scalar identifier N available to the subroutine. We could communicate A, B, and N to SUBR by making them elements of the argument list; however, when we have subroutines that need several arguments, the argument list becomes unnecessarily long. The COMMON statement, then, is another way to present arguments to a subroutine. The order of identifiers in a COMMON statement actually determines the order in which they are stored. To ensure proper communication between a main program and a subroutine via COMMON, the identifiers should be in the same order in both COMMON statements. As a result of the COMMON statements in the preceding example, we could picture the storage allocation as shown below.

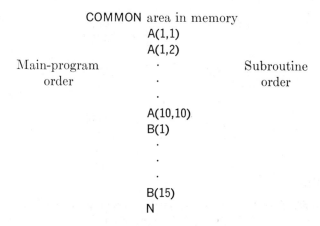

COMMON area in memory
A(1,1)
A(1,2)

Main-program   Subroutine
order   order

A(10,10)
B(1)

B(15)
N

If we interchange A and B in the COMMON statement in the subroutine,

```
DIMENSION A(10,10), B(15)
COMMON A, B, N
        .
        .
        .
END
SUBROUTINE SUBR (XX,YY)
DIMENSION A(10,10), B(15)
COMMON B, A, N
        .
        .
        .
END
```

then the main program and the subroutine will have different COMMON definitions, hence different "views" of the COMMON portion of memory. This situation is shown in the diagram below. The discrepancy, and hence the error, is obvious. When the subroutine refers to an element of B, it actually gets the value of an element in A.

COMMON

Main program	Subroutine
A(1,1)	B(1)
A(1,2)	B(2)
.	.
.	.
A(2,5)	B(15)
.	A(1,1)
.	.
A(10,10)	.
B(1)	.
.	.
B(15)	A(10,10)
N	N

EQUIVALENCE

The EQUIVALENCE statement is not used as much as the COMMON statement. The general form of the EQUIVALENCE statement is

$$\text{EQUIVALENCE } (L_1, L_2, \ldots , L_n), (L_1, L_2, \ldots , L_n), \ldots$$

where the subscripted L's are location references. The EQUIVALENCE statement allows the programmer to give more than one name (location reference) to a particular location. The location references, L_i, can be array identifiers, a scalar name, or a subscripted array variable. All the following statements are acceptable:

> DIMENSION X (100), Y (10,10)
> EQUIVALENCE (X(1), Y(1,1)), (A, B)
> EQUIVALENCE (X,Y)
> EQUIVALENCE (X(1), A)
> EQUIVALENCE (X(20), B)

The effect of an EQUIVALENCE statement is that it superimposes the locations referred to in the statement onto the same area in memory. In these statements, defining x and y to be equivalent puts them in the same place in memory. Below is shown the result of two EQUIVALENCE statements.

```
DIMENSION X(100), Y(10,10)
EQUIVALENCE (X,Y)
EQUIVALENCE (X(1), A), (X(78), B)
C   A AND B ARE SCALAR IDENTIFIERS.
```

Common Locations

A, X(1) ⌷⎯⎯⎯⎯⎯⎯⎯⎯⎯⌷ Y(1,1)

X(2) ⌷⎯⎯⎯⎯⎯⎯⎯⎯⎯⌷ Y(1,2)

.
.
.

X(10) ⌷⎯⎯⎯⎯⎯⎯⎯⎯⎯⌷ Y(1,10)

X(11) ⌷⎯⎯⎯⎯⎯⎯⎯⎯⎯⌷ Y(2,1)

.
.
.

B, X(78) ⌷⎯⎯⎯⎯⎯⎯⎯⎯⎯⌷ Y(8,8)

.
.
.

X(100) ⌷⎯⎯⎯⎯⎯⎯⎯⎯⎯⌷ Y(10,10)

12-4 INPUT–OUTPUT STATEMENTS

The fourth category of FORTRAN, input-output statements, is the least standard part of the language. This is unfortunate, because much of the usefulness of a computer depends on the convenience of presenting information to the machine and then obtaining results from the machine. The variance in input-output statements makes it necessary to discuss the subject only generally. We will cover the two most common types of input-output statements after a short discussion of the actual input-output devices.

The various pieces of input-output equipment are usually lumped together into the more general term *peripheral devices*. The sole purpose of peripheral devices is to present information to a computer (input) and obtain information from a computer (output). The actual information is encoded onto two primary media: punched tabulating cards and magnetic tape. A third, but less common, medium is punched paper tape. The table below lists the more common peripheral devices and their function.

Device	Function
Card reader	Input, tabulating cards
Card punch	Output, tabulating cards
Magnetic-tape drive	Input and output, magnetic tape
Printer	Output, printer paper
Paper-tape reader	Input, paper tape
Paper-tape punch	Output, paper tape
Typewriter	Input and output (very limited)

In a way, the peripherals are the most interesting part of digital computers, because they provide means of interaction between men and machines. As an example of this, a new peripheral device, the cathode-ray tube, is gaining wider acceptance. The cathode-ray tube is essentially a primitive television screen, and is used primarily as an output device. As such, it represents the current trend in making computers more "man-oriented." A cathode-ray tube, when used as an output device, will present the computer user with a graph of a function, rather than table of numbers which formerly were graphed by hand. Some cathode-ray tubes can even be used as an input device; however, this is very limited. Some of the major airlines use cathode-ray tubes coupled with large computers, at their reservation desks.

In order to use any of the peripheral devices coupled to a computer, it must be possible for the computer to refer to them. Computers have machine instructions for this purpose. The FORTRAN language is able to refer to peripherals via the input-output statements. The simpler of the two more common input-output schemes we will discuss associates a verb with each peripheral device. In this scheme, if we wish our output to appear on a printer, the output statement will begin with the word PRINT. If we want to obtain input data from a card reader, the input statement will begin with the word READ. The table below shows the verbs associated with each peripheral device.

Peripheral device	Associated verb
Card reader	READ
Card punch	PUNCH
Printer	PRINT
Typewriter (input)	ACCEPT
Typewriter (output)	TYPE
Magnetic tape (input)	READ INPUT TAPE
Magnetic tape (output)	WRITE OUTPUT TAPE
Paper tape (input)	READ PAPER TAPE
Paper tape (output)	PUNCH PAPER TAPE

Input-output statements can be used to make programs more flexible, particularly when a program is written as an algorithm. We have already encountered a situation that demonstrates the advantage of flexibility. The first time we considered a program to multiply matrices, we wrote it specifically for 4 by 4 matrices. When we made this into a subroutine, we wrote the subroutine to handle any size up to 10 by 10 matrices. Continuing in the matrix multiplication example, consider how the values of the elements are defined in the program. One way would be to use replacements:

$$A(1,1) = 3.2$$
$$A(1,2) = 0$$
.

.

.

$$A(4,4) = 67.3$$
.

.

.

$$A(1,3) = 2.7$$
.

.

.

This would work, but only for the matrices defined by the replacement statements. If we wanted to form the product of two other matrices, we would have to define them by separate statements. A better way to communicate our matrices to a computer would be to define them as input data that would be read in when the program executed. If we did this, then we could multiply different matrices simply by providing different input data when the program executes.

Variables are defined to be input or output data by means of an *input-output list*. An input-output list is a list (in the linguistic sense of Chap. 11) of variable names. If we wished to define the variables X, Y, and N as input data, we would do this using the input-output list

X, Y, N

Now we indicate the peripheral device from which the values of X, Y, and N will be obtained by using the verb associated with the peripheral device. If we wanted to supply the values of X, Y, and N on tabulating cards, the input device would be the card reader. Our input statement would be

READ X, Y, N

If we wanted to print out these values, we would use the statement

PRINT X, Y, N

There is an additional specification to be made, but this specification includes so many options that we will mention it only briefly. Referring again to reading the values of X, Y, and N from a tabulating card, we must also specify where the values of the variables appear on the card. This specification is contained in a statement known as a FORMAT *statement*. The FORMAT statement, as its name suggests, indicates to the computer the format of the data on the input (or output) medium. For example, a FORMAT statement could be used to indicate that the value of X is in the first 10 columns of the card, the value of Y is in the second 10 columns of the card, and the value of N is in the last 4 columns. For our purpose, we need only say that a FORMAT statement completely describes the physical arrangement of data on an input (or output) medium. Since this specification is necessary, we will show how FORMAT statements are used. We will not discuss the many subtle features of FORMAT statements.

FORMAT statements always have a statement label. To specify the arrangement of variables that appear in an input-output list, the input-output statement includes the label of the FORMAT statement that actually describes the data. In our earlier example of reading in the values of X, Y, and N, the full input statement would be

READ N_1, X, Y, N
N_1 FORMAT (⟨description⟩)

where N_1 can be any statement label. Now the READ statement does three things: it defines the variables X, Y, and N to be input data, it tells the computer that their values will be read in from a card reader, and it refers to a FORMAT statement that describes where the values of X, Y, and N will appear on the card that is read. If we wished to print out the values of X, Y, and N, the full output statement would be

PRINT N_2, X, Y, N
N_2 FORMAT (⟨description⟩)

where the FORMAT statement N_2 may indicate an arrangement that is not the same as the input format.

We will conclude the chapter with a sample FORTRAN program that illustrates many of the features of the FORTRAN language. The only missing part of this program is the actual FORMAT statements. Before doing this program, we will mention the second common scheme for input-output statements.

The second type of input-output-statement scheme uses numbers, rather than verbs, to specify peripheral devices. The words READ and WRITE are used to define whether the variables are input or output. This scheme has two forms of statements:

$$\text{READ } (N_1, \ N_2) \ \langle \text{input-output list} \rangle$$
$$\text{WRITE } (N_1, \ N_2) \ \langle \text{input-output list} \rangle.$$

The numbers in parentheses are the peripheral-device number N_1 and the associated FORMAT statement label N_2. The only difference between these two schemes is that the first refers to peripheral devices by an associated verb, while the second associates a number with each device to accomplish the reference. Both schemes convey the necessary information to the computer. We conclude this section with a table of peripheral devices and their associated verbs. Their associated device numbers are an arbitrary convention.

Peripheral device	Associated verb	Associated number
Card reader	READ	5
Card punch	PUNCH	1
Printer	PRINT	6
Typewriter (input)	ACCEPT	2
Typewriter (output)	TYPE	3
Magnetic tape (input)	READ INPUT TAPE	4
Magnetic tape (output)	WRITE OUTPUT TAPE	7
Paper tape (input)	READ PAPER TAPE	8
Paper tape (output)	PUNCH OUTPUT TAPE	9

12-5 SAMPLE PROGRAM

Our sample program will solve a system of simultaneous linear equations of the form

$$a_{11}x_1 + a_{12}x_2 + \cdots + a_{1n}x_n = b_1$$
$$a_{21}x_1 + a_{22}x_2 + \cdots + a_{2n}x_n = b_2$$
$$\cdots \cdots \cdots \cdots \cdots \cdots \cdots \cdots \cdots$$
$$a_{n1}x_1 + a_{n2}x_2 + \cdots + a_{nn}x_n = b_n$$

If we define the matrices A, B, and X by

$$A = (a_{i,j})$$
$$B = (b_i)$$
$$X = (x_i)$$

we can then write our system of equations as

$$A \cdot X = B$$

Our program will solve this system for the solution matrix X. The program will require as input the matrices A and B and the size of the system, which will be the value of the variable NDIM. We will use a subroutine, named INVERT, to compute the inverse of the matrix A. With this inverse, we can obtain the solution in the following manner.

$$A \cdot X = B$$
$$(A^{-1} \cdot A) \cdot X = A^{-1} \cdot B$$
$$I \cdot X = A^{-1} \cdot B$$
$$X = A^{-1} \cdot B$$

The program will compute the inverse of A, store it in the array AINV, and then form the product $A^{-1} \cdot B$. This product will be stored in the X array and then be printed as output.

```
C       PROGRAM TO SOLVE SIMULTANEOUS LINEAR
C       EQUATIONS.  A IS THE COEFFICIENT MATRIX,
C       B IS THE CONSTANT MATRIX, AND X IS
C       THE SOLUTION MATRIX.  THE MAXIMUM SIZE
C       OF A SYSTEM IS 20 EQUATIONS IN 20 UNKNOWNS.
C
C
        DIMENSION A(20,20), AINV(20,20), X(20), B(20)
C
C       OBTAIN VALUES OF A, B, AND N FROM CARD
C       INPUT DATA.
C
        READ 1, N
    1   FORMAT (⟨description⟩)
        READ 2, A, B
    2   FORMAT (⟨description of A, B⟩)
C       VALUES OF A, B, N ARE NOW DEFINED.
        IF (N — 1) 3,3,4
    3   STOP
C       N MUST BE GREATER THAN 1.
    4   CALL INVERT (A, AINV, N)
C       NOW AINV CONTAINS COMPUTED INVERSE OF A.
C       FORM PRODUCT AINV * B.
        DO 5 I = 1,N
```

```
          X(I) = 0.0
          DO 5 J = 1,N
    5     X(I) = X(I) + AINV(I,J) * B(J)
C         NOW X CONTAINS COMPUTED SOLUTION.   PRINT RESULTS.
          PRINT 6, A, B, X, AINV
    6     FORMAT (⟨description of A, B, X, and AINV⟩)
          STOP
          END
          SUBROUTINE INVERT (A, AINV, N)
          DIMENSION A(20,20), AINV(20,20), AI(20,40)
C         SUBROUTINE BASED ON FLOWCHART IN FIGURE 8, CHAPTER 9.
C
C         CREATE MATRIX AI
          DO 1 I = 1, N
          K = I + N
          DO 1 J = K, N
          AI (I,J) = A(I,J)
          IF (I−J) 3,2,3
    3     AI(K,J) = 1.0
          GO TO 1
    2     AI(K,J) = 0.0
    1     CONTINUE
C         NOW RIGHT HALF OF AI IS AN IDENTITY MATRIX.
          NN = 2 * N
          DO 4 J = 1, N
          AI(J,J) = 1.0
          DO 5 L = 2,NN
    5     AI(J,L) = AI(J,L)/AI(J,J)
C         LOOP 5 DIVIDES EACH ELEMENT OF ROW J BY AI(J,J)
          DO 6 I = 1, N
          IF(I−J), 7,6,7
    7     DO 8 L = 2, NN
    8     AI(I,L) = AI(I,L) − AI(I,J) * AI(J,L)
    6     CONTINUE
    4     CONTINUE
C         NOW RIGHT HALF OF AI IS INVERSE OF A.
          DO 9 I = 1,N
          K = I + N
          DO 9 J = 1,N
    9     AINV(I,J) = AI(K,J)
          RETURN
          END
```

EXERCISES

12-1. Which of the following constants are permitted by the FORTRAN
       syntax?

a.	36278	b.	-123
c.	$17A3C_{16}$	d.	3.01×10^8
e.	$3.01E + 08$	f.	$3.01E + 2.5$
g.	1,234,567	h.	1234567

       If any of these are not permitted, explain why.

12-2. Examine the expressions below to see if they are permitted by the
       syntax of FORTRAN. If any are not permitted, explain why.

       a. ((A(I,J) * SQRT(X)) ** 2)/(2.3 **)
       b. 1A + 3.2
       c. I1A + 3.2
       d. (3*(X**2) + 2*X) + 6.2*SQRT (Y(J,K))
       e. (3X ÷ 2y) + 62.7
       f. (3.6 + 2.8) + 26.3*X)

12-3. Write expressions in FORTRAN that correspond to the mathematical
       expressions below.

       a. $3^x \cdot x^2 + y^2$ b. $\log_e x$

       c. $\dfrac{\cos^2 x + \sin x}{e^{2x} + \ln x}$

12-4. Referring to the program on p. 377, what is the value of the variable
       ISUM after the loop is complete?

12-5. Write a program to compute

       $$\text{ISUMSQ} = 1^2 + 2^2 + 3^2 + \cdots + n^2$$

       using the idea on p. 377.

12-6. In Chap. 9, when we discussed the binary-chopping square-root
       algorithm, we indicated that it might be wise to stop the program after
       a certain number of iterations. We can keep track of the number of
       iterations in a location (I on p. 375) by using the replacement

       $$I = I + 1$$

       after each iteration. When a location is incremented in this manner,
       it is often called a counter. Insert a counter into the square-root
       program, and use an IF statement to prevent the program from making
       more than 200 iterations.

12-7. Counters can be used in conjunction with IF statements to simulate DO-loops. Write a program that will replace the DO-loop below, using a counter and an appropriate IF statement.

$$
\begin{aligned}
&\text{ISUM} = 0 \\
&\text{DO 1 J} = 1,\ \text{N} \\
&1\ \text{ISUM} = \text{ISUM} + \text{J}
\end{aligned}
$$

12-8. We can use the program on p. 378 as part of a program to compute the standard deviation of a statistics sample. Suppose the elements are stored in an array X. Write FORTRAN programs for finding the standard deviation of a sample using the formulas below.

Mean:

$$
\mu = \frac{\sum_{i=1}^{n} x_i}{n}
$$

Standard deviation:

$$
\sigma = \frac{\sqrt{\sum_{i=1}^{n} (\mu - x_i)^2}}{n - 1} \tag{1}
$$

$$
\sigma = \frac{\sqrt{\sum_{i=1}^{n} x_i^2 - \frac{1}{n}\left(\sum_{i=1}^{n} x_i\right)^2}}{n - 1} \tag{2}
$$

Notice that the program for formula (2) needs only one DO-loop, while formula (1) requires one loop to compute the average and a second loop that uses the average to compute the standard deviation.

12-9. Convert your program for

$$
\sigma = \frac{\sqrt{\sum_{i=1}^{n} x_i^2 - \frac{1}{n}\left(\sum_{i=1}^{n} x_i\right)^2}}{n - 1}
$$

into a subroutine that can be called by

CALL STANDEV (X, N, AVG, SIG)

where X is an array containing the sample data, N is the number of elements in the array, and AVG and SIG are the locations in which the average and standard deviation are returned.

12-10.   Write a FUNCTION subprogram to compute $\sum_{i=1}^{n} (i!)$, given the value of n.

12-11.   The reader may have noticed that we stopped giving the Backus normal form description of FORTRAN statements with the DO statement. The reason we stopped is that the rest of the statements had fewer options; hence there was no need to summarize them in a production. As an exercise in the use of Backus normal form as a descriptive tool, develop the three types of GO TO statements (GO TO, Assigned GO TO, and Computed GO TO).

12-12.   Referring to the program described in Exercise 12-9, show how you could use a COMMON statement to remove X and N from the calling sequence.

12-13.   In Chap. 9, when we discussed matrix inversion, we mentioned a few improvements for the algorithm. Revise the sample program in Sec. 12-5 to include these features.

12-14.   Write FUNCTION subprogram to generate random numbers using the multiplicative generator

$$r_1 = 17$$
$$r_{i+1} = kr_i \bmod (m)$$

with $k = 3125$, $m = 2^{16}$.

12-15.   Use your random-number-generator FUNCTION as part of a program for approximating π (see Fig. 9-12).

COBOL

INTRODUCTION

COBOL (COmmon Business-oriented Language) is a programming language designed to aid in the solution of business-oriented problems. It was conceived at a meeting in Washington, D.C., composed of computer users and manufacturers, in 1959. At that meeting (Conference on Data Systems Languages, or CODASYL) specifications for COBOL were submitted to the conference leaders. Since that time several refined versions of COBOL have emerged, each refinement adding more options to the language.

Recall from Chap. 12 the similarity between the FORTRAN language and conventional mathematics notation. In this chapter you will notice the similarity between COBOL and ordinary English statements. This similarity to written English is deliberate and is one of the more important design features of the language. This feature makes most COBOL programs self-documenting. That is, upon reading a COBOL source program, a human being can usually comprehend what the programmer has intended. This and other attributes of the language make it easy to learn and easy to teach.

13-1 THE COBOL PROGRAM DIVISIONS

Every COBOL program is segmented into four parts, hereafter referred to as divisions. Each division exists so as to answer certain questions about the program and the problem it is to solve. The division names and the questions answered in that division follow:

> Identification division
> > Who has written this program?
> > When and where was it written?
> > What is the name of this program?
> Environment division
> > Which computer will be used?
> > Which peripheral devices will be used?
> Data division
> > How are the data (input and output) described?
> > How are intermediate data (non-input-output) described?
> Procedure division
> > How will the data be processed?
> > What steps must be followed to solve the problem?

This chapter is intended to merely describe the COBOL language. The reader will not become an expert COBOL programmer upon completing this chapter. It should be noted that each computer manufacturer should have his own set of COBOL instruction manuals, where idiosyncrasies of his COBOL language processor (see Chap. 11) and his computer are pointed out.

13-2 COBOL STRUCTURE

In reading about the structure of any computer language, we will come across elements that make up the language. In relation to COBOL, this will begin with the COBOL character set. This is a set of 51 characters, 37 of which, when properly combined, make up the next class of element, called a *word*.

Words are then combined, sometimes with the remaining characters, to form *clauses* and *statements*. The statements are combined to form *sentences*. Sentences may then be combined to form a *paragraph*. Paragraphs can be combined to form *sections*. One or more sections combine to form a *division* (see Fig. 13-1).

The four divisions previously mentioned are present in every COBOL source program. The source program (usually key-punched on tab cards) is fed to the computer and translated by the COBOL language processor. Output of this translation is the COBOL object program. This process is referred to as a compilation, and we say that the source program has been compiled by

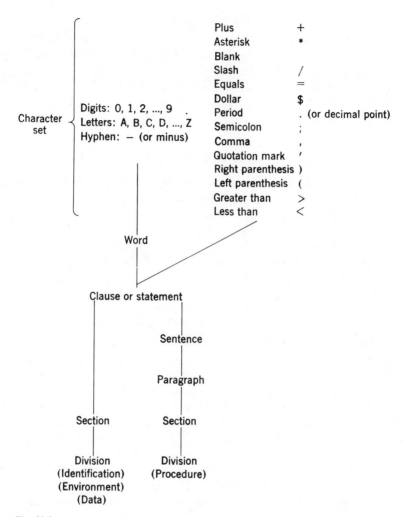

Fig. 13-1

the processor. The object program is a series of machine-language instructions and data which correspond to the instructions and data first defined in the source program. The object program can reside on punched cards or any other output medium that can be read later by the computer. The object program is then fed to the computer via this medium and, when completely read, will begin executing, starting at the first executable instruction in the object program.

Some care must be taken in the writing of COBOL source programs. In particular, we must know something about the computer on which the compilation will take place.   When constructing the environment, data, and procedure divisions of a COBOL source program, we should be aware of the computer to which the source program will be fed.   This machine is called the *source computer*.   For this reason the above-mentioned divisions are referred to as *machine-dependent*.   However, we need not concern ourselves about the *source computer* when constructing the identification division.   Thus the identification division is referred to as being *machine-independent*.

13-3 FILES, BLOCKS, RECORDS, AND ITEMS

Certain concepts are important enough to require special consideration in this chapter.   The heading of this section names four of these concepts, referring to the way data are described in relation to a COBOL program.   We will define each and provide some examples.

An *item*, more specifically, an elementary item, is a unit of data that cannot be broken down into subcategories and still make sense.   For example, a unit of data defined as "day of the month" can be any of the numbers 1, 2, 3, 4, 5, 6, 7, . . . , 28, 29, 30, 31, depending on what month is referred to.   If we subdivided a particular day of the month, say, 16, into 1 and 6, we could not make sense out of the individual numbers 1 and 6.   Of course, we could refer to the 1 as the tens digit of 16 and the 6 as the units digit of 16, but this would be out of context.   However, if we had a unit of data defined as "date," this could be any configuration of numbers in which the first ranges between 1 and 12, the second ranges between 1 and 31, and the last is some two-digit configuration corresponding to a year in the twentieth century.   For example, 3, 30, 38 would be a valid unit of data defined under "date."   Note that "date" could be broken up into three subcategories, each a logical part of "date."   Thus the unit of data "date" is not an elementary item.

A *record* is a group of related elementary items.   In the second example above, the unit of data "date" can be called a record.

Consider now a fictitious employee whose name is John Smith; his Social Security number is 123-45-6798.   He is a lathe operator and worked 52 hours last week, the week of March 30, 1970.   His hourly rate of pay is $5.   If this information is thought of as residing somewhere in the main memory portion of some computer, it is referred to as a *logical record*.   However, if the information is residing on some input-output medium, like the punched card, it is referred to as a *physical record*.   A physical record is sometimes called a *block*. Certain manufacturers refer to a physical record as a collection of one or more logical records.   We point out here that the definitions for logical record and physical record are not standard.   The reader is referred to particular manuals associated with a specific computer.

A *file* is said to be a set of blocks.   Thus, if we spoke of 10 employees like John Smith with employee information similar to the above, then the data on all the employees could be referred to as a file.   Again we direct the reader to particular computer manuals.

13-4 A SIMPLE APPLICATION

A problem will be defined in this section.   We state what is to be supplied as input and what is desired as output.   Then a flowchart will be constructed showing the logical flow of thought in seeing the problem to its final conclusion. In the next section, a COBOL source program will be constructed to solve the problem.

Problem

There are many avenues open to the average man if he seeks to borrow money.   However, because of the many different ways that interest charges are stated, people become confused about interest rates, carrying charges, discounts, and similar terminology.   When money is borrowed over an extended period, the payments can be made weekly or monthly.   Thus it would be convenient if some formula could be had that gives an indication of the annual interest rate.   The following formula has been used by the Federal Reserve System and is meant to give the borrower a single rule of thumb no matter how the loan and charges are stated:

$$I = \frac{200MD}{P(N + 1)}$$

where I = annual interest rate, in percent   ANN-INT
          P = principal borrowed   PRINCI
          N = number of payments to close out the loan   TOTPMTS
          M = number of payments in a year   PYR
          D = cost of the loan (total debt minus P)   LNCST
This is the formula that will be used in our program.

Solution

We will assume that, for a given principal, the payments are made on a weekly or monthly basis.   The symbols on the right, above, are the names that will be assigned to these numbers in the COBOL program.   We also know the term of the loan (that is, the number of years to discharge the total debt).   The input can now be described.   On a tab card will appear the fixed weekly or monthly payment, a two-character symbol that tells if the payment is weekly or monthly, the period of the loan in years, and finally, the amount borrowed (the principal).   The information on a single loan appears on a single tab card (see Fig. 13-2). Thus the tab card will be our input medium. For each single

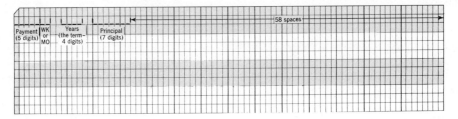

Fig. 13-2 An input card.

card the program is to print a line of output. On each line the input information is to be printed, together with the values I (annual interest rate, in percent) and D (the cost of the loan). See Fig. 13-3. Furthermore, we are to print a

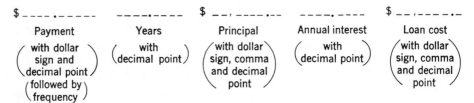

Fig. 13-3 An output line. The words above do not appear; only digits and symbols where indicated.

line whenever a new card is read. After reading the last card and printing the last line, the job is ended (that is, the program is terminated). We point out that many COBOL programs could be written to solve the defined problem, perhaps better than the one given here. The program in the text is merely representative.

The flowchart to accomplish our problem appears in Fig. 13-4.

13-5 THE COBOL SOURCE PROGRAM

The source program is constructed with the identification division first, followed by the environment, data, and finally, the procedure divisions. The divisions must appear in that order; however, we will begin with a discussion of the "word" and then the procedure division. Doing this, the construction of the environment and data divisions will become more meaningful.

You were introduced to the notion of word in Sec. 13-2. It now becomes necessary to describe the word concept in more detail.

A word is a combination of at most 30 characters chosen from the letters A to Z, the digits 0 to 9, and the hyphen; but the hyphen cannot appear as the

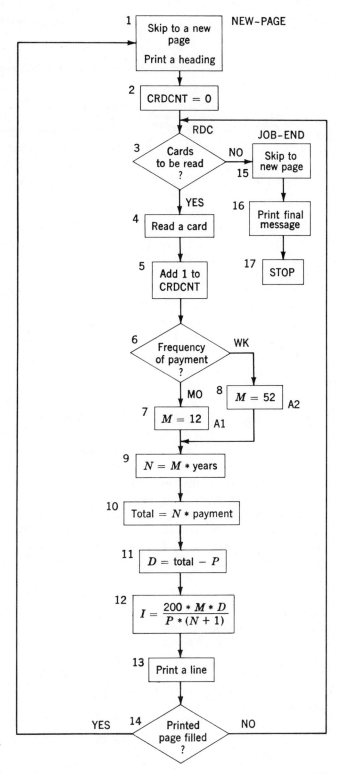

Fig. 13-4 Flowchart for sample problem.

first or last character of a word.   The more common types of words will now be defined.

Data name: A word which contains at least one alphabetic character.   It can name an elementary item or several elementary items within a record or records.   A data name first appears defined in the data division and is manipulated in the procedure division.   The data name does not represent an explicit value.   The item for which the data name appears takes on different values during the execution of a program.

Procedure name: A word made up of any of the permissible characters for word.   It must be followed by a period, then a space.   It appears in the procedure division only and is used to name a section or paragraph.   By use of the procedure name, one statement can refer to another statement.   This means that one section or paragraph can refer to another section or paragraph.   Data names and procedure names are selected by the programmer.   However, they must not be reserved words (defined below).

Literal: A string of characters whose value is immediately known because its value is precisely the string of characters appearing.   There are two types of literal words, nonnumeric and numeric.

> *Nonnumeric literal:* A special kind of word because it can be longer than 30 characters and it is made up of any character (except the quotation mark) in the COBOL character set.   The nonnumeric literal must be bounded on both ends by quotation marks.

> *Numeric literal:* A string of characters made from the digits 0 to 9.   The string may be preceded by a plus or a minus sign.   The sign, if present, must begin the word.   Also, a decimal point may appear in the word anywhere except as the last character.   The numeric literal is not enclosed in quotes.

Figurative constants: Values which have been assigned fixed data names. The more common fixed data names are ZERO and SPACE.   The first represents the numerical value zero.   The second represents one or more blanks or spaces. ZERO, ZEROS, and ZEROES can be used interchangeably.   Similarly for SPACE and SPACES.

Reserved words: Words that have been given special meaning.   They are precisely spelled and cannot be used outside of their special meaning.   A list of reserved words appears in the Appendix to this chapter.   Figurative constants are reserved words.   One of the more common types of reserved word is the verb.

Verb: A reserved word which, when used, signifies an action to be taken. Some verbs that we will meet are READ, ADD, MULTIPLY, and MOVE.   *A verb always begins a statement.*

We will see other words defined later in the chapter.   Now let us get to the program.

The Procedure Division

Every COBOL source program has a procedure division that begins with the two words **PROCEDURE DIVISION.**

The procedure division contains the steps (instructions) needed to solve a given problem. The computer will follow these steps during the execution of a program. We will write the instructions needed to accomplish the tasks defined in each box of our flowchart. Later, the instructions will be described in more detail.

```
                        ┌─────────────────┐   NEW–PAGE
                        │  Skip to a new  │
                        │      page       │
                        │                 │
                      1 │  Print a heading│
                        └─────────────────┘
```

NEW-PAGE.
    MOVE   'PAYMENT   YEARS   PRINCIPAL   ANN INT   LN COST'
       TO HEAD-LINE.
    WRITE HEAD-LINE AFTER ADVANCING 0 LINES.

NEW-PAGE is a paragraph name and will be described later.

In the first statement (the MOVE statement), the information between the quote marks (this is a nonnumeric literal) is moved exactly as it appears from some internal portion of storage to an internal portion of storage whose name we have assigned to be HEAD-LINE. The nonnumeric literal and HEAD-LINE are called the operands of the move statement. The next statement (the WRITE statement) instructs the computer to write (in our case, print) the information appearing internally at HEAD-LINE, on the printer. In the WRITE statement you see the clause AFTER ADVANCING 0 LINES. This is a special clause which instructs the printer to skip to a new page before printing a line. Different manufacturers will have different rules governing this clause.

Thus, after a skip to a new page, the heading line will be printed. Box 1 is complete. In the above two statements, the words MOVE, TO, WRITE, AFTER, ADVANCING, and LINES are reserved words. Box 2 is next.

2.   │   CRDCNT = 0 │

CRDCNT is a name assigned to a portion of memory containing a number that will increase by one each time a new card is read. CRDCNT is short for "card count." Remember, we intend to read a card, then print a line, etc. So this number, which has the name CRDCNT, is also an indication of how many lines have been printed.   The instruction to accomplish box 2 is

MOVE ZEROS TO CRDCNT.

In this statement the verb is MOVE and the operands are ZEROS (a figurative constant) and CRDCNT (data name of an elementary item).

Next we have

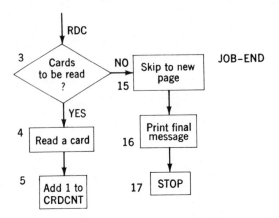

The statements needed to accomplish the above are

RDC.   READ INPUT-FILE; AT END GO TO JOB-END.
ADD 1 TO CRDCNT.

The reserved words are READ, AT, END, GO, TO, ADD, and TO.   INPUT-FILE is a data name, more specifically, a file name.   JOB-END is a procedure name. 1 is a numeric literal, and CRDCNT is a data name.   RDC is a paragraph name; we will see the reason for its existence later.

The READ statement, together with the AT END portion, accomplishes the tasks defined in boxes 3, 4, and 15.   INPUT-FILE is the name we have assigned to the file of tab cards that will be used as input to the program.   The ADD statement accomplishes box 5.   Note the similarity between the COBOL statement and ordinary English.   This was one of the intentions of the COBOL developers: to make a COBOL source program easily readable.

Now the next box asks a question: Is the payment weekly or monthly? This can be answered only after a portion of the input card is examined. Before we describe how this is done, something will be said about the organization of data in this program.   It has been stated that the file of tab cards (or deck of tab cards) has been given the name INPUT-FILE.   Now, obviously, INPUT-FILE is composed of tab cards, each one of which can be called a record. Just as the name INPUT-FILE has been assigned to the file of cards, we must assign a name to the record that belongs to INPUT-FILE. The name DATA-CARD is selected. DATA-CARD also becomes the name of a portion of memory where the data appearing on a tab card will be held. When the next card from the input file is read, these new data will replace the former data in the DATA-CARD portion of memory. Thus the former data will be destroyed. Referring to Fig. 13-2 we see that each DATA-CARD has four pieces of information present. Each piece can be called an elementary item, which must be named also, so that it can be referred to in the program. We choose to name these items PAYMENT, an obvious choice; FREQ, for frequency of payment; YRS, for the term of the loan; and PRINCI, for principal (the amount borrowed). See Fig. 13-5. Now, at the conclusion of box 4, the items from the DATA-CARD reside in memory. See Fig. 13-6.

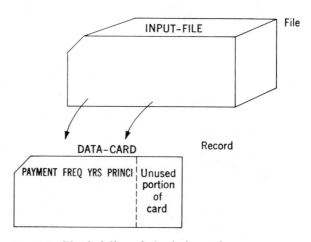

Fig. 13-5   Physical file and physical record.

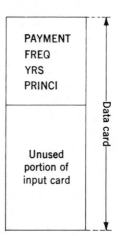

Fig. 13-6 Data card is the name of that portion of memory which holds the information shown above.

INPUT-FILE is a file-name; DATA-CARD is a record name; and PAYMENT, FREQ, YRS, and PRINCI are data names.

Now let us get to box 6.   In order to respond properly to the question of

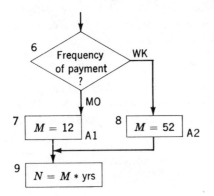

box 6, we must examine the item named FREQ.   Only two configurations can occur in FREQ on the card.   The item will consist of the two characters, WK signifying a weekly payment, or the item will be MO, signifying a monthly payment.   Thus, after the input card is read, the memory position named FREQ will hold WK or MO.

In boxes 6 to 8 a question is asked about the item FREQ, and then a certain action is taken, depending on the answer to that question.   The COBOL statements to accomplish boxes 6 to 9 are

```
        IF FREQ IS EQUAL TO 'MO' GO TO A1.
        MOVE 52 to PYR.
        GO TO A2.
A1.     MOVE 12 TO PYR.
A2.     MULTIPLY YEARS BY PYR GIVING TOTPMTS ROUNDED.
```

The reserved words in the IF and MULTIPLY statements are IF, IS, EQUAL, TO, GO, TO, MULTIPLY, BY, GIVING, and ROUNDED.

The first statement, the IF statement, states a condition about FREQ and points to the next instruction to be executed if that condition is true.   If the condition is not true, the statement immediately following the IF is executed. If the item FREQ is the same as the two characters between the quote marks, MO (a nonnumeric literal), then the statement with name A1 is executed next. Statement A1 accomplishes box 7.   (In that statement, 12 is a numeric literal.) However, if the item FREQ is not the same as MO, then it must be WK, for these are the only two configurations possible.   (Note that we are assuming that the input card always has the properly key-punched data.)   This means that the condition defined in the IF statement is not true.   In this case, the next instruction in sequence is executed.   The instruction following the IF statement accomplishes box 8.   (In that statement, 52 is a numeric literal.)   Following the first MOVE statement we see the GO TO statement.   This statement causes a break in the normally sequential nature of statement execution.   (Sequential means one after the other.)   When the GO TO statement is executed, control is transferred to the statement with name A2.   In effect, we are "branching around" the statement with name A1.   In the FORTRAN language, symbols like A1 and A2 were called *statement labels*.   In COBOL they are called *paragraph names*, a special class of procedure name.

In Sec. 13-2 it was mentioned that sentences are combined to form a paragraph.   To be specific, a paragraph is made up of a paragraph name and one or more sentences.   Moreover, a sentence is made up of one or more statements.   From this, you should be able to see that the smallest paragraph is made up of a paragraph name and one statement.   Now a paragraph ends where the next paragraph begins.   In our example you will see that the statement with name A1 is a paragraph consisting of one statement.   The MULTIPLY statement begins the next paragraph, because it has its own name, A2. In this statement, the operand TOTMPTS is a data name that we have assigned to the product of *years* (the term of the loan) and payments per year.   TOTPMTS corresponds to N (see flowchart and formula) and is short for "total number of payments."

You will note that the last word of the MULTIPLY statement is ROUNDED. This is a reserved word, and is needed for our particular application.   The reasons follow.

The internal value of PYR will be 52 or 12.   The internal value of YEARS will be some number with a two-digit fractional part and a two-digit integer part.   (You will see in the data division why this is so.)   For example, YEARS might have the value 2.25 or 20.00 or 2.75.   The first number represents a loan term of $2\frac{1}{4}$ years (27 months, or 117 weeks).   The second number represents a loan term of 20 years (240 months, or 1,040 weeks), and the third number a loan term of $2\frac{3}{4}$ years (33 months, or 143 weeks).

The product of YEARS and PYR has the name TOTPMTS.   This product must be an integer.   Without the word ROUNDED, the product would be truncated to the nearest integer.   For example:

| | | | | TOTPMTS | |
LOAN TERM	YEARS	PYR	PRODUCT	TRUNCATED	ROUNDED
27 months	2.25	52	117.00	117	117
28 months	2.33	12	27.96	27	28

So you see that in our particular application the word ROUNDED is needed in the MULTIPLY statement.

Next in the flowchart is box 10.

10. | TOTAL = N * PAYMENT |

Here the total debt, in dollars, is sought.   It is obtained by multiplying the total number of payments by the individual fixed periodic payment.   The instruction to accomplish this is

MULTIPLY TOTPMTS BY PMT GIVING TOTDEBT

The data names in the above statement are TOTPMTS, PMT, and TOTDEBT.

In box 11 we seek the cost of the loan.

11. | D = TOTAL − P |

The cost D of the loan is found by subtracting the principal P from the total debt.   Thus

SUBTRACT PRINC FROM TOTDEBT GIVING LNCOST.

The key words here are SUBTRACT, FROM, and GIVING.   The data names are PRINC, TOTDEBT, and LNCOST.

Now we can compute the annual interest, since all numbers needed are present, either having been read in (P, the principal) or having been calculated (M, the payments per year; D, the cost of the loan; N, the total number of payments).

Box 12 carries the formula

12. $$I = \frac{200 * M * D}{P(N + 1)}$$

The statement to accomplish box 12 is

COMPUTE ANN-INT EQUALS (200 * PYR * LNCST) / (PRINC * (TOTPMTS + 1)).

In the above statement, the only key words are COMPUTE and EQUALS. The symbols *, /, and + are called arithmetic operators and signify multiplication, division, and addition, respectively.   The parentheses are used to enhance readability, but more importantly, they are used to specify the order in which operations are to occur.   In general, operations within the parentheses are performed first. When a pair of parentheses appear within another pair, the innermost operation is performed first. In our statement, TOTPMTS + 1 is calculated first. The sum is then multiplied by PRINC. This product is our denominator. Next, the product of 200, PYR, and LNCST is calculated. This is our numerator. Finally, the numerator is divided by the denominator, and the result is the annual interest that we seek. It is assigned the data name ANN-INT and is held internally at some memory position.

At this point, all data that we wish to have printed are held internally, either having been read in (payment, frequency of payment, the term, principal) or having been calculated (annual interest, loan cost). When the data have been moved to the proper internal storage positions (this is a very important point and will be covered later), the output line can be printed. The statement needed is

WRITE OUTLINE AFTER ADVANCING 1 LINES

OUTLINE is the name of an internal portion of storage where the data to be printed appear. The verb WRITE, together with the words AFTER ADVANCING 1 LINES, causes a line to be printed on the next available position of the printer.

So far we have stepped through the flowchart with instructions to accomplish the reading of one input card and the printing of its associated output line. Keep in mind the fact that this will be done repeatedly: read a card, print a line, read a card, print a line, etc. If the number of input cards is large, sooner or later a page will be filled with printed lines. When this happens, we will want to go to a new page and continue the process. After every printed line, box 14 asks the question: Is a printed page filled?

You will notice from the flowchart (Fig. 13-3) that for every printed output line a card must have been read. If we have kept track of the number of cards read, this will tell us the number of lines that have been printed. This has been done beginning at box 2 and continuing at box 5. The number with name CRDCNT has been keeping track for us.

Now we have selected 50 as the number of lines that will fill up a page. If a page of printer paper is 11 inches long by 15 inches wide (somewhat of a standard), then 50 is an acceptable number. The important thing to remember here is that we as programmers select the number.

Two statements can accomplish box 14.

```
IF CRDCNT IS EQUAL TO 50 GO TO NEW-PAGE.
GO TO RDC.
```

The first statement states the condition on CRDCNT that will cause a new page to be started. The GO TO portion of the IF statement causes a branch to the statement with header NEW-PAGE (another way of saying this is, the paragraph with paragraph name NEW-PAGE.) if CRDCNT is equal to 50. If CRDCNT is *not* equal to 50, the next statement, GO TO RDC, in sequence will be executed. This statement causes a branch to the statement with header RDC (that is, the paragraph with paragraph name RDC). RDC is short for "read a card." Referring to box 3 and the associated statements, we see that RDC begins a set of instructions that causes the reading of an input card. Thus, when the GO TO RDC is executed, this begins another read-a-card print-a-line cycle.

Similarly, when a page is filled, we want to begin the cycle, but only after a new page appears and the heading line has been printed. This is accomplished when a branch occurs to the paragraph NEW-PAGE.

One portion of the flowchart remains to be covered. It begins after a "NO" response from box 3. That is, it begins when there are no more cards to be read. Boxes 15 and 16 are repeated here for convenience.

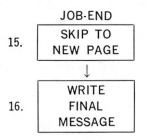

The associated statements are

```
JOB-END.  MOVE SPACES TO HEAD-LINE.
MOVE 'END OF JOB' TO HEAD-LINE.
WRITE HEAD-LINE AFTER ADVANCING 0 LINES.
STOP RUN.
```

JOB-END is a paragraph name beginning this portion of the program. In the first move statement, the operands are SPACES and HEAD-LINE. Recall that HEAD-LINE is the internal portion of storage that holds the data appearing as the first line (the heading line) of every page. Refer to box 1 and its associated instructions. Now we as programmers have decided to use the portion of storage named HEAD-LINE as the portion that will hold our final message. But before new information is placed there, the old information must be deleted. The first statement replaces every character appearing at HEAD-LINE by a space (the blank character). The next MOVE statement causes the characters between the quote marks to be moved from a certain position of storage to HEAD-LINE. Next, the WRITE statement is executed, and this means that all the data appearing in HEAD-LINE are printed as the first line of a new page. Thus the final message is seen to be END OF JOB.

Finally, box 17, together with its associated instruction, is given. This signals the end of the stated problem.

17. | STOP |

STOP RUN.

Now the end of any procedure division in a COBOL source program is the source line after which no further statements appear. Since no statements will appear after STOP RUN, this is the end of the program.

The Data Division

Every COBOL source program has a data division that begins with the two words

DATA DIVISION.

As mentioned in Sec. 13-1, the data division describes input and output data and also non-input-output data that the program needs for manipulation. It is in this division that the data names used in the procedure division first appear. In our problem the input data consist of a deck of cards, that is, a file of cards. This file is made up of individual cards or records. In the data division we select a name for the file. The name we select is referred to as a *file name*, a special kind of data name. In addition, we must select a name for an individual record, that is, a *record name*. Finally, we select names for each item in the record that will be manipulated in the procedure division.

The output data consist of a set of printed lines. Each line represents a record in the output file of printed lines. Names must be selected for the output file and an individual output record. Finally, we must select names for each item in the record that will appear as a printed item. The names selected for input and output data are given in Fig. 13-7. Note that the four input items from a card appear as printed items. All the names selected identify data items, either files or records or elementary items. The names also identify that portion of computer storage where the data items are held. You may wonder why different names were selected even though these items repre-

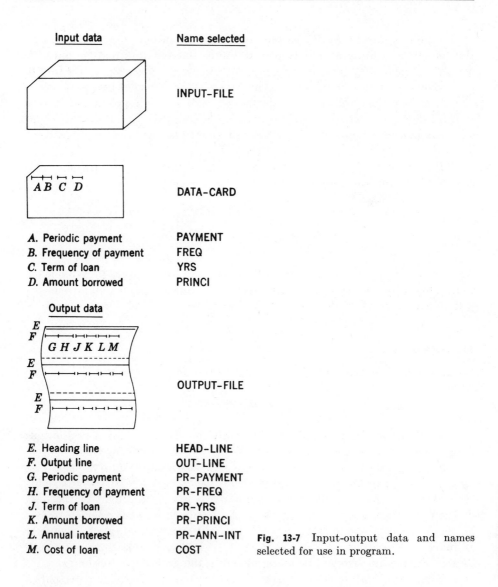

Input data   Name selected

INPUT-FILE

DATA-CARD

A. Periodic payment   PAYMENT
B. Frequency of payment   FREQ
C. Term of loan   YRS
D. Amount borrowed   PRINCI

Output data

OUTPUT-FILE

E. Heading line   HEAD-LINE
F. Output line   OUT-LINE
G. Periodic payment   PR-PAYMENT
H. Frequency of payment   PR-FREQ
J. Term of loan   PR-YRS
K. Amount borrowed   PR-PRINCI
L. Annual interest   PR-ANN-INT   **Fig. 13-7** Input-output data and names
M. Cost of loan   COST   selected for use in program.

sent the same value. This is so because of one of the rules for data-name formation: No two data names can be spelled exactly the same. This ensures uniqueness of names. (There is another means for ensuring uniqueness. It will be described after the notion of qualification is introduced, later in the chapter.)

Input and output data are defined and described in a portion of the data division called the file section, and those two words begin the section.

FILE SECTION.

Appearing next is the file-description entry

```
FD INPUT-FILE;
    LABEL RECORDS ARE OMITTED;
    RECORDING MODE IS F;
    DATA RECORD IS DATA-CARD.
```

The above entry describes the structure of the file of input cards. Beginning this entry is the reserved word FD, which is short for file description. It must appear as the first word of the file-description entry. Next appears the file name. This is the name that we, as programmers, have selected to name the file being described, which in this case happens to be INPUT-FILE. (It could just as easily have been any name, as long as the rules for data-name formation were not violated: rules governing uniqueness of name, reserved words, etc.).

The parts of the FD entry that appear between semicolons are called *clauses*. The clause serves to further describe the file. In our entry we see the LABEL RECORDS clause, the RECORDING MODE clause, and the DATA RECORD clause.

In the LABEL RECORDS clause all words are reserved words. This is a required clause in an FD entry. In order to explain the function of this clause properly, a knowledge of *labels* is required. In this text, the notion of label will not be discussed. The reader is referred to labels as described by a particular computer manufacturer.

The RECORDING MODE clause describes how data will be represented on the external medium which we have named INPUT-FILE. The F means each record of the input file will have a fixed length, namely, 80 characters (one character per card column).

Finally, the DATA RECORD clause assigns a name to the individual records of INPUT-FILE. Thus each card of the input file will have the record name DATA-CARD. A record name is a data name that we as programmers assign to a record.

This concludes the file-description entry. You will note that certain information has been provided concerning the file. We have described its physical structure, we have named it, and finally, the records within this file have been named. Next comes the record-description entry, where we must specify certain characteristics of the input record (the tab card).

Brief mention will be made here of the concept of *level*. This concept is basic for an understanding of the data division. Frequently, there is a need to specify subdivisions of an input record in order to "get at" pieces of data within that record. In our case, the record called **DATA-CARD** contains pieces of data that we must "get to" in order to solve our problem.

In the COBOL language, there is an exact way to specify the subdividing of records. This is accomplished through a system of *level numbers*, in which the lowest number is identified with the most inclusive piece of data, namely, the record. Higher numbers identify pieces of data within the record. The lowest level number is 1 or 01. Now let us construct the record-description entry for our input record.

```
01  DATA-CARD.
      02  PAYMENT; PICTURE 999V99; DISPLAY.
      02  FREQ; PICTURE AA.
      02  FILLER; PICTURE XX.
      02  YRS; PICTURE 99V99; DISPLAY.
      02  FILLER; PICTURE XX.
      02  PRINCI; PICTURE 99999V99; DISPLAY.
      02  FILLER; PICTURE X(58).
```

The first line begins with level number 01, followed by the record name that we as programmers have selected, **DATA-CARD**. Following these and signified by the higher level number 02 are the elementary items that belong to the record **DATA-CARD**. They appear above in exactly the same order that they will appear on the input record, which in our problem is the 80-column tab card. All the items are said to be *at the elementary item level*. Each line below the 01 line consists of the level number 02, followed by a data name or the reserved word **FILLER**. The word **FILLER** is used to specify an unused portion of a record. In our case it specifies unused (always blank) card columns (see Fig. 13-2). After the data name or **FILLER** comes the reserved word **PICTURE**, followed by certain strings of characters. It is called the **PICTURE** clause. The word **PICTURE** and its character string determine the *category* of an elementary item that has just been named in the line. An elementary item is *categorized* as being in one of five groups: alphabetic, numeric, alphanumeric, alphanumeric-edited, and numeric-edited. Finally, the character string gives the exact size of (number of positions in) the elementary item. In the first 02 level line we see the data name **PAYMENT**, followed by the **PICTURE** clause. The character string is 999V99. Each 9 identifies a character position of the elementary item which contains a digit. Since it appears first after the 01 level entry, this means **PAYMENT** will appear in the first five columns of an input card. The V indicates the location of an assumed decimal point—not an actual, physically present decimal point, but an assumed one. This means that the five digits of **PAYMENT**, after being read into the computer's memory unit, will be represented internally as a number with a decimal point following the third digit. The first three digits are called the integer part of **PAYMENT**. The last two are called the fractional part. The method of internal representation depends on the particular computer manufacturer. Examples of valid PAY-MENT data items on a card are 56213, 00145, and 01200.

Following the PICTURE clause is the reserved word DISPLAY. This word indicates that the characters (five digits) comprising the item PAYMENT will appear in a form oriented toward the punched card or the printed page.

The next 02 level item has the name FREQ. This line describes the frequency-of-payment portion of an input card (see Fig. 13-2). The PICTURE clause associated with FREQ has the character string AA. This means that the item FREQ will be composed of two characters, each one of which can be only a letter of the alphabet or a space. In our problem the two characters punched in columns 6 and 7 on an input card will be MO or WK.

Next is the FILLER line with PICTURE clause, having character string XX. This line specifies two blank columns of an input card, in particular, columns 8 and 9. An X in a character string means that the character position in an item can contain any allowable character, including a blank.

The years portion of an input card (the term) is described in the next line. The data name selected is YRS. The PICTURE clause describes YRS as a four-digit item, with an *assumed* decimal point following the second digit. Examples of valid and invalid YRS items are

Valid:	0200	Invalid:	2.00	decimal point not allowed
	0350		12 5	blank position not allowed
	2500		34500	too many digits
	0225		500	not enough digits

The YRS data item occupies columns 10 to 13 of an input card. Next is another FILLER line, which describes the blank columns 14 and 15. The "principal" portion of an input card is described on the next line. The name we have selected is PRINCI. The PICTURE clause describes a data item seven positions long (the V does not contribute toward the length or size of a data item) in which each position is one of the digits 0 to 9. Examples of valid and invalid PRINCI data items are

Valid:	0743200	Invalid:	12500.00	decimal point not allowed
	0050000		378000	not enough digits
	0002500		$500,000	dollar sign not allowed
	0250000			

The PRINCI data item occupies columns 16 to 22.

Finally, the final FILLER line indicates that 58 columns will be unused. (X(58) is another way of writing 58 X's in succession.) See Fig. 13-2.

Next must come the file-description entry for our output file.

As with all file-description entries, it must begin with the reserved word FD. The complete entry follows:

```
FD  OUTPUT-FILE;
      RECORD CONTAINS 53 CHARACTERS;
      LABEL RECORDS ARE OMITTED;
      RECORDING MODE IS F;
      DATA RECORDS ARE HEAD-LINE, OUT-LINE.
```

The file name OUTPUT-FILE has been selected. The RECORD CONTAINS clause, although not required, is used here to indicate how many characters will appear on a printed line. The remaining clauses serve the same purpose as those in the file-description entry for INPUT-FILE. However, the last clause (the DATA RECORD clause) is used to name the records associated with OUTPUT-FILE. The record names selected are HEAD-LINE and OUT-LINE.

The record-description entries are next.

```
01  HEAD-LINE.
    02  FILLER; PICTURE X(53).
```

The record HEAD-LINE will be the printed line that appears at the top of every new printed page; that is, it will be the heading line. Now the reserved word FILLER indicates an unused portion of a record. Also, the PICTURE clause has character string X(53). This means that 53 characters will initially constitute the record HEAD-LINE. So if this record is printed as is, an uncertain configuration of characters will appear. Thus, if a proper heading line is to appear at the top of every new page, the desired characters making up the heading line must first be placed in the logical record HEAD-LINE. This is accomplished in the procedure division by the first MOVE statement.

The other printed line that appears has the record name OUT-LINE.

```
01  OUT-LINE.
    02  FILLER; PICTURE XX.
    02  PR-PAYMENT; PICTURE $$$$.99.
    02  PR-FREQ; PICTURE AA.
    02  FILLER; PICTURE XX.
    02  PR-YRS; PICTURE 99.99.
    02  FILLER; PICTURE XX.
    02  PR-PRINCI; PICTURE $$$,$$9.99.
    02  FILLER; PICTURE X(5).
    02  PR-ANN-INT; PICTURE ZZZ.99.
    02  FILLER; PICTURE XX.
    02  COST; PICTURE $$$,$$9.99.
```

All FILLER lines above will ultimately represent blank character positions on a printed line. The second 02 level entry has data name PR-PAYMENT, short for printed payment. The PICTURE clause has a seven-character string, four currency symbols, a decimal point, and two 9's.   The four currency symbols have the following effect on the printed form of the item **PR-PAYMENT**: If the internal representation of **PR-PAYMENT** has one, two, three, or four leading zeros in its integer part, replace these by blanks; then replace the rightmost blank by a currency symbol.   Used in this way, it is referred to as a floating-currency symbol.   The decimal point, when used in this format, will always appear as a printed character just to the left of two trailing digits.   (Remember that 9's in a **PICTURE** clause identify a character position that will contain a digit.)   Examples of internal values and printed data items for **PR-PAYMENT** follow.   The caret signifies an assumed decimal point.

PR-PAYMENT

Internal value	Printed form (b = blank)
0001ᴧ56	bb$1.56
0025ᴧ682	b$25.68
000ᴧ01	bbb$.01
0346ᴧ72	$346.72
00000	bbb$.00
100ᴧ00	$100.00
027ᴧ689	b$27.68
03672ᴧ45	See below

The last example will not be properly printed.   This is so because of a certain rule governing the use of the floating-currency symbol; the number of nonzero digits in the integer part of a value must be one less than the number of currency symbols used.   In the last example above, four nonzero digits appear, thus violating the rule.   Manufacturers will have different methods for alerting the programmer that the rule has been violated.

Next comes the printed frequency-of-payment line.   We have given it the data name **PR-FREQ**.   Its associated **PICTURE** clause describes it as being two characters in length, each character being a letter of the alphabet or a space. In our problem this two-character item will be **WK** or **MO**.

The next non-**FILLER** line has **PR-YRS** as data name, short for printed-years (the term of the loan).   The **PICTURE** clause describes **PR-YRS** as having a length of five characters, the first two characters and the last two characters being digits, and the third character being a decimal point.

Examples

PR-YRS

Internal value	Printed form
02ᴧ287	02.28
002ᴧ15	02.15
25ᴧ00	25.00
000ᴧ05	00.05

After the next FILLER line comes the line that describes the printed-principal data item. It has the data name PR-PRINCI. Note that the character string of the PICTURE clause has 10 characters in it: five currency symbols, a comma, three 9's, and a decimal point. Used in this way, the comma is called an *insertion symbol;* that is, a comma is inserted, if needed, in the final form of PR-PRINCI. The currency symbol in this application is referred to as the floating-currency symbol (since its final position floats through five positions). The 9's and the decimal point are used as in previous PICTURE clauses.

Examples

PR-PRINCI

Internal value	Printed form (b = blank)
00678₄235	bbb$678.23
02524₄78	b$2,524.78
25000₄00	$25,000.00
00000₄50	bbbbb$0.50

Note that the comma appears if needed.

A brief mention is now made about the PICTURE clause of the next FILLER line. Here the character string is X(5). This is merely another way of writing XXXXX.

The next line describes the data item that we have named PR-ANN-INT. This is short for printed annual interest. Its PICTURE clause has six characters in its character string. The two 9's and the decimal point are used as in previous PICTURE clauses. The three Z's have the following effect on the printed form of the item PR-ANN-INT. If the internal representation of PR-ANN-INT has one, two, or three heading zeros in its integer part, replace these by blanks.

Examples

PR-ANN-INT

Internal value	Printed form (b = blank)
000₄023	bbb.02
024₄59	b24.59
007₄503	bb7.50
123₄00	123.00

After the last FILLER line, the data item that we have named COST is described. This is the item representing the cost of the loan. Note that its PICTURE character string is identical with that of PR-PRINCI. Its function is the same.

In all the 02 level entries above, the respective PICTURE character strings define the maximum number of characters that will comprise the respective item. For example, the PR-PAYMENT item will occupy a maximum of seven positions on a printed line; that is, the size of the item will be seven positions long. The first FILLER entry describes a portion of the printed line two positions in length.

The sum of all the sizes is 53. This means the printed line will be 53 characters long. (Most commercial printers have a certain maximum length associated with their printed lines. This maximum is usually larger than 53. The extra positions will be automatically "blanked out," so that no characters will appear to the right of printer position 53.) That is, the OUT-LINE record will be 53 characters in length. This is consistent with the RECORD CONTAINS clause of the file-description entry.

This completes the discussion of the FILE SECTION portion of the DATA DIVISION.

The next section of the DATA DIVISION describes data items that are not part of external files. This section is called the working-storage section and must begin with the reserved words

WORKING-STORAGE SECTION.

Before the working-storage section is described in detail, some mention should be made of external and internal data representation.

Data appearing on a tab card or data printed are said to be external data. These data, when held in the computer's storage unit, are said to be internal data. Data items in this class are called DISPLAY type. Another kind of internal data exists when data are created and used only within the computer's storage unit. In this class are data items called COMPUTATIONAL. The internal representation of a DISPLAY type and the internal representation of a COMPUTATIONAL type are different. (The difference will be specified when you read the reference manual associated with a particular computer.) An important difference between the two types is this: Only with the COMPUTATIONAL type can valid arithmetic operations be performed. So if a data item is read into the computer from a card, that item is a DISPLAY type. Now, if the item is to be used in some arithmetic operation (an ADD, SUBTRACT, MULTIPLY, DIVIDE, or some combination of these), the item must be changed internally to a COMPUTATIONAL type. This is easily accomplished by use of the MOVE statement in the PROCEDURE division. We will see an application of this in our program.

Now all the entries in the WORKING-STORAGE SECTION will be given:

    77 PYMT; PICTURE S999V99; USAGE COMPUTATIONAL.
    77 YEARS; PICTURE S99V99; USAGE COMPUTATIONAL.

```
77  PRINC; PICTURE S99999V99; USAGE COMPUTATIONAL.
77  CRDCNT; PICTURE S99; USAGE COMPUTATIONAL.
77  TOTPMTS; PICTURE S9999; USAGE COMPUTATIONAL.
77  PYR; PICTURE S99; USAGE COMPUTATIONAL.
77  TOTDEBT; PICTURE S9999999V99; USAGE COMPUTATIONAL.
77  LNCST; PICTURE S9999999V99; USAGE COMPUTATIONAL.
77  ANN-INT; PICTURE S999V99; USAGE COMPUTATIONAL.
```

Each entry has the special level number 77. This level number is used only in the WORKING-STORAGE SECTION and only with elementary data items (items that cannot be subdivided). In addition to the special level number, each entry has a programmer-assigned data name, a PICTURE clause, and a USAGE clause. Let us examine the first entry.

First of all, you are reminded that the data name identifies a portion of computer storage where the data item is held. The data name PYMT will identify that portion of storage where the computational form of PAYMENT is held. The data names are similar, and this is deliberate. The PICTURE clause of PYMT has a character string that begins with S. This means that an operational sign (plus or minus) will be part of the internal representation for PYMT. The 9's in the character string identify where digits will occur. The V indicates the presence of an *assumed* decimal point. The particular arrangement of characters in the PICTURE character string defines the *category* in which this data item, PYMT, belongs (see record-description entry for DATA-CARD). The category is *numeric*.

Do not confuse the terms category and type. There are five *categories* of data and two *types* of data. Categories describe data items as they appear internally. Types describe how the data item will be used:

Categories	*Types*
Alphabetic	DISPLAY
Numeric	COMPUTATIONAL
Alphanumeric	
Alphanumeric-edited	
Numeric-edited	

The USAGE clause states how the data item will be used; that is, it describes the type. Now note that five 9's appear in the PICTURE character string. This means that five digits will be used to express the value of PYMT internally. Five 9's were selected (rather than three 9's or two or seven, etc.) because only five digits were used to express the DISPLAY type of data item PAYMENT. So it would make no sense to express the COMPUTATIONAL form of PAYMENT with a different number of digits. A similar argument holds for the data items named YEARS and PRINC. These are the COMPUTATIONAL forms of the DISPLAY types YRS and PRINCI.

The item named CRDCNT appears next. Referring back to the PRO-CEDURE division, you will recall that CRDCNT is a name assigned to a number that will increase by one each time a line is printed. The highest value this number can assume is 50. (See Fig. 13-4 and associated PROCEDURE statement.) Moreover, the number is always an integer, and its range is between 0 and 50.

The PICTURE clause of CRDCNT describes an item in the numeric category. From the character string it is seen that two digits comprise CRDCNT. The S (always needed for an item in the numeric category) indicates an operational sign. Finally, the USAGE clause ends the entry.

The item with name TOTPMTS is described next. The name is short for total number of payments. It is an item in the numeric category described internally by four digits with an operational sign. No decimal point is needed here, since the item will always be an integer. (See Fig. 13-4 and associated instruction.)

Next comes the item named PYR. Referring to the PROCEDURE division, you will see that PYR can assume only the values 12 and 52. So two digits are sufficient to represent PYR internally.

The line describing item named TOTDEBT is next. TOTDEBT is short for total debt, and the value TOTDEBT assumes comes from the product of "total number of payments" (TOTPMTS) and "the periodic payment" (PYMT). From the TOTDEBT PICTURE clause you see that the integer part of the value consists of seven digit positions; the fractional part, two digits. An example will show why the character string is so constructed.

The number we have named TOTDEBT is the product of two numbers named TOTPMTS and PYMT. Now PYMT is a number with three digits for its integer part and two digits for its fractional part (as seen from its PICTURE clause). Also, TOTPMTS can be no larger than a four-digit integer (as seen from its PICTURE clause). Some typical values are given below for TOTPMTS and PYMT, together with their product TOTDEBT.

Total number of payments	Periodic payment	Product
465	36.75	17,088.75
520	300.00	156,000.00
900	900.00	810,000.00
9,000	900.00	8,100,000.00
9,145	922.25	8,433,996.25
9,999	999.99	9,998,900.01

The last example shows the largest values that TOTPMTS and PYMT can assume inside the computer. (Their PICTURE clauses restrict them to these maximum values.)   On the right you see the largest value the product can assume.   Note that its integer part consists of seven digits, its fractional part two digits.   Then the PICTURE clause for this product should describe a numeric item with nine digits, seven for integer part and two digits for fractional part.   This is precisely what we have in the PICTURE clause for the product TOTDEBT.

The item LNCST has an identical character string, for similar reasons.

The next line describes the item named ANN-INT, short for annual interest. Now, we are assuming that the initial input data will lead to an annual interest figure less than 1,000 percent.   The PICTURE clause for ANN-INT describes a numeric item whose value cannot validly exceed 999.99.

This completes the description for the WORKING-STORAGE SECTION, the last section of the DATA DIVISION for our program.

The Environment Division

The next division discussed will provide information about certain physical characteristics of a computer in relation to our data-processing problem.   It is called the environment division, and begins with those two words.

ENVIRONMENT DIVISION.

In this division the computer on which our program will be compiled is specified.   Also, the computer on which our program will be executed is specified.   (These two computers need not be the same.)

Two sections will appear in our ENVIRONMENT DIVISION.   The first begins with the two reserved words CONFIGURATION SECTION.   This section deals with the characteristics of the source computer (on which our source program will be compiled) and the object computer (on which our object program will be executed).   The complete section follows:

CONFIGURATION SECTION.
SOURCE-COMPUTER.   IBM-360   H50.
OBJECT-COMPUTER.   IBM-360   H50.

The reserved words in the second and third lines are SOURCE-COMPUTER and OBJECT-COMPUTER.   Since our problem is rather simple, all we need do is name the source computer and the object computer.   Note that the *names* are the same.   This means the COBOL program will be compiled and executed on the same computer (the IBM 360 computer, model 50).   Each manufacturer will have his own set of characters for computer name.

The next section in the ENVIRONMENT DIVISION is called the input-output section.   It provides information needed to control transmission of data between external devices and the *object program*. The input-output section will have within it a file-control paragraph. It is in this paragraph that external files are named. Each named file is then associated with some external device.

The complete input-output section follows:

```
INPUT-OUTPUT SECTION.
FILE-CONTROL
SELECT INPUT-FILE ASSIGN TO 'SYSIN' UNIT-RECORD 2540R UNIT.
SELECT OUTPUT-FILE ASSIGN TO 'SYSPRINT' UNIT-RECORD 1403 UNIT.
```

Note that the FILE-CONTROL paragraph is composed of two statements, called SELECT statements. In each statement the reserved words are SELECT, ASSIGN, UNIT-RECORD, TO, and UNIT. The words INPUT-FILE and OUTPUT-FILE have been selected by us to name our files of input data (a deck of cards) and output data (a page or more of printed lines). In this section we see first use of these programmer-selected file names INPUT-FILE and OUTPUT-FILE.

The words SYSIN and SYSPRINT are called external names. They refer to an input and an output device, respectively. The word 2540R is a name for a specific device number. In this case it is the card-reader portion of IBM corporation's model 2540 card-reader punch. The word 1403 is the device number of IBM Corporation's model 1403 line printer.

The form of external names and device numbers will vary according to the specifications of particular manufacturers.

This completes the description of the ENVIRONMENT DIVISION for our program.

The Identification Division

This division (the first to appear in any COBOL program) identifies the source program (by its very appearance) and provides a name for the object program. This name is selected by the programmer.

The identification division for our program is as follows:

```
                    IDENTIFICATION DIVISION.
                    PROGRAM-ID.  'INTEREST'.
                    AUTHOR.  S.M. DEANGELO.
```

The first line begins the IDENTIFICATION DIVISION in any COBOL program. The next line is called the program identification (PROGRAM-ID) paragraph. The word between the quote marks is the program name. It is selected by the programmer, and this is the name that identifies the object program. PROGRAM-ID is a reserved word. Finally, the reserved word

AUTHOR begins the author paragraph. Other paragraphs may appear which serve to identify the program further. This completes the identification division for our program. Thus, in the preceding four sections of this chapter, we have tried to describe each division as it applied to a particular problem. The complete program appears in Fig. 13-8 on coding forms.

You will notice certain statements in the procedure division that were not described in the chapter section on that division. The first is the OPEN statement appearing just after the PROCEDURE DIVISION line.

The OPEN statement serves to "get the files ready for processing." This statement prepares the files for the oncoming READ statement. OPEN must appear before any READ statement is executed; however, the OPEN need be

```
        IDENTIFICATION DIVISION.
        PROGRAM-ID. 'INTEREST'
        AUTHOR. S. M. DE ANGELO.

        ENVIRONMENT DIVISION.
        CONFIGURATION SECTION.
        SOURCE-COMPUTER. IBM-360 H50.
        OBJECT-COMPUTER. IBM-360 H50.
        INPUT-OUTPUT SECTION.
        FILE-CONTROL.
            SELECT INPUT-FILE ASSIGN TO 'SYSIN' UNIT-RECORD 2540R UNIT
            RESERVE NO ALTERNATE AREAS.
            SELECT OUTPUT-FILE ASSIGN TO 'SYSPRINT' UNIT-RECORD 1403
            UNIT.

        DATA DIVISION.
        FILE SECTION.
        FD  INPUT-FILE;
            LABEL RECORDS ARE OMITTED;
            RECORDING MODE IS F;
            DATA RECORD IS DATA-CARD.
        01  DATA-CARD.
            02 PAYMENT; PICTURE 999V99; DISPLAY.
            02 FREQ; PICTURE AA.
```

```
            02 FILLER; PICTURE XX.
            02 YRS; PICTURE 99V99; DISPLAY.
            02 FILLER; PICTURE XX.
            02 PRINCI; PICTURE 99999V99; DISPLAY.
            02 FILLER; PICTURE X(58).
        FD  OUTPUT-FILE
            RECORD CONTAINS 53 CHARACTERS;
            LABEL RECORDS ARE OMITTED;
            RECORDING MODE IS F;
            DATA RECORDS ARE HEAD-LINE, OUT-LINE.
        01  HEAD-LINE.
            02 FILLER; PICTURE X(53).
        01  OUT-LINE.
            02 FILLER; PICTURE XX.
            02 PR-PAYMENT; PICTURE $$$$.99.
            02 PR-FREQ; PICTURE AA.
            02 FILLER; PICTURE XX.
            02 PR-YRS; PICTURE 99.99.
            02 FILLER; PICTURE XX.
            02 PR-PRINCI; PICTURE $$$,$$9.99.
            02 FILLER; PICTURE X(5).
            02 PR-ANN-INT; PICTURE ZZZ.99.
            02 FILLER; PICTURE XX.
            02 COST; PICTURE $$$,$$9.99.
```

Fig. 13-8 Sample source program.

```
       WORKING-STORAGE SECTION.
       77  PYR; PICTURE S99; USAGE COMPUTATIONAL.
       77  PYMT; PICTURE S999V99; USAGE COMPUTATIONAL.
       77  YEARS; PICTURE S99V99; USAGE COMPUTATIONAL.
       77  PRINC; PICTURE S99999V99; USAGE COMPUTATIONAL.
       77  CRDCNT; PICTURE S99; USAGE COMPUTATIONAL.
       77  TOTPMTS; PICTURE S9999; USAGE COMPUTATIONAL.
       77  TOTDEBT; PICTURE S9999999V99; USAGE COMPUTATIONAL.
       77  LNCST; PICTURE S9999999; USAGE COMPUTATIONAL.
       77  ANN-INT; PICTURE S999V99; USAGE COMPUTATIONAL.

       PROCEDURE DIVISION.
           OPEN INPUT, INPUT-FILE; OUTPUT, OUTPUT-FILE.
       NEW-PAGE.
           MOVE '     PAYMENT   YEARS    PRINCIPAL    ANN-INT   LN COST '
               TO HEAD-LINE.
           WRITE HEAD-LINE AFTER ADVANCING 0 LINES.
           MOVE SPACES TO OUT-LINE.
           MOVE ZEROS TO CRDCNT.
       RDC.
           READ INPUT-FILE; AT END GO TO JOB-END.
           ADD 1 TO CRDCNT.
           MOVE PAYMENT TO PYMT.
           MOVE YRS TO YEARS.
```

```
           MOVE PRINCI TO PRINC.
           IF FREQ IS EQUAL TO 'MO' GO TO A1.
           MOVE 52 TO PYR.
           GO TO A2.
       A1. MOVE 12 TO PYR.
       A2. MULTIPLY YRS BY PYR GIVING TOTPMTS ROUNDED.
           MULTIPLY TOTPMTS BY PYMT GIVING TOTDEBT.
           SUBTRACT PRINC FROM TOTDEBT GIVING LNCST.
           COMPUTE ANN-INT = (200 * PYR * LNCST) / (PRINC * (TOTPMTS +
               1)).
           MOVE PYMT TO PR-PAYMENT.
           MOVE FREQ TO PR-FREQ.
           MOVE YEARS TO PR-YRS.
           MOVE PRINC TO PR-PRINCI.
           MOVE ANN-INT TO PR-ANN-INT.
           MOVE LNCST TO COST.
           WRITE OUT-LINE AFTER ADVANCING 1 LINES.
           IF CRDCNT IS EQUAL TO 50 GO TO NEW-PAGE.
           GO TO RDC.
       JOB-END.
           MOVE SPACES TO HEAD-LINE.
           MOVE ' END OF JOB' TO HEAD-LINE.
           WRITE HEAD-LINE AFTER ADVANCING 0 LINES.
           CLOSE INPUT-FILE, OUTPUT-FILE.
           STOP RUN
```

Fig. 13-8 (*Continued*)

executed only once before a series of **READ** statements.   (This is exactly what happens in our program.)   In the **OPEN** statement, the reserved words are **OPEN, INPUT,** and **OUTPUT.**   The words **INPUT-FILE** and **OUTPUT-FILE** are programmer-selected.   Note that, as far as COBOL is concerned, the words **INPUT** and **INPUT-FILE** are two completely different words.   Similarly for the words **OUTPUT** and **OUTPUT-FILE.**

Next the **CLOSE** statement, which appears just preceding the **STOP RUN** statement, serves to terminate the processing of files.   This means that the peripheral devices and files associated with the input-output functions are, in a sense, "closed" to further input-output activity.

The next series of statements to be considered are the three successive MOVE statements appearing in the RDC paragraph. In the description of the WORKING-STORAGE SECTION, mention was made of two *types* of data, DISPLAY and COMPUTATIONAL. Each of the three MOVE statements in the RDC paragraph has the following effect: The data item (a DISPLAY type) specified by the first operand is converted during the move to a COMPUTATIONAL type. This converted data item is then placed in memory at a position specified by the second operand.

Similarly, five MOVE statements in the A2 paragraph effectively convert data items from COMPUTATIONAL to DISPLAY. The five COMPUTATIONAL items are PYMT, YEARS, PRINC, ANN-INT, and LNCST, and their DISPLAY counterparts are PR-PAYMENT, PR-YRS, PR-PRINCI, PR-ANN-INT, and COST.

PAYMENT	YEARS	PRINCIPAL	ANN-INT	LN COST
$63.00MC	01.00	$725.00	7.89	$31.00
$85.00MO	02.00	$2,000.00	1.92	$40.00
$15.00WK	02.89	$1,800.00	17.21	$450.00
$63.64MC	01.00	$725.00	9.84	$38.68
$125.00MC	25.00	$20,000.00	6.97	$17,500.00
$43.86MO	01.00	$500.00	9.71	$26.32
$22.95MC	02.00	$500.00	9.75	$50.80
$15.97MC	03.00	$500.00	9.71	$74.92
$12.49MC	04.00	$500.00	9.74	$99.52
$10.40MC	05.00	$500.00	9.75	$124.00
$87.72MC	01.00	$1,000.00	9.71	$52.64
$45.89MO	02.00	$1,000.00	9.73	$101.36
$31.94MC	03.00	$1,000.00	9.71	$149.84
$24.97MC	04.00	$1,000.00	9.72	$198.56
$20.79MC	05.00	$1,000.00	9.73	$247.40
$219.30MC	01.00	$2,500.00	9.71	$131.60
$114.71MC	02.00	$2,500.00	9.71	$253.04
$79.85MO	03.00	$2,500.00	9.71	$374.60
$62.42MO	04.00	$2,500.00	9.72	$496.16
$51.96MO	05.00	$2,500.00	9.71	$617.60
$306.11MC	01.00	$3,500.00	9.14	$173.32
$159.72MC	02.00	$3,500.00	9.14	$333.28
$110.93MO	03.00	$3,500.00	9.14	$493.48
$86.53MC	04.00	$3,500.00	9.14	$653.44
$71.89MC	05.00	$3,500.00	9.14	$813.40
$10.26WK	01.00	$500.00	13.15	$33.52
$5.44WK	02.00	$500.00	13.02	$65.76
$3.84WK	03.00	$500.00	13.12	$99.04
$20.52WK	01.00	$1,000.00	13.15	$67.04
$10.88WK	02.00	$1,000.00	13.02	$131.52
$7.68WK	03.00	$1,000.00	13.12	$198.08
$30.65WK	01.00	$1,500.00	12.27	$93.80
$16.18WK	02.00	$1,500.00	12.06	$182.72
$11.38WK	03.00	$1,500.00	12.15	$275.28
$40.68WK	01.00	$2,000.00	11.31	$115.36
$21.39WK	02.00	$2,000.00	11.12	$224.56
$14.98WK	03.00	$2,000.00	11.15	$336.88
$50.67WK	01.00	$2,500.00	10.58	$134.84
$26.56WK	02.00	$2,500.00	10.38	$262.24
$18.54WK	03.00	$2,500.00	10.39	$392.24

Fig. 13-9 Sample output.

Note that the MOVE statement, MOVE FREQ TO PR-FREQ, is not a conversion from COMPUTATIONAL to DISPLAY. The items referred to by FREQ
and PR-FREQ are both DISPLAY types. This MOVE statement merely takes the
item referred to by FREQ (part of an input record) and places it in memory at a
position referred to by PR-FREQ (part of an output record).

Sample output for our problem appears in Fig. 13-9.

13-6 THE COBOL CODING FORM

From Fig. 13-8 it is clear that certain portions of the source program always
begin in certain positions on the coding form. Each position on the form
corresponds to a column on an 80-column tab card. Each form line corresponds
to one tab card. A coding line is broken up into margins and areas defined as
follows:

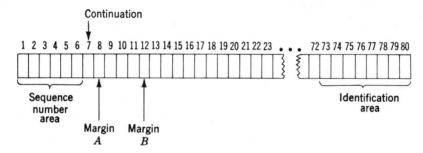

Sequence *numbers* are optional and may be used by the programmer to
number his coding lines. The identification area (columns 73 to 80) may be
used to identify the program. The use of this area is optional. Refer to
specific reference manuals for further description of the sequence-number area
and the identification area.

As we know, every COBOL source program has an identification division,
environment division, data division, and procedure division. Each division
begins with its associated *division header*. This division header must always
begin in margin A with the division name and the word DIVISION separated by a space. The word DIVISION is always followed by a period. No
other characters may appear on the division header line. See Fig. 13-8.

Section names start in margin A, with the name and the word SECTION
separated by a space. The word SECTION is followed by a period. No other
characters may appear on the same line as the section header.

In the data division a section is made up of data-description entries. In
our problem, the data division has two sections: first, the FILE SECTION, which
is made up of two file-description (FD) entries; then the WORKING-STORAGE
SECTION, which is made up of nine data-description entries. See Fig. 13-8.

In the environment and procedure divisions a section is made up of paragraphs. In our problem, the environment division is made up of two sections. First the CONFIGURATION SECTION, which is made up of two paragraphs; then the INPUT-OUTPUT SECTION, which is made up of one paragraph. The procedure division of our problem has no sections in it, only paragraphs. See Fig. 13-8.

Data-division Entries

Data-division entries, more specifically, file-description entries, begin with an alphabetic indicator (such as FD) or a level *number*. Each indicator or number is followed by a space, then by the file name, followed by a sequences of clauses describing the file. Each clause *may* be terminated by a semicolon followed by a space, except the last, which is always terminated by a period followed by a space. See Fig. 13-8, data division.

The alphabetic level indicator always begins in margin A. Its associated file name begins in margin B, followed by descriptive information, if any. Record-description entries are next.

The first level number 01 in a hierarchy begins in margin A. Its record name follows in margin B. All entries subordinate in the record description are begun with a higher level number in margin B, with the number and the associated name separated by one or more spaces. This is how our COBOL record description is constructed (see Fig. 13-8). Note that the 01 line and subordinate entries are terminated by periods. This is mandatory.

Paragraph

A paragraph name starts in margin A and ends with a period followed by a space. Remember that a paragraph is made up of one or more sentences. The first sentence of a paragraph begins in margin B of the same line (if it was a short paragraph name like A2 of our program) or in margin B of the next line (if it was a long paragraph name like NEW-PAGE of our program).

When the sentences of a paragraph require more than one line, the continuation is as described in the following paragraphs.

Continuation

A sentence or any entry in a COBOL program that requires more than one line is continued by starting the continuation in margin B.

A hyphen in column 7 of the continuation line means that the character in margin B is a continuation of the last word or numeric literal written in the preceding line.

If there is no hyphen in column 7, then it is assumed that the last character of the preceding line is followed by a space.

Fig. 13-10 Examples of continuation. (*a*) Continuation of nonnumeric literal; (*b*) continuation example where no hyphen is needed in column T. (The statement could have been written on one line.)

Often nonnumeric literals must be continued because they cover many columns. The rule is: Place a hyphen in column 7; place a quote mark in margin B. Now continue in a normal manner, beginning in column 13, the coding of the nonnumeric literal. Examples can be seen in Fig. 13-10.

13-7 QUALIFICATION

It was mentioned on p. 424 that every data name used in a source program must be unique. Uniqueness can be accomplished in one of two ways: first, by spelling (constructing) each data name uniquely; second, through the process of qualification.

Consider the following example of qualification. A furniture dealer sells and delivers his merchandise. His bookkeeping department included in each transaction record the date of sale and the date of delivery. Furthermore, assume that the two sets of data have been described as follows:

DATE-OF-SALE   DATE-OF-DELIVERY
DAY   DAY
MONTH   MONTH
YEAR   YEAR

Each set is referred to as a hierarchy of names. The name DATE-OF-SALE is said to be at a higher level than DAY, MONTH, or YEAR. Similarly for DATE-OF-DELIVERY.

If MONTH is referenced (for example, in the PROCEDURE DIVISION), it would not be clear which MONTH was meant. Reference to MONTH would be made unique by qualifying MONTH with DATE-OF-SALE or DATE-OF-DELIVERY, depending on what was intended. Qualification is specified by using one of the reserved words OF or IN.

For example, if we wanted to reference the month on which the merchandise was delivered, it must be referred to as

MONTH OF DATE-OF-DELIVERY

Here DATE-OF-DELIVERY is called a qualifier of MONTH.

The highest level of qualifier in a hierarchy is the file name, and it thus cannot be qualified.   So we can have hierarchies set up as

File name
　　　Record name
　　　　　Data name

The file name qualifies the record name, which qualifies the data name.

The above example indicates hierarchies which exist in the data division. Hierarchies can also exist in the procedure division.   Here they are set up as

Section name
　　　Paragraph name

Qualification would be needed if two sections had the same paragraph name within.

For example:

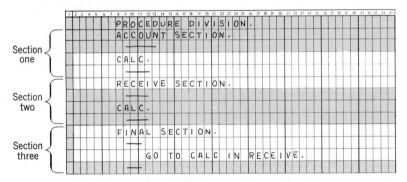

CALC is a paragraph name, ACCOUNT, RECEIVE, and FINAL are section names.

The GO TO statement in section 3 indicates a desire to branch to the CALC paragraph of section 2.   The GO TO statement must appear in this form to achieve the desired result.   GO TO CALC would be incorrect.   However, if we were within the section where CALC appears, then CALC need not be qualified.

The rules for qualification follow:

1. Each qualifier must be at a higher level but within the same hierarchy as the name it qualifies.

2. The same name may not appear at two levels in a hierarchy.

3. If a data name is assigned to more than one data item, the data name must be qualified each time it is referred to in the procedure, environment, and data divisions.

4. A paragraph name must never be duplicated within a section. When a paragraph name is qualified by a section name, the word SECTION does not appear. A paragraph name need not be qualified when referred to from within the same section.
5. A name can be qualified even though it does not need qualification.

13-8 NOTATIONAL RULES

In the rest of this chapter we will discuss clauses and statements in a more general way. Rules governing the construction of clauses and statements in a COBOL paragram are specific and precise. A set of symbols (somewhat standard) are used to describe these rules. The symbols are brackets [ ] and braces { }. These symbols, together with the specifically arranged elements of a clause or statement, are called the *general format* of that clause or statement. By elements, we mean uppercase words, lowercase words, level numbers, connectives, and special characters. A special character is one that is not a digit and not a letter of the alphabet (see Fig. 13-1). A connective is a word or a punctuation character (or a combination of these) that associates a name with its qualifier or links operands written in a series.

When you see an underlined uppercase word in the general format, it means that the word is required when this format is used. Uppercase words not underlined are optional to the programmer and may or may not be used in the COBOL source program.

Lowercase words not subsequently defined indicate that programmer-supplied names must be constructed (according to the rules for formation of COBOL words).

Before an example is given, the word *identifier* is defined.

An identifier is a *data name*, with proper qualifiers, if needed, to make specific reference to a data item.

Now let us show the general format for the MOVE statement:

$$\underline{\text{MOVE}} \left\{ [\text{CORRESPONDING}] \begin{matrix} \text{identifier-1} \\ \text{literal} \end{matrix} \right\} \underline{\text{TO}} \ \{\text{identifier-2}\} \ \cdots$$

The brackets [ ] enclosing any portion of a general format mean that the enclosed portion may or may not be present. The programmer has the option. So in the MOVE statement, the word CORRESPONDING is optional. This word will be explained later.

The braces { } enclosing any portion of a general format mean that a selection must be made among the *vertically stacked* possibilities within. The possibilities will be written in lowercase. So, in the first set of braces, there is a choice between an identifier and a literal. Either must appear when the MOVE statement is written. Since CORRESPONDING is not part of the vertical stack, it is not one of the mandatory possibilities. The second set of braces encloses only one possibility, which must appear when the MOVE statement is written.

The three dots . . . , called the ellipsis, have special meaning in a general format. They indicate where repetition may occur if the programmer deems it necessary. The part that may be repeated is found as follows.

Find the right bracket] or right brace }, immediately to the left of the ellipsis. Scan left until you find the matching left bracket [or left brace {. The part that may be repeated lies between the indicated pair of grouping symbols.

In our example the ellipsis applies to identifier 2 (the second identifier). Identifier 1, or literal, represents the sending area, while identifier 2 and the ellipsis . . . represent the receiving area.

Note that the ellipsis could have been replaced by

{identifier-3}{identifier-4}

and so on.

13-9 FORMAT–IDENTIFICATION DIVISION

The general format for the identification division follows:

IDENTIFICATION DIVISION.
PROGRAM ID.—program-name
[AUTHOR.—comment-paragraph]
[INSTALLATION. comment-paragraph]
[DATE-WRITTEN. comment-paragraph]
[DATE-COMPILED. comment-paragraph]
[SECURITY. comment-paragraph]
[REMARKS. comment-paragraph]

A comment paragraph is any combination of characters organized to convey a message implied by the associated key word.

The program name is a programmer-supplied word. Some manufacturers restrict the size and form of this word. Refer to specific manuals. You should note that the first two entries must appear when the identification division is constructed.

13-10 FORMAT–ENVIRONMENT DIVISION

The environment division specified the configuration of the source computer and object computer. This is done in a section of the environment division called the configuration section.

Another section of the environment division contains information needed to control transmission of data between external devices and the object program. This is the input-output section. Each section is made up of several paragraphs.

ENVIRONMENT DIVISION.

CONFIGURATION SECTION.

SOURCE-COMPUTER. source-computer entry

OBJECT-COMPUTER. object-computer entry

[SPECIAL NAMES. special-names entry]

INPUT-OUTPUT SECTION.

FILE-CONTROL. file control entry

[I-O CONTROL. input-output control entry]

As you can see, the configuration section is made up of three paragraphs, two of which must appear. The input-output section consists of two paragraphs, one of which is mandatory. Each section and paragraph begins in margin A of a coding line. Each entry above can begin just after the period space of its paragraph name. But subsequent lines of the entry must begin in margin B.

Each organization responsible for a COBOL compiler will define the source-computer entry and the object-computer entry. The reader is referred to manuals supplied by such an organization. Hereafter, organizations (such as manufacturers) responsible for a COBOL compiler will be called *implementors*.

The special names entry provides a means of relating external-device names (defined by the implementor) to programmer-defined names (also called mnemonic names).

Refer to specific manuals for elaboration on this clause.

The FILE CONTROL paragraph names each file (by a file name) and allows us to assign hardware devices and specify alternate input-output areas.

The general format for the FILE CONTROL paragraph is

FILE-CONTROL. {SELECT [OPTIONAL] file-name-1

ASSIGN TO [integer-1] implementor-name-1

[implementor-name-2] . . . .

$$\left[\text{FOR MULTIPLE} \begin{Bmatrix} \text{REEL} \\ \text{UNIT} \end{Bmatrix} \right] \left[\text{, RESERVE} \begin{Bmatrix} \text{integer} \\ \text{NO} \end{Bmatrix} \text{ALTERNATE} \right.$$

$$\left. \left[\begin{Bmatrix} \text{AREA} \\ \text{AREAS} \end{Bmatrix} \right] \right] \Big\} \cdots$$

Each file described in the *data division* must be named once as file-name-1 in the FILE CONTROL paragraph following the key word SELECT. Each SELECTED file must have a file-description entry in the data division. (There are certain exceptions to this, but we will not pursue them.)

The key word OPTIONAL is required for input files that might not be presented each time the object program is run.

The use of integer-1 means that the number of input-output devices assigned to file-name-1 will be equal to integer-1. If no integer is specified, the compiler determines the number.

ASSIGN associates the file names file-name-1 with an input-output device. The names for these devices are defined by the implementor.

MULTIPLE REEL is used when the number of tape units assigned might be less than the number of reels in the file.

MULTIPLE UNIT is used when the number of disk or drum devices assigned might be less than the number of devices in the file.

The RESERVE clause lets the programmer modify the number of input-output areas set aside by the COBOL compiler. When integer is used instead of NO, the compiler sets aside integer additional areas in addition to the minimum area. The implementor specifies what is the minimum area and what is the additional area for the particular hardware device.

The use of the NO option is obvious.

The optional I-O-CONTROL paragraph specifies alternate input-output techniques; points at which rerun is to be established; memory area shared by different files; and the location of files on a single reel. The general format follows:

I-O CONTROL.

[APPLY implementor-defined I-O technique ON file-name-1

[, file-name-2] . . .] . . .

$$
\left[
\begin{array}{l}
; \text{ RERUN } \left[\text{ON} \begin{Bmatrix} \text{file-name-3} \\ \text{implementor-name} \end{Bmatrix} \right] \\[2em]
\text{EVERY} \begin{Bmatrix} \left\{ \text{END OF} \begin{Bmatrix} \text{REEL} \\ \text{UNIT} \end{Bmatrix} \right\} \text{ of file-name-4} \\ \text{integer-1 RECORDS} \\ \text{integer-2-CLOCK UNITS} \\ \text{condition-name} \end{Bmatrix}
\end{array}
\right] \ldots
$$

[; SAME [RECORD] AREA FOR file-name-5 {; file-name-6} . . .] . . .

$$
\left[
\begin{array}{l}
; \text{ MULTIPLE FILE TAPE CONTAINS file-name-7} \\
\text{[POSITION integer-3][,file-name-8 [POSITION integer-4]] . . .}
\end{array}
\right] \cdots
$$

The **APPLY** clause would be used when alternate input-output techniques are made available by the implementor.   The concept of input-output technique would be elaborated upon in the implementor's reference manuals.

The **RERUN** clause is used if the programmer wishes to rerun the program again at a later time.   When certain conditions specified in the **RERUN** clause occur the contents of storage are written on file-name-3 or implementor name, together with certain control information.   This control information allows the program to be restarted again from the point that the dump occurred.

The **SAME AREA** clause is used when the programmer wants two or more files to share the same storage area.

The **MULTIPLE FILE** clause is used when a single tape reel can contain two or more files in a single program.   Integer-3 and integer-4 specify which **POSITION** the files are in.

Punctuation

Commas and semicolons are shown in the general formats of the environment division.   Wherever you see a comma, it can be used or omitted or replaced by either of the two forms

AND

, AND

All semicolons are optional; they may be included or omitted.

13-11   FORMAT–DATA DIVISION

The data division describes in detail all data that the object program works on or with.   This division consists of several sections, two of which will be covered in this text.

First is the file section, which describes data that enter or leave storage. The data are originally described as a file and then further described in terms of records.

Next is the working-storage section, which describes data items that are originated internally.   The general format follows:

DATA DIVISION

⌈ FILE SECTION.   ⌉
| file-description-entry |
⌊ record-description-entry ⌋

⌈ WORKING-STORAGE SECTION. ⌉
⌊ record-description entry   ⌋

As you can see, each section is optional and can be omitted if not needed.

Each section name begins in margin A.   Its associated entry also begins in margin A.

The file-description entry provides information about the physical structure of a file.   It also identifies the file and provides a means of identifying records that are contained in this file.   The general format for file-description entry follows.

FD file-name [; <u>RECORDING MODE IS</u> mode]

$$\left[; \underline{BLOCK} \text{ CONTAINS [integer-1 } \underline{TO}\text{] integer-2 } \begin{Bmatrix} \underline{RECORDS} \\ \underline{CHARACTERS} \end{Bmatrix} \right]$$

[; <u>RECORD CONTAINS</u> [integer-3 <u>TO</u>] integer-4 CHARACTERS]

$$; \text{ LABEL } \begin{Bmatrix} \underline{RECORDS} \text{ ARE} \\ \underline{RECORD} \text{ IS} \end{Bmatrix} \begin{Bmatrix} \underline{STANDARD} \\ \underline{OMITTED} \\ \text{data-name-1 [, data-name-2] . . .} \end{Bmatrix}$$

$$\left[; \underline{VALUE\ OF} \text{ data-name-3 IS } \begin{Bmatrix} \text{data-name-4} \\ \text{literal-1} \end{Bmatrix} \right.$$

$$\left. \left[, \text{data-name-5 IS } \begin{Bmatrix} \text{data-name-6} \\ \text{literal-2} \end{Bmatrix} \right] \text{ . . .} \right]$$

$$; \underline{DATA} \begin{Bmatrix} \underline{RECORDS} \text{ IS} \\ \underline{RECORDS} \text{ ARE} \end{Bmatrix} \text{ data-name-7 [,data-name-8] . . .}$$

The RECORDING MODE clause is optional and should be used when data formats can vary on external devices.   See implementor's reference manual.

The BLOCK clause is used to define the minimum size (integer-1) and maximum size (integer-2) of a physical record.   If only integer-2 is shown, it refers to the exact size.   The CHARACTERS option refers to the number of characters in the physical record.   RECORDS refers to records with a block.

The RECORD CONTAINS clause specifies the size, in CHARACTERS of a data record.   The information in this clause appears again in the record-description entry (see below).

The LABEL clause must appear in every file-description entry.   It specifies whether labels are present or not.   If present, this clause identifies the label.   This clause is commonly used in conjunction with tape files.

The VALUE OF clause defines a name for an item in a label record.   Label records usually appear at the beginning and end of tape files.

The DATA RECORDS clause provides a means for naming data records within the file named file-name.   The words given by data-name-7 and data-name-8 are referred to as record names since they name data records.

The entire file-description-entry paragraph must be ended with a period, followed by space.   FD always begins in margin A, followed in margin B by its file name and subsequent information. Lines after FD are to begin in margin B. Semicolons are optional to the user.

Record-description entries describe in great detail the records first defined in a file-description entry. They also describe elementary data items originated internally. The full general format for a record-description entry contains many options, some of which should be studied at a later time. For this reason we show a partial general format for a record-description entry.

$$\text{level-number} \begin{Bmatrix} \underline{\text{data-name-1}} \\ \underline{\text{FILLER}} \end{Bmatrix} [;\ \underline{\text{REDEFINES}}\ \text{data-name-2}]$$

$$\begin{Bmatrix} \left[;\ \underline{\text{SIZE}}\ \text{IS}\ \text{integer-1} \begin{Bmatrix} \text{CHARACTERS} \\ \text{DIGITS} \end{Bmatrix} \right] \\ [;\ \underline{\text{PICTURE}}\ \text{IS}\ \text{character-string}] \end{Bmatrix}$$

$$\left[;\ \underline{\text{USAGE}}\ \text{IS} \begin{Bmatrix} \text{COMPUTATIONAL} \\ \text{DISPLAY} \end{Bmatrix} \right]$$

$$\left[;\ \underline{\text{SYNCHRONIZED}} \begin{Bmatrix} \text{LEFT} \\ \text{RIGHT} \end{Bmatrix} \right]$$

$$[;\ \underline{\text{JUSTIFIED}}\ \underline{\text{RIGHT}}]$$

$$[;\ \underline{\text{VALUE}}\ \text{IS}\ \text{literal}]$$

The semicolons are optional to the user. With level numbers we specify the hierarchy of data within a record. Level numbers are also used to identify data items in the working-storage section. The level number 77 is used for this purpose in the working-storage section. Level numbers in the range from 01 to 49 are used in the file section, with 01 used exclusively at the beginning of a hierarchy. Successively higher-level numbers are used to identify subordinate data items within a hierarchy. Although higher-level numbers must be used, they need not be consecutive. Level number 01 thus identifies a record.

When there are no data subordinate to a data item, it is referred to as an *elementary data item*.

The FILLER option is used to name an unused portion of a record. When FILLER is used, the PICTURE clause must be used.

The REDEFINES clause, when used, must immediately follow data-name-1. It is not used with FILLER. This clause permits the same storage area to be used by different data items.

If data-name-1 is an elementary item, then either the SIZE or PICTURE clause must be used.

The SIZE clause specifies the length in characters or digits of an elementary data item.

The PICTURE clause specifies through its character string the length of an elementary data item. Certain combinations of characters in the string determine the category of the elementary item. Its category can be alphabetic (constructed from the letters A to Z), numeric (constructed from the digits 0 to 9 and the signs $+$ or $-$), or alphanumeric (composed of any allowable characters).

The PICTURE clause also allows the programmer to accomplish editing. Editing is a feature whereby the programmer, by using the MOVE statement, can automatically add to or delete characters from an elementary data item. This feature was used in the example of this chapter.

At the risk of opening many doors for criticism, the PICTURE clause will not be discussed further. Many fine descriptions exist in a wide variety of publications, including implementor reference manuals.

The USAGE clause specifies the manner in which a data item is represented in computer storage. With the COMPUTATIONAL or DISPLAY option, the programmer can indicate how the data are to be used.

The SYNCHRONIZED clause specifies how the elementary item is to be positioned within the computer. The LEFT option means that the item will begin at the left boundary of a computer word. The RIGHT option means that the item will terminate at the right boundary of a computer word.

The JUSTIFIED clause, used only with elementary items, specifies how a receiving area should represent data within it. (A receiving area is an area in storage where data are received, for example, the second operand of a MOVE statement.) When the JUSTIFIED clause is used, the following sequence occurs. Assume the receiving area is described with JUSTIFIED RIGHT. If the sent data are larger than the receiving area, the leftmost characters are truncated. If the receiving area is larger, the sent data are stored in the receiving area, with its rightmost characters in the rightmost position of the receiving area. Spaces are filled in on the left.

The VALUE clause allows the programmer to define the initial value of a data item in the WORKING-STORAGE SECTION.

Punctuation

Punctuation in the data division is defined as in the environment division (see p. 447).

13-12 FORMAT–PROCEDURE DIVISION

The general format for the procedure division is shown in Fig. 13-11.

```
PROCEDURE DIVISION
{section-name SECTION            }
{paragraph-name {sentence} . . .}  . . .
```

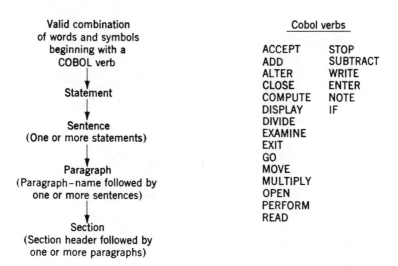

Fig. 13-11 Relationship of terms making up the procedure division.

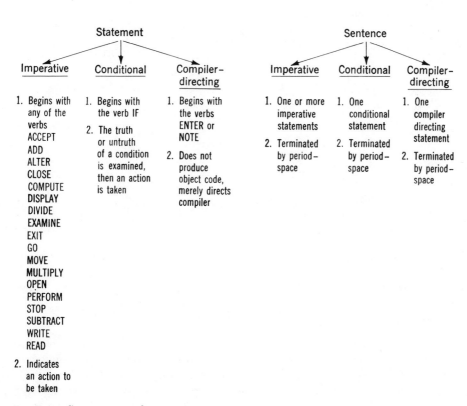

Fig. 13-12 Statements and sentences.

We have previously mentioned section names and paragraph names. (See flowchart boxes 6 to 8, and associated statements. See also Sec. 13.6.) A good way of introducing sentence is given by Fig. 13-11. The first option under PROCEDURE DIVISION is called the *section header*. A sentence always ends with a period followed by a space. Separators (the semicolon or the word THEN) may be used between statements. Sentences and statements are further defined as in Fig. 13-12.

Arithmetic Expressions

An arithmetic expression is a combination of identifiers and literals separated by the arithmetic operators as shown:

Operator	Meaning
+	Addition
—	subtraction
*	multiplication
/	division
**	exponentiation

When used, each operator must be preceded by and followed by a space. A few arithmetic expressions follow:

$$(X + Y) ** 2 \qquad \text{means} \qquad (x + y)^2$$

$$(A + B) / D \qquad \text{means} \qquad \frac{a + b}{d}$$

$$A + B / D \qquad \text{means} \qquad a + \frac{b}{d}$$

The result of an arithmetic expression is always an elementary numeric item.

Conditions

In Fig. 13-12, under conditional statement, the word condition is introduced. In COBOL there are several kinds of conditions, each of which may be true or false; depending on its truth or untruth, different paths (branches) are taken in the program. The three conditions (there are others) that will be discussed here are relation, sign, and class.

the relation condition

The general format for the relation condition is

$$\begin{Bmatrix} \text{identifier-1} \\ \text{literal-1} \\ \text{arithmetic-expression-1} \end{Bmatrix} \begin{matrix} \text{relational-} \\ \text{operator} \end{matrix} \begin{Bmatrix} \text{identifier-2} \\ \text{literal-2} \\ \text{arithmetic-expression-2} \end{Bmatrix}$$

The relational-operator has its own general format:

$$\begin{Bmatrix} \begin{Bmatrix} \text{IS [NOT] GREATER THAN} \\ \text{IS [NOT]} > \end{Bmatrix} \\ \begin{Bmatrix} \text{IS [NOT] LESS THAN} \\ \text{IS [NOT]} < \end{Bmatrix} \\ \begin{Bmatrix} \text{IS [NOT] EQUAL TO} \\ \text{IS [NOT]} = \end{Bmatrix} \end{Bmatrix}$$

Entries to the left and right of the relational-operator are called operands. Certain events occur when the operands are numeric, nonnumeric, equal size, and unequal size. For detailed description of these occurrences the reader is referred to manuals.

the sign condition

The general format for the sign condition is

$$\begin{Bmatrix} \text{identifier} \\ \text{arithmetic-expression} \end{Bmatrix} \text{IS [NOT]} \begin{Bmatrix} \text{POSITIVE} \\ \text{NEGATIVE} \\ \text{ZERO} \end{Bmatrix}$$

the class condition

Here the operand is examined for class NUMERIC or class ALPHABETIC. The general format is

$$\text{identifier IS [NOT]} \begin{Bmatrix} \text{ALPHABETIC} \\ \text{NUMERIC} \end{Bmatrix}$$

ALPHABETIC means consisting entirely of the characters A to Z and space. NUMERIC means consisting entirely of the digits 0 to 9 with or without a sign $(+,-)$.

The general formats of COBOL verbs will now be described.

ACCEPT and DISPLAY

ACCEPT identifier [FROM device-name]

This verb is used when low volumes of data are to be read from the named device. Similarly, the verb DISPLAY is used to write out (or punch out) low volumes of data (like a single piece of data) on a named device. Its general format is

$$\text{DISPLAY} \begin{Bmatrix} \text{literal-1} \\ \text{identifier-1} \end{Bmatrix} \begin{bmatrix} , \text{literal-2} \\ , \text{identifier-2} \end{bmatrix} \ldots$$
[UPON device-name]

ADD

There are several forms of the ADD statement. Each general format is given. The action taken is an addition of two or more operands, the sum being stored.

Form 1

$$\text{ADD} \begin{Bmatrix} \text{identifier-1} \\ \text{literal-1} \end{Bmatrix} \begin{bmatrix} , \text{identifier-2} \\ , \text{literal-2} \end{bmatrix} \ldots \text{TO identifier-3}$$
[ROUNDED][; ON SIZE ERROR imperative-statement]

Form 2

$$\text{ADD} \begin{Bmatrix} \text{identifier-1} \\ \text{literal-1} \end{Bmatrix} \begin{Bmatrix} \text{identifier-2} \\ \text{literal-2} \end{Bmatrix} \begin{bmatrix} , \text{identifier-3} \\ , \text{literal-3} \end{bmatrix} \ldots$$
GIVING identifier-4 [ROUNDED]
[; ON SIZE ERROR imperative statement]

Form 3

ADD CORRESPONDING identifier-1 TO identifier-2 [ROUNDED]
[; ON SIZE ERROR imperative-statement]

In form 1 the values of the operands to the left of TO are added, and the result is added to identifier-3. The final result appears at identifier-3.

In form 2, the values of the operands to the left of GIVING are added together. The result is stored as the new value of identifier-4.

In form 3, data items in a hierarchy are added to and stored in corresponding data items of a different hierarchy.

In all forms each operand cannot exceed 18 decimal digits and all literals must be numeric.

In forms 1 and 2 all identifiers must be elementary numeric items.

The COBOL compiler normally truncates if a result has decimal places greater than the number of decimal places allowed for that result. However, if ROUNDED is specified, rounding occurs instead of truncation.

The SIZE ERROR option provides a path to take if a result exceeds the largest value that can be contained in storage provided for that result.

The SUBTRACT verb is next.

SUBTRACT

Form 1

SUBTRACT $\begin{Bmatrix} \text{identifier-1} \\ \text{literal-1} \end{Bmatrix} \begin{bmatrix} , & \text{identifier-2} \\ , & \text{literal-2} \end{bmatrix}$ . . . FROM identifier-3 [ROUNDED]

[; ON SIZE ERROR imperative-statement]

Form 2

SUBTRACT $\begin{Bmatrix} \text{literal-1} \\ \text{identifier-1} \end{Bmatrix} \begin{bmatrix} , & \text{literal-2} \\ , & \text{identifier-2} \end{bmatrix}$ . . . FROM $\begin{Bmatrix} \text{literal-3} \\ \text{identifier-3} \end{Bmatrix}$

GIVING identifier-4 [ROUNDED]

[; ON SIZE ERROR imperative-statement]

Form 3

SUBTRACT CORRESPONDING identifier-1 FROM identifier-2 [ROUNDED]

[; ON SIZE ERROR imperative-statement]

In form 1 all operands preceding FROM are added together, and this sum is subtracted from identifier-3.

In form 2 all operands to the left of FROM are added. The sum is subtracted from literal-3 or identifier-3. The result is stored as the new value of identifier-4.

In form 3 items in hierarchy defined by identifier-1 are subtracted from and stored in corresponding items in the hierarchy defined by identifier-2.

The ROUNDED and SIZE ERROR options hold as in the ADD statement. Sizes of literals and identifier are defined as in the ADD also.

The MULTIPLY statement is next.

MULTIPLY

Form 1

$$\underline{\text{MULTIPLY}} \begin{Bmatrix} \text{identifier-1} \\ \text{literal-1} \end{Bmatrix} \underline{\text{BY}}\ \text{identifier-2} \ [\underline{\text{ROUNDED}}]$$
$$[;\ \text{ON} \ \underline{\text{SIZE}} \ \underline{\text{ERROR}} \ \text{imperative-statement}]$$

Form 2

$$\underline{\text{MULTIPLY}} \begin{Bmatrix} \text{identifier-1} \\ \text{literal-1} \end{Bmatrix} \underline{\text{BY}} \begin{Bmatrix} \text{identifier-2} \\ \text{literal-2} \end{Bmatrix} \underline{\text{GIVING}}\ \text{identifier-3} \ [\underline{\text{ROUNDED}}]$$
$$[;\ \text{ON} \ \underline{\text{SIZE}} \ \underline{\text{ERROR}} \ \text{imperative-statement}]$$

In form 1 the product appears at identifier-2. For size of operands, ROUNDED, and SIZE ERROR, see the ADD statement.

Finally, we have the DIVIDE verb.

DIVIDE

Form 1

$$\underline{\text{DIVIDE}} \begin{Bmatrix} \text{identifier-1} \\ \text{literal-1} \end{Bmatrix} \underline{\text{INTO}}\ \text{identifier-2} \ [\underline{\text{ROUNDED}}]$$

Form 2

$$\underline{\text{DIVIDE}} \begin{Bmatrix} \text{identifier-1} \\ \text{literal-1} \end{Bmatrix} \underline{\text{INTO}} \begin{Bmatrix} \text{identifier-2} \\ \text{literal-2} \end{Bmatrix} \underline{\text{GIVING}}\ \text{identifier-3} \ [\underline{\text{ROUNDED}}]$$

Form 3

$$\underline{\text{DIVIDE}} \begin{Bmatrix} \text{identifier-1} \\ \text{literal-1} \end{Bmatrix} \underline{\text{BY}} \begin{Bmatrix} \text{identifier-2} \\ \text{literal-2} \end{Bmatrix} \underline{\text{GIVING}}\ \text{identifier-3} \ [\underline{\text{ROUNDED}}]$$

The ON SIZE ERROR option can appear in all forms. It was omitted for brevity. In form 1 the quotient appears at identifier-2.

COMPUTE

With the COMPUTE statement certain more elaborate arithmetic may be performed.

<u>COMPUTE</u> identifier-1 [ROUNDED] EQUALS

$\left\{\begin{array}{l}\text{literal}\\\text{identifier-2}\\\text{arithmetic-expression}\end{array}\right\}$ [; ON <u>SIZE</u> <u>ERROR</u> imperative-statement]

The word EQUALS may be replaced by the equal sign =. Identifier-1 assumes the value of the operand to the right of EQUALS.

Example

COMPUTE INC-TX = 21

is equivalent to

MOVE 21 TO INC-TX

ALTER

The ALTER statement allows the programmer to alter (or change) a certain sequence of operations. It changes the direction of an already coded GO TO statement.

<u>ALTER</u> procedure-name-1 <u>TO</u> <u>PROCEED</u> TO procedure-name-2
[, procedure-name-3 <u>TO</u> <u>PROCEED</u> TO procedure-name-4] . . .

When the ALTER statement is executed, the GO TO statements in paragraphs named procedure-name-1, procedure-name-3 is changed. Internally, the GO TO statements are modified to GO TO procedure-name-2, GO TO procedure-name-4.

The following rules apply to the procedure names.

Procedure-name-1, procedure-name-3, . . . are paragraph names. Each paragraph contains only one sentence: a GO TO procedure-name.

Procedure-name-2, procedure-name-4, . . . are paragraph names or section names.

Example

```
STRT. _____
CHK. GO TO TEMP.

TEMP. _____

      ALTER CHK TO PROCEED TO WRAP-UP
      GO TO STRT.
WRAP-UP. _____
```

In the example, the first time the GO TO in CHK is executed, a branch will be made to TEMP.   The second time the GO TO in CHK is executed, a branch will be made to WRAP-UP.

CLOSE

The CLOSE statement terminates the processing of input and output data with respect to the mediums (tapes, disks, cards, printed page) on which they reside.

$$
\text{CLOSE file-name-1} \begin{bmatrix} \text{REEL} \\ \overline{\text{UNIT}} \end{bmatrix} \text{WITH} \begin{Bmatrix} \text{NO REWIND} \\ \overline{\text{LOCK}} \end{Bmatrix}
$$

$$
\begin{bmatrix} \text{, file-name-2} \begin{bmatrix} \text{REEL} \\ \overline{\text{UNIT}} \end{bmatrix} \begin{bmatrix} \text{WITH} \begin{Bmatrix} \text{NO REWIND} \\ \overline{\text{LOCK}} \end{Bmatrix} \end{bmatrix} \end{bmatrix} \; . \; . \; .
$$

The CLOSE statement will apply to files with names file-name-1, file-name-2, ...

UNIT will be defined by each implementor.   REEL and WITH NO REWIND apply only to files that reside on tape.

Certain events occur when the CLOSE statement is executed.   The events depend on the medium involved and the type of data representation on that medium.   Dependent also is the type of file (input or output or both).

The reader is referred to implementor manuals for details.

EXAMINE

The EXAMINE statement causes the program to count (when TALLYING is used) the number of times a character is used.   It can also replace (when REPLACING is used) the number of times by another character.

$$
\text{EXAMINE identifier} \begin{Bmatrix} \text{TALLYING} \begin{Bmatrix} \text{UNTIL FIRST} \\ \overline{\text{ALL}} \\ \overline{\text{LEADING}} \end{Bmatrix} \text{literal-1} \begin{bmatrix} \text{REPLACING BY} \\ \text{literal-2} \end{bmatrix} \\ \text{REPLACING} \begin{Bmatrix} \text{ALL} \\ \overline{\text{LEADING}} \\ \overline{\text{UNTIL FIRST}} \end{Bmatrix} \text{literal-3 BY literal-4} \end{Bmatrix}
$$

The identifier must always be a DISPLAY item.   Each character of identifier is examined, and actions are taken, depending on which option (TALLYING or REPLACING) is used.   Each literal above may be a figurative constant (like ZERO or BLANK).   The count created by the use of TALLYING is held in a special storage location called TALLY.

Example

EXAMINE PART-NO REPLACING LEADING ZEROS BY BLANKS.
    Before EXAMINE   After EXAMINE. b = Blank
    PART-NO. 0022646   PART-NO. bb22646

EXIT

This verb acts as an exit point for a subroutine. A subroutine in COBOL is a section or a paragraph.

    EXIT is always preceded by a paragraph name. Furthermore, EXIT always appears as a sentence by itself.

paragraph-name EXIT.

GO TO

This statement causes a "branch" to another part of the procedure division.

Form 1

GO TO [procedure-name]

Form 2

GO TO procedure-name-1 [, procedure-name-2] . . . , [procedure-name-n]
    DEPENDING ON identifier

    Form 1 with a procedure name causes a familiar "branch." When an ALTER statement appears in a program, then the GO TO being altered has the first form, without procedure name but with a preceding paragraph name.

    When form 2 is used, the branch occurs to procedure-name-1, procedure-name-2, . . . , procedure-name-n, if the value of identifier is 1, 2, . . . , n. If identifier is none of these values, the GO TO has no effect.

MOVE

The MOVE statement causes a movement of data from a storage area to one or more storage areas.

$$\text{MOVE [CORRESPONDING]} \begin{Bmatrix} \text{identifier-1} \\ \text{literal} \end{Bmatrix} \text{TO \{identifier-2\} . . .}$$

The operands to the left of TO (identifier-1 or literal) are referred to as the sending area, while to the right of TO we have operands representing the receiving area.

Example

```
01  EMPLOYEE-NO
    02   ID PICTURE 999
    02   DIV PICTURE 99
    02   DEPT PICTURE 99
    02   SECN PICTURE 99
01  NEW-EMPLOYEE-NO
    02   ID PICTURE 999
    02   DIV PICTURE 99
    02   DEPT PICTURE 99
    02   SECN PICTURE 99
MOVE CORRESPONDING NEW-EMPLOYEE-NO TO EMPLOYEE-NO.
```

Before move in storage	After move in storage
ID 678	ID 527
DIV 07	DIV 26
DEPT 72	DEPT 63
SECN 29	SECN 17
ID 527	ID 527
DIV 26	DIV 26
DEPT 63	DEPT 63
SECN 17	SECN 17

Certain moves are "illegal." For example, a numeric item must not be moved to an alphabetic receiving area. Check the implementor reference manual.

OPEN

The OPEN statement initiates certain setup operations of input and output files. The OPEN statement does not accomplish the reading or writing of a data record. This is done by the READ or WRITE statement. However, OPEN must be executed before the first READ or WRITE statement for a file.

$$\text{OPEN} \left[\text{INPUT} \left\{ \text{file-name} \begin{bmatrix} \text{REVERSED} \\ \text{WITH } \underline{\text{NO}} \text{ REWIND} \end{bmatrix} \right\} \cdots \right]$$

$$[\text{OUTPUT} \{ \text{file-name} [\text{WITH } \underline{\text{NO}} \text{ REWIND}] \} \cdots]$$

The REVERSED and NO REWIND options are used when files reside on tape. Assume a file of records resides on a tape. When neither REVERSED nor NO REWIND appears, the OPEN statement causes the tape to be positioned at its beginning.

When REVERSED appears, the programmer must make sure the tape is positioned at the end of the file. A subsequent READ statement causes the file to be read in reverse order.

When NO REWIND is specified, the tape must be positioned at the beginning of the file.

A second OPEN statement for a specific file cannot be executed before the execution of a CLOSE statement for that file.

Example

Legal
OPEN INPUT TAX-FILE.
READ TAX-FILE.
READ TAX-FILE.
CLOSE TAX-FILE.
OPEN TAX-FILE.

Illegal
OPEN INPUT TAX-FILE
READ TAX-FILE
READ TAX-FILE
OPEN TAX-FILE
CLOSE TAX-FILE

PERFORM

With the PERFORM statement, a programmer can execute one or more procedures a specified number of times. He can also execute these procedures until a specific condition is satisfied. When the procedures have been properly executed, control is returned automatically to the normal sequence of execution.

One form of the PERFORM is similar to the notion of subroutine in FORTRAN. Another form is similar to the notion of looping in FORTRAN.

Form 1

PERFORM procedure-name-1 [THRU procedure-name-2]

Usually, the PERFORM statement appears in the normal sequence of operations. When it is executed, control is transferred to the first statement of procedure-name-1. There is an automatic return to the statement following the PER-FORM. The procedure names can be paragraph names or section names. If procedure-name-2 is specified, all statements within it are executed prior to the return.

Form 2

PERFORM procedure-name-1 [THRU procedure-name-2]

$$\begin{Bmatrix} \text{identifier-1} \\ \text{integer-1} \end{Bmatrix} \text{ TIMES}$$

In form 2, the procedures referred to are executed a number of times. That number is given by identifier-1 or integer-1. It must be a nonnegative integer.

Form 3

PERFORM procedure-name-1 [THRU procedure-name-2] UNTIL condition

In form 3, the procedures referred to are executed until the condition specified in the PERFORM statement becomes true.

Form 4

PERFORM procedure-name-1 [THRU procedure-name-2]

$$\text{VARYING identifier-1 FROM} \begin{Bmatrix} \text{literal-1} \\ \text{identifier-2} \end{Bmatrix}$$

$$\text{BY} \begin{Bmatrix} \text{literal-2} \\ \text{identifier-3} \end{Bmatrix} \text{UNTIL condition}$$

In form 4, identifier-1 begins at a certain starting value. That value is given by literal-1 or identifier-2. The condition is then examined. If false, the procedures referred to are executed once. Then identifier-1 is incremented by literal-2 or identifier-3, and the condition is examined again. This cycle continues until the condition is true. When true, control is returned to the statement after PERFORM. If the condition was true to begin with, the procedures are not executed.

The following comments refer to all forms. In the referred procedures, certain statements (like GO TO or another PERFORM) might appear which would take us out of the referred procedures before their normal conclusion. In this case, procedure-name-2 should be a paragraph name. The paragraph should consist solely of an EXIT statement.

Some examples of PERFORM statements are

```
PERFORM TAX-ROUTINE.
PERFORM TAX-ROUTINE 5 TIMES.
PERFORM WRITE-OUT UNTIL LINE-COUNT EQUALS ZERO.
PERFORM GROSS-PAY VARYING ID-NO FROM DEPT-NO BY
    ONE UNTIL CARD-COUNT EQUALS ZERO.
```

STOP

The STOP statement halts the object program either permanently or temporarily.

$$\underline{\text{STOP}} \begin{Bmatrix} \text{literal} \\ \underline{\text{RUN}} \end{Bmatrix}$$

When RUN is used, an implementor-defined ending procedure is called in. When literal is used, this literal is displayed on an output device, and the program continues execution.

READ

The READ statement makes *available* the next logical record from an input file. When end of file is detected, a specified imperative statement can be executed.

$$\underline{\text{READ}} \text{ file-name RECORD } [\underline{\text{INTO}} \text{ identifier}]$$
$$; \text{ AT } \underline{\text{END}} \text{ imperative-statement}$$

An OPEN statement must be executed before the first READ statement for a file.

If the last record has been read and another READ is attempted, the imperative statement is executed.

When a file is made up of more than one record, these records automatically share the same storage area.

It is important to keep in mind that after the execution of the imperative statement, the file must be CLOSED, followed by OPEN again, before a READ for that file is given.

WRITE

The WRITE statement releases a logical record to an output medium. It can also be used for page and line positioning when the output device is a printer.

$$\underline{\text{WRITE}} \text{ record-name } [\underline{\text{FROM}} \text{ identifier-1}]$$
$$\left[\begin{Bmatrix} \underline{\text{BEFORE}} \\ \underline{\text{AFTER}} \end{Bmatrix} \text{ ADVANCING } \begin{Bmatrix} \text{identifier-2} \\ \text{integer} \end{Bmatrix} \text{ LINES} \right]$$

Note that the WRITE statement requires a record name, not a file name. Of course, the record named is part of a file defined in the file section of the data division.

An OPEN statement for the file containing the record name must have been executed before any WRITE statement for that file.

The ADVANCING option allows the programmer to control vertical page and line positioning.

IF

The IF statement causes a condition to be evaluated. The subsequent action of the object program depends on whether the value of the condition is true or false.

$$\text{IF condition} \begin{bmatrix} \text{THEN} \\ ; \end{bmatrix} \begin{Bmatrix} \text{statement-1} \\ \text{NEXT SENTENCE} \end{Bmatrix}$$

$$\begin{bmatrix} \text{THEN} \\ ; \end{bmatrix} \begin{Bmatrix} \text{OTHERWISE} \\ \text{ELSE} \end{Bmatrix} \begin{Bmatrix} \text{statement-2} \\ \text{NEXT SENTENCE} \end{Bmatrix}$$

If the condition is true, statement-1 is executed. If false, the sentence after IF is executed when ELSE is omitted. When ELSE is present, statement-2 is executed.

When NEXT SENTENCE is used, control always passes to the next sentence after IF, regardless of the condition.

ENTER

This statement allows the programmer to use another language in his program, provided the implementor has made provisions for it.

ENTER language-name [routine-name]

The implementors will specify the details on how the other language is to be written.

NOTE

NOTE character-string

This sentence allows the programmer to write comments. The comments will appear on the source program printout, but will not be compiled.

The comments always end with a period followed by a space.

13-13 PUNCTUATION

A comma shown in any of the formats above may be replaced by either of the two forms

AND
, AND

Also, a semicolon can be used between statements.

APPENDIX

COBOL Reserved Words

ABOUT
ACCEPT
ACCESS
ACTUAL
ADD
ADDRESS
ADVANCING
AFTER
ALL
ALPHABETIC
ALPHANUMERIC
ALTER
ALTERNATE
AN
AND
APPLY
ARE
AREA
AREAS
ASCENDING
ASSIGN
AT
AUTHOR

BEFORE
BEGINNING
BITS
BLANK
BLOCK
BY

CF
CH
CHARACTERS
CHECK
CLASS
CLOCK-UNITS
CLOSE
COBOL
CODE
COLUMN
COMMA
COMPUTATIONAL
COMPUTE
CONSTANT
CONFIGURATION
CONTAINS
CONTROL
CONTROLS
CONVERSION
COPY

CORRESPONDING
CURRENCY

DATA
DATE-COMPILED
DATE-WRITTEN
DE
DECIMAL-POINT
DECLARATIVES
DEFINE
DEPENDING
DESCENDING
DETAIL
DIGITS
DISPLAY
DIVIDE
DIVIDED
DIVISION
DOLLAR
DOWN

ELSE
END
ENDING
ENTER
ENVIRONMENT
EQUAL
EQUALS
ERROR
EVERY
EXAMINE
EXCEEDS
EXIT
EXPONENTIATED

FD
FILE
FILE-CONTROL
FILE-LIMIT
FILE-LIMITS
FILLER
FINAL
FIRST
FLOAT
FOOTING
FOR
FORMAT
FROM

GENERATE
GIVING
GO

GREATER
GROUP

HASHED
HEADING
HIGH-VALUE
HIGH-VALUES
HOLD

I-O
I-O-CONTROL
IDENTIFICATION
IF
IN
INCLUDE
INDEX
INDEXED
INDICATE
INITIATE
INPUT
INPUT-OUTPUT
INSTALLATION
INTO
INVALID
IS

JUSTIFIED

KEY
KEYS

LABEL
LAST
LEADING
LEAVING
LEFT
LESS
LIBRARY
LIMIT
LIMITS
LINE
LINE-COUNTER
LINES
LOCATION
LOCK
LOW-VALUE
LOW-VALUES
LOWER-BOUND
LOWER-BOUNDS

MEMORY
MINUS

MODE	QUOTE	SOURCE
MODULES	QUOTES	SOURCE-COMPUTER
MOVE		SPACE
MULTIPLE	RANDOM	SPACES
MULTIPLIED	RANGE	SPECIAL-NAMES
MULTIPLY	RD	STANDARD
	READ	STATUS
NEGATIVE	RECORD	STOP
NEXT	RECORDING	SUBTRACT
NO	RECORDS	SUM
NOT	REDEFINES	SUPERVISOR
NOTE	REEL	SUPPRESS
NUMBER	RELEASE	SYMBOLIC
NUMERIC	REMARKS	SYNCHRONIZED
	RENAMES	
OBJECT-COMPUTER	RENAMING	TALLY
OBJECT-PROGRAM	REPLACING	TALLYING
OCCURS	REPORT	TAPE
OF	REPORTING	TERMINATE
OFF	REPORTS	THAN
OH	RERUN	THEN
OMITTED	RESERVE	THROUGH ⎫ Equivalent
ON	RESET	THRU ⎭
OPEN	RETURN	TIMES
OPTIONAL	REVERSED	TO
OR	REWIND	TYPE
OTHERWISE	RF	
OUTPUT	RH	UNEQUAL
OV	RIGHT	UNIT
OVERFLOW	ROUNDED	UNTIL
	RUN	UP
PAGE		UPON
PAGE-COUNTER	SA	UPPER-BOUND
PERFORM	SAME	UPPER-BOUNDS
PF	SD	USAGE
PH	SEARCH	USE
PICTURE	SECTION	USING
PLACES	SECURITY	
PLUS	SEEK	VALUE
POINT	SEGMENT-LIMIT	VALUES
POSITION	SELECT	VARYING
POSITIVE	SELECTED	
PREPARED	SENTENCE	WHEN
PRIORITY	SEQUENCED	WITH
PROCEDURE	SEQUENTIAL	WORDS
PROCEED	SET	WORKING-STORAGE
PROCESS	SIGN	WRITE
PROCESSING	SIGNED	
PROGRAM-ID	SIZE	ZERO
PROTECT	SORT	ZEROES
		ZEROS

Note: Of course, the list to become familiar with is the one that appears in the manuals put out by your implementor.

EXERCISES

13-1.   How many divisions appear in a COBOL program?   Name them.

13-2.   Name the characters that can be combined to form a COBOL word. Construct 10 COBOL words.

13-3.   Name the divisions that are machine-dependent.

13-4.   a.   Define elementary item.   From your definition are the following elementary items: b.   Social Security number; c.   zip code 60616?

13-5.   Are these valid data names?

    a.   67425   b.   CHERRY-PINK
    c.   ZERO   d.   Z5
    e.   SECONDARY-THERMOSTATIC-   f.   ONE-HUNDRED-
        TRANSFORMER

13-6.   Are these valid procedure names?

    a.   67425   b.   ZERO
    c.   CHERRY-PINK   d.   TWELVE
    e.   THIRTEEN-   f.   -FOUR

13-7.   Are these valid nonnumeric literals?

    a.   'THIRTEEN'
    b.   'ZERO'
    c.   'SECONDARY-THERMOSTATIC-TRANSFORMER'
    d.   '12-24-48A

13-8.   Are these valid numeric literals?

    a.   1   b.   —24.65
    c.   200—   d.   306A
    e.   16.   f.   SEVEN

13-9.   Replace box 14 by an equivalent box.

13-10.   Are these valid?

    a.   PROCEDUREDIVISION
    b.   WORKING STORAGE SECTION
    c.   I/O SECTION
    d.   I/O CONTROL
    e.   DATA DIVISION

13-11.   Answer true or false (T or F).

    a.   All data names must be spelled uniquely in a source program.

    b.   A hyphen must always be used in column 7 to indicate continuation.

    c.   Paragraph names always start in margin B.

    d.   Alphabetic level indicators begin in margin A.

    e.   Record-description entries always begin with an 01 level number.

    f.   The record name associated with an 01 level number begins in margin B.

13-12.   a.   Assume that FINAL is a paragraph name in the TAX SECTION of a PROCEDURE DIVISION.   Can FINAL be a paragraph name in the PAY SECTION of that same PROCEDURE DIVISION?

    b.   If the programmer desired to branch to FINAL in the TAX SECTION while the program was executing in the PAY SECTION, would the following statement accomplish the branch?

GO TO FINAL IN TAX SECTION.

    c.   Can there be two paragraphs named FINAL in the TAX SECTION?

13-13.   a.   State the optional entries that may appear in the identification division.

    b.   In the environment division, state the mandatory paragraphs that must appear in the configuration section; the input-output section.

13-14.   Answer true or false.

    a.   The data-division file section describes external data.

    b.   The data-division working-storage section describes data originated internally.

    c.   The environment-division file-control paragraph assigns hardware devices.

    d.   FILE SECTION and WORKING-STORAGE SECTION each must appear on a line by itself.

    e.   A file-description entry always begins with the level number 01.

13-15.   Name the three kinds of sentences.

13-16.   Assume two storage locations hold DEPT. If DEPT has the value 92:

    a.   What effect would the following statement have?   ADD 6 TO DEPT; ON SIZE ERROR GO TO REDO.   MOVE A TO B.

    b.   What effect would the following statement have?   ADD 16 TO DEPT; ON SIZE ERROR GO TO REDO.   MOVE A TO B.

ANSWERS TO SELECTED EXERCISES

CHAPTER 2

1a. Literals: A, h
   Explicit real number: 2
b. Literals: x, a, b
   Explicit real numbers: none
e. Literals: none
   Explicit real numbers: 10, 20, 10

3b. $15\frac{1}{2}$
d. $-6x + 6y$
f. $101\frac{1}{75}$
h. $11\frac{1}{3}$
j. 682

4a. 2
c. $\frac{1}{2}$
e. $-6\frac{1}{7}$

5b. Equal
c. Not equal
d. Equal

6a. Not prime
b. Prime
d. Not prime
j. Not prime

7a. 9
b. 9
c. $\frac{1}{4}$
d. 1

8a. $7\frac{1}{105}$
b. $37\frac{1}{30}$
c. $\frac{7}{10}$

11a. $q = 2 \qquad r = 0$
c. $q = -3 \qquad r = 0$
e. $q = 1 \qquad r = 14$

12a. $\frac{3}{7} < \frac{5}{8}$
   $-\frac{2}{3} < \frac{3}{2}$
b. $a^2 > a$
c. $a^2 < a$

14a. a
b. 279,936
c. 262,144
e. $\frac{1}{5}$

15a. x^3/y
b. xy^2z^3
d. $5x^2y^2$

469

16a. 11
  b. 74
  c. 8
  d. 651
  f. 196
  k. 18,852

17. No, because 6 is not a base 5 number

18a. 1.5×10^{-5}
  b. 9.3×10^{7}

20. Rounded: Truncated:
  a. 0.464   0.463
  c. 0.001   0.000

23a. 0.3314×10^{3}
  d. For a) 0.017% when truncation is used
          0.013% when rounding is used

24a. 0.0263×10^{3}
     0.0000982×10^{3}
  b. 0.7655×10^{0}

28a. $\pm \frac{1}{2}$
  d. ± 11

29a. 0.2
  c. 0.16

30b. $(x^2 + yz + y^3)\sqrt[3]{y}$

  c. $\left(\dfrac{1+a}{b}\right)\sqrt{\dfrac{a}{b}}$

33a. $-3 = \log_5 \frac{1}{125}$
  b. $4 = \log_3 81$
  g. $\frac{2}{3} = \log_{27} 9$

34b. $\frac{1}{10} = 10^{-1}$
  c. $64 = 8^2$

37a. -5
  b. -4
  f. 0
  k. 5

38a. $a(1-b)$
  b. $-3b$
  c. $c(a+b)$
  d. $4(5x+3)$
  e. $\frac{1}{8}$
  f. $19b - 3a + 5$

39a. $(x-y) + (4a-b)$
  b. $-(-x+y-2a)$

41c. $6\frac{7}{8}$
  e. 90

CHAPTER 3

1a. $7x^2 - 33x - 10$
  b. $36x^4 - 1$
  c. $6a^2x^2 + 3a^2x + 2ax^2 - 12ax + 4a - 7x - 28$
  f. $a^2 - b^2$
  g. $a^4 - 2a^2b^2 + b^4$

3b. $f(c) = ac^2 + bc + c$
  c. $G\left(\dfrac{1}{x}\right) = \dfrac{1+4x}{1-2x}$ $G(0) = -2$
     $G(4) = 4$
  d. $F[H(x)] = 7x + 7$
  f. $2xh + h^2 - h$
  g. $\dfrac{1}{g(x)} = \dfrac{x+1}{x-1}$

5. $g(x-2) = 2x - 1$
   $g(x^2 + 1) = 2x^2 + 5$

7a. $z(x-y)^2$
  b. $-4y(x+y)[x^2 + (x+2y)^2]$
  d. $(\frac{1}{4} + b^2)(\frac{1}{2} - b)(\frac{1}{2} + b)$
  f. $bx(12b^2x - 75z^2)$

8a. $x[x(3x-4) - 2] + 5$

9a. $x^3 - x^2 + 11x - 5$ degree 3

10a. $x = \frac{3}{7}$
  c. $x = 32$
  d. $x = 6$
  e. $x = 5$
  f. $x = -3\frac{9}{5}$

11a. $\dfrac{11x + y}{36}$
  b. 0
  d. $\dfrac{a^2 + 8a - 4}{a(a^2 - 4)}$

12. 16, 17

13. 12

17a. $6x^2 - 6x - 6$ $a = 6,$
       $b = -6,$ $c = -6$
  c. $2x^2 - 2x - 2$ $a = 2,$
       $b = -2,$ $c = -2$

18a. $x = \pm 4$
  b. $x = \pm 2\sqrt{2}$

19a. $x^2 + 8x + 16$

20a. $x_1 = 4$ $x_2 = -16$
b. $x_1 = 1$ $x_2 = -5$

21a. $(x - 6)(x - 4)$
b. $(3x - 2)(2x - 3)$
d. $(7x + 4)(7x + 11)$

22b. $x_1 = 4$ $x_2 = 1$
c. $x_1 = 8$ $x_2 = -2$
f. $y_1 = 2$ $y_2 = -1$

23a. $x = 3$
b. $x = 2$ and $x = 1$

24a. Roots imaginary
b. Roots real and unequal
$x_1 = \frac{1}{4}$ $x_2 = 1$

27. 10, 12, 14

31a. x intercept $(10, 0)$
y intercept $(0, 5)$

33a. Minimum $(2, -5)$
b. Minimum $(3, -4)$
c. Maximum $(1, 9)$

CHAPTER 4

8. $C = 325.00$ $A = 425.00$

9. $S = 430$ $L = 110$

10a. $a = 3$ $b = 1$
b. $a = 2$ $b = 1$
d. $x = 2.75$ $y = 2.25$

14a. Inconsistent
c. Dependent

16. $m = \frac{5}{4}$ $b = \frac{15}{4}$

18a. 69
c. -18
d. 82
e. -7

20a. $k = 6$
b. Any $k \neq 6$

21a. $m = -2$ $n = -18$
b. -2 any $n \neq -18$
c. any $m \neq -2$ any n

22a. 4 is a factor of all elements of column 3 in the matrix at left.

23a. $x = -\frac{27}{28}$ $y = -\frac{123}{28}$
$z = \frac{25}{28}$
b. $x = 1$ $y = 1$ $z = 1$

CHAPTER 5

1a. $\begin{bmatrix} 6 & -4 & 3 \\ 1 & .5 & -10 \\ 13 & -\frac{3}{2} & 1 \end{bmatrix}$ $\begin{bmatrix} 1 & 2 & 3 & 0 \\ 0 & 1 & 2 & 3 \\ 1 & 0 & 2 & 3 \\ 0 & -2 & 1 & 3 \end{bmatrix}$

b. $\begin{bmatrix} 7 \\ 1 \\ 0 \end{bmatrix}$ $\begin{bmatrix} 1 \\ -1 \\ 1 \\ 1 \end{bmatrix}$

3. Rank $A = 1$
rank $B = 2$
rank $C = 2$

6a. $\begin{bmatrix} 1 & 9 \\ 2 & 6 \\ 15 & -8 \end{bmatrix}$

b. $\begin{bmatrix} 5 & -5 \\ -4 & 4 \\ -3 & 10 \end{bmatrix}$

c. Same as a.
d. $\begin{bmatrix} -5 & 5 \\ 4 & -4 \\ 3 & -10 \end{bmatrix}$

g. The 3×2 zero matrix

7a. Not possible
b. Not possible
c. Possible
d. Not possible
e. Possible
f. Possible
g. Possible
h. Not possible

8. $x = 10$ $y = 10$ $z = 5$

11b. $\begin{bmatrix} 1 & 0 & 0 & 0 \\ 0 & 1 & 0 & 0 \\ 0 & 0 & 1 & 0 \\ 0 & 0 & 0 & 1 \end{bmatrix}$

d. 1
e. $C = \begin{bmatrix} 2 & -5 \\ -3 & 6 \\ 4 & -8 \end{bmatrix}$ $E = \begin{bmatrix} 4 \\ -5 \\ 9 \end{bmatrix}$

12. For matrix A $\begin{bmatrix} -47 & -5 & -11 \\ 46 & -10 & -2 \\ -7 & -5 & 9 \end{bmatrix}$

13.
$$A^{-1} = \begin{bmatrix} .47 & -.46 & .07 \\ .05 & .1 & .05 \\ .11 & .02 & -.09 \end{bmatrix}$$

16. 4 by 3; if E is n by m and F is m by p, then product is n by p.

17a.
$$\begin{bmatrix} 1 & \frac{1}{2} & \frac{1}{3} \\ \frac{1}{2} & \frac{1}{3} & \frac{1}{4} \\ \frac{1}{3} & \frac{1}{4} & \frac{1}{5} \end{bmatrix}$$

18a. Only A is symmetrical

20. $w = 50 \qquad o = 20 \qquad c = 30$

CHAPTER 6

1a. $\dfrac{2n + 1}{2^n} \qquad n = 0, 1, \ldots$

c. $(-1)^{n-1} \dfrac{n + 1}{n} \qquad n = 1, \ldots$

2.
a_0	a_1	a_2	a_3	a_4	a_5
1	2	6	24	60	168

3a. $a_n = 10 - (n - 1)4$
 b. $a_n = a_{n-1} + d$

4a. $a_n = 50(\frac{1}{2})^{n-1} \qquad n = 1, 2, \ldots$
 c. $a_n = 10^{n-1} \qquad n = 1, 2, \ldots$

6a. $S_{11} = 66$
 b. $k(k + 1) = S_k$

8a. 111.56662
 b. $S_n = \dfrac{1 - (1 + r)^n}{1 - (1 + r)}$

10a. $1\frac{4}{9}$
 b. $2\frac{1}{99}$
 c. $\frac{1}{3}$
 d. $\frac{1}{30}$

13a. 10100

16a. 01001
 b. 10010100
 c. $-.000101$

18a. $2^7 - 1 \qquad -2^7$
 b. $2^{n-1} - 1 \qquad -2^{n-1}$

20.
	F	E
a.	01010000	0011
b.	01000000	1101
c.	10110000	0011
d.	11111110	0000

e. 01000000   0101
f. 01111100   0101
g. 01000000   0001
h. 11000000   0001

21a. Not correct
 b. Yes
 c. Six bits cannot hold -35

23b. 3567_8

24b. No; it is -2^8
 c. 400_8

26a. $1EF6_{16} \qquad 17366_8$ fourth number

28c. 17777_8

29. $F, E, D, C, B, A, 9, 8$

30a. .110101
 b. .010111

CHAPTER 7

1a. Professors are absent-minded and students are lazy.
 b. It is the case that either professors are absent-minded or students are lazy, and librarians dislike noise.
 c. Either it is the case that either professors are not absent-minded or librarians dislike noise, or students are not lazy.
 d. It is the case that either students are not lazy or professors are not absent-minded, and librarians do not dislike noise.
 e. Librarians dislike noise and students are not lazy.
 f. Professors are not absent-minded, and either students are not lazy or librarians dislike noise.

2. p: Boating is a safe sport.
 q: Many people are foolish.
 r: October is too hot.
 s: October is too cold.
 t: Indian summer is late.
 a) $p \lor q$ b) $\sim(p \lor q)$
 c) $\sim r \lor \sim s$ d) $(\sim r \lor \sim s) \lor t$

4a. If I study the material for my course then I understand the material for my course.

d. If I do not understand the material for my course then I will not pass my course.

5. *p*: I step on the accelerator.
   q: I stop the car.
   r: I step on the brake.
   a. $p \rightarrow \sim q$
   e. $r \rightarrow \sim p$
   g. $(\sim(\sim r \rightarrow p)) \wedge (\sim(\sim p \rightarrow r))$

7a. $A = \{x:(x = n^2) \wedge (1 \leq n \leq 5)\}$ (*n* is a natural number)

d. $D = \{x:(x = n^3) \text{ and } (1 \leq n \leq 5)\}$ (*n* is a natural number)

9c. $A + B = (A - B) \cup (B - A)$ (defn.)
    $B + A = (B - A) \cup (A - B)$ (defn.)
    $(B - A) \cup (A - B) = (A - B) \cup (B - A)$ (commutative law, see Chapter 8) $\therefore B + A = A + B$

12b. $A \cap B$ is the solution to the system of equations
$$2y - x = 3$$
$$y + 2x = 9$$

CHAPTER 8

2.

Original Proof	Dual Proof

$$A + (A \cdot B) \equiv A \cdot 1 + A \cdot B \qquad A \cdot (A + B) \equiv (A + 0) \cdot (A + B)$$
$$\equiv A \cdot (1 + B) \qquad\qquad \equiv A + (0 \cdot B)$$
$$\equiv A \cdot (B + 1) \qquad\qquad \equiv A + (B \cdot 0)$$
$$\equiv A \cdot 1 \qquad\qquad\qquad \equiv A + 0$$
$$\equiv A \qquad\qquad\qquad\quad \equiv A$$

3. Prove $A + (A' \cdot B) \equiv A + B$
   Using distributive law: $A + (A' \cdot B) \equiv (A + A') \cdot (A + B)$
   $$\equiv 1 \cdot (A + B)$$
   $$\equiv (A + B) \cdot 1$$
   $$\equiv A + B$$

6.

Account number	Current balance	Soc. Sec. number	
31	2423	1211	0

11111111	000000000000	00000000000	Account number mask

00000000	111111111111	00000000000	Current balance mask

9a. $A \cdot (B + B')$
 d. $(A \cdot B') + (A' \cdot B)$

10c.

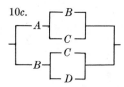

15a. Simplify $F \equiv A' \cdot B' + A' \cdot B + A \cdot B'$
   $$\equiv A' \cdot B' + B \cdot (A' + A)$$
   $$\equiv (A' \cdot B') + B \cdot 1$$
   $$\equiv B + (B' \cdot A')$$
   $$\equiv B + A'$$

16. "Atomic" functions for conjunctive normal form:

A	B	$A' + B'$	$A' + B$	$A + B'$	$A + B$
0	0	1	1	1	0
0	1	1	1	0	1
1	0	1	0	1	1
1	1	0	1	1	1

Suppose we are given a function F defined by the table below

A	B	F	
0	0	1	
0	1	0	$\leftarrow(A + B')$ creates a 0 in this row in a product
1	0	0	$\leftarrow(A' + B)$ creates a 0 in this row in a product
1	1	1	

Then,

$$F \equiv (A + B') \cdot (A' + B)$$

17. The expression $A + (A \cdot B)$ interpreted in terms of Boolean computer instructions is
OR$(A,$ AND $(A,B))$
For A: 1100
B: 1010
we have

$$\text{AND } (A,B) = 1 \quad 0 \quad 0 \quad 0$$
$$A = 1 \quad 1 \quad 0 \quad 0$$
$$\text{OR}(A, \text{ AND } (A,B)) = 1 \quad 1 \quad 0 \quad 0$$

All the laws of Boolean algebra hold for Boolean computer instructions.

CHAPTER 9

9.1 Binary Chopping

1. $a = 9$, $\epsilon = 0.05$
after 8 trials $X = 2.98828125$
(after 11 trials, $X = 3.00146484375$ ($\epsilon = 0.005$))
3. When the algorithm is used for $a = 1$, the series of midpoints converges to 1 (which is $\sqrt{1}$). The left endpoint always changes, until the current value of X_I is within ϵ distance of 1.

9.2 Binomial Coefficients

1. Given a set A having 10 elements, there are
   a. 120 subsets of three elements
   d. 120 subsets of seven elements
5. a. $^{35}\!/_{128}$ is the probability of 3 heads in 7 tosses
   b. $^{21}\!/_{128}$

9.3 Binary Search

1. a. Monotone increasing: 1, $1\frac{1}{4}$, $1\frac{1}{2}$, 2, 3, 4
   c. Monotone non-decreasing: 1, $1\frac{1}{4}$, $1\frac{1}{2}$, 2, 2, 3, $3\frac{1}{2}$, $3\frac{1}{2}$, 4

5. The main similarity between the binary search and the binary chopping square root algorithm is that at each iteration, (approximately) one-half of the possibilities are eliminated, thus assuring a rapid convergence.

9.4   Matrix Inversion

4.
$$\begin{bmatrix} -186\!\big/_{234} & 174\!\big/_{234} & 222\!\big/_{234} & -90\!\big/_{234} \\ -33\!\big/_{234} & 12\!\big/_{234} & 96\!\big/_{234} & 18\!\big/_{234} \\ 237\!\big/_{234} & -150\!\big/_{234} & -264\!\big/_{234} & 126\!\big/_{234} \\ 57\!\big/_{234} & -42\!\big/_{234} & -102\!\big/_{234} & 54\!\big/_{234} \end{bmatrix} = A^{-1}$$

9.5   Random Numbers

1. *a.* $18 \equiv 4 \bmod 7$
   c. $11 \equiv 4 \bmod 7$
   g. $5 \equiv 1 \bmod 2$
4. $r_1 = 3$
   $r_{i+1} \equiv 2 \cdot r_i \bmod 19$

$r_1 = 3$	$r_{11} = 13$
$r_2 = 6$	$r_{12} = 7$
$r_3 = 12$	$r_{13} = 14$
$r_4 = 5$	$r_{14} = 9$
$r_5 = 10$	$r_{15} = 18$
$r_6 = 1$	$r_{16} = 17$
$r_7 = 2$	$r_{17} = 15$
$r_8 = 4$	$r_{18} = 11$
$r_9 = 8$	$r_{19} = 3$
$r_{10} = 16$	$r_{20} = 6$

9.6   Nim

1. Flowchart to find j such that $2^j \leq$ EORSUM. Method: We consider (EORSUM -2^j) for $j = 0$, 1, 2, ... At first, (EORSUM -2^j) is negative. Increase j until the expression becomes positive, then the correct value of j is obtained.

CHAPTER 10

1. Largest integer 32767:   0111   1111   1111   1111 $(2^{15} - 1)$
   Smallest integer -32768:   1000   0000   0000   0000 (-2^{15})

3. Maximum F: $\left(1 - \dfrac{1}{2^{22}}\right)$

   max floating point number $= \left(1 - \dfrac{1}{2^{22}}\right) 2^{255}$

   Maximum E: $+255$

   $= 2^{255} - 2^{233}$

4. The value of E indicates the number of binary places to the right (for E positive) or left (E negative) that the binary point of the fraction should be shifted.

9. Take $E = 0$.   Then the fraction part is
   $F = .01$ 01 01 01 01 01 01 01 01 01 01
   $= \dfrac{1,398,021}{4,194,064}$

10*a.* 010000
     000000
  b. 011100
     000001
  e. 010000
     001111

  g. 110000
     000000
  h. 011111
     000010

11*a.* $2\frac{1}{2}$

16. 0.0034

CHAPTER 11

1. If computer A is to be upward compatible with computer B, the instruction set of A must be a subset of the instruction set of B.

2a. Yes
 b. No
 c. Yes
 d. No
 e. No
 f. No

3f. No

CHAPTER 12

1. a, b, e, and h are permitted

2. c and d are permitted

3a. $(3**X) * (X**2 + Y**2)$

4. ISUM = 55

7.   ISUM = 0
       J = 1
    1 ISUM = ISUM + J
       J = J + 1
       IF (J-N) 1, 1, 2
    2 CONTINUE

12. Include the statement
    COMMON X, N
    in the main program and in the subroutine.

14. C MAIN PROGRAM CALLS RANDOM
    C NO. GENERATOR
    C WITH STATEMENT   "R = F(R)."
    C INITIALLY,
    C R = 17.
       FUNCTION F(R)
       M = 2**16
       F = MOD(3125*R,M)
       RETURN
       END

CHAPTER 13

1. Four; Identification, Environment, Data, Procedure

2. Digits: 0 thru 9   Hyphen: -

   Letters: A thru Z

   INCOME TAX
   ACCOUNTS-PAYABLE
   ACCOUNTS-RECEIVABLE
   GLIP-GLOP
   PLGWYP
   OVER-DRAWN
   ALGWEP
   MUGWUMP
   BOOZE
   CHURCH

3. Environment, Data, Procedure

4c. No

5a. No, they are all numeric characters
 b. Yes
 c. No, ZERO is a reserved word
 d. Yes
 e. No, over thirty characters
 f. No, hyphen can't terminate the word

7a. Yes
 b. Yes
 c. Yes
 d. No, there must be a final quotation mark.

8a. Yes
 b. Yes
 c. No, the sign must not end the word.
 d. No, there must not be an alphabetic character present.
 e. No, the decimal point must not be the last character.
 f. No, a numeric literal must only be made up of digits.

9a.

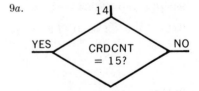

10a. No, there must be a space between PROCEDURE and DIVISION.
  b. No, there must be a hyphen between WORKING and STORAGE.
  c. No. It must read INPUT-OUTPUT SECTION.

d. No. It must read I-0 CONTROL

e. Yes

Remember, to be used properly, the answers to *a*, *b*, *c*, *d*, and *e* must begin in column 8.

11a. False. When qualification is used data names can be spelled the same.

b. False, see Fig. 13-10

c. False

d. True

e. True

f. True

13a. AUTHOR, INSTALLATION, DATE-WRIT-TEN, DATE-COMPILED, SECURITY, REMARKS, each with its associated comment-paragraph.

b. SOURCE-COMPUTER,   OBJECT-COM-PUTER, FILE CONTROL

14. *a*) True, *b*) True, *c*) True, *d*) True, *e*) False; it begins with FD not 01.

15. Imperative, conditional, compiler-directing

16a. The move statement would be executed, not the GO TO, because 6 + 92 = 98 and 98 can be held in the two locations for DEPT. Thus there is no size error.

b. A branch would occur to REDO. This happens because 16 + 92 yields a number too large to be held in DEPT.

INDEX